INTRODUCTION TO MOLECULAR IMMUNOLOGY

INTRODUCTION TO MOLECULAR IMMUNOLOGY

Second Edition

Alfred Nisonoff

BRANDEIS UNIVERSITY

SINAUER ASSOCIATES, INC.
SUNDERLAND, MASSACHUSETTS

THE COVER:
Schematic drawing of the three-dimensional structure of
the human IgG molecule, based on X-ray crystallographic
analysis. See page 82. Courtesy of David R. Davies.

INTRODUCTION TO MOLECULAR IMMUNOLOGY
Second Edition

Copyright © 1984, 1985 by Sinauer Associates Inc.

Library of Congress Cataloging in Publication Data

Nisonoff, Alfred.
    Introduction to molecular immunology.

    Includes bibliographical references and index.
    1. Immunochemistry.   2. Immunoglobulins.
3. Molecular biology.   I. Title.
QR183.6.N57   1984   616.07'9   83-20259
ISBN 0-87893-595-9

Printed in U.S.A.

9 8 7 6 5 4 3 2

CONTENTS

PREFACE TO
THE SECOND EDITION

This edition will be published two years after the book originally appeared in the spring of 1982. This, the publisher informs me, is an uncommonly short interval between editions. The revision was made necessary, first, by a rapid accumulation of data on the structure of the glycoproteins encoded by the major histocompatibility complex and on the organization of genes within the complex. This topic is covered in the new Chapter 12. The arrangement and function of the genes that encode the immunoglobulins (Chapter 6) is another subject on which a considerable amount of new information has become available. I have attempted to update this key chapter to late 1983. A third chapter, Chapter 11, "Mechanisms of Action in the Complement System," has received several additions and deletions to the text, as well as new figures and tables. The rest of the book required fairly minor revisions, in most cases made to accommodate newly-acquired information.

Our experience with the First Edition suggests that the book is proving useful for investigators entering the field of immunology as well as for students in introductory courses.

ALFRED NISONOFF
January, 1984

PREFACE TO THE FIRST EDITION

During the 1960s a number of important discoveries in cellular immunology provided a basis for intensive research in that area. As a consequence, our knowledge of the subject has greatly increased during the past decade; this has been reflected in the content of textbooks on general and cellular immunology. At the same time, significant progress has been made in molecular immunology, particularly in such areas as the organization of genes controlling the immunoglobulins, the preparation and applications of monoclonal antibodies, and the molecular basis of idiotypy. In addition, many details of the structure of immunoglobulins have been clarified during the past several years. It is the purpose of this book to provide an introduction to the basic principles of molecular immunology, incorporating these important recent discoveries.

A major part of the text deals with the structural properties, evolution, and genetics of immunoglobulins. Separate chapters cover the specificities of antihapten antibodies, monoclonal antibodies, methods for purification and assay of antibodies, and properties of the human complement system. An appendix contains the amino acid sequences of a few immunoglobulins of particular interest and a description of the structural properties of antigens that are under control of the major histocompatibility complex. Amino acid sequences are also presented, where applicable, in the main body of the text.

The book is designed as a text for an introductory course in molecular immunology. A second purpose is to provide a text that is complementary to those that emphasize cellular immunology, for use in an introductory course in general immunology. It has been necessary to be selective in the coverage of topics in molecular immunology. I have tried to stress subjects that are of general interest and that are essential to an understanding of the mechanisms of immunity.

I wish to acknowledge the contributions of Drs. Edmundo Lamoyi, Lisa A. Steiner, Edward S. Golub, Harvey Colten, and Mr. Steven M. Rosen, each of whom made invaluable comments on the text.

ALFRED NISONOFF
December, 1981

INTRODUCTION TO MOLECULAR IMMUNOLOGY

1

ANTIGENS AND ANTIBODIES: GENERAL CONSIDERATIONS

The science of immunology can be conveniently divided into two major branches: humoral and cellular. Both humoral and cellular immune responses are essential components of our defenses against pathogenic bacteria, viruses, and parasites. CELLULAR IMMUNITY is mediated by a class of white blood cells called LYMPHOCYTES. These cells originate from stem cells in the bone marrow and migrate to the thymus gland, where they undergo differentiation before emigrating to the peripheral lymphoid organs (spleen, lymph nodes); such cells, which have been processed in the thymus, are referred to as T lymphocytes or T CELLS. T cells can destroy cells infected by various types of viruses or intracellular bacteria. HUMORAL IMMUNITY, or the humoral response, is mediated by ANTIBODIES, which are protein molecules synthesized by another class of lymphocyte, called B CELLS. B cells also originate from stem cells in the bone marrow but do not enter the thymus. B cells are found in all peripheral lymphoid organs, and the antibodies they secrete are found throughout the blood, lymphatics, and in exocrine secretions (e.g., milk). In many cases, the production of antibodies by B cells requires cooperative interactions with T cells.

This text will deal with humoral immunity and the properties of antibodies and not with the other arm of the immune system, i.e., cellular immunity.

ANTIGENS

An ANTIGEN may be defined as a substance that can induce an IMMUNE RESPONSE. Such a response may consist of antibody production or of stimulation of immunologically active T cells. The antigen can

1

react with those antibodies or with receptors on those T cells that it stimulates. Antibodies and receptors exhibit specificity for the inducing antigen; in general they will not react with substances unrelated to the antigen, although they may cross-react with related, but nonidentical, substances. For example, antibodies to human cytochrome c will cross-react with many mammalian cytochromes c, although the reaction is strongest with the inducing antigen (the IMMUNOGEN). Antibodies are produced by all vertebrates but not by invertebrates.

From the standpoint of infectious disease, the significant antigens are, as already noted, bacteria, viruses, and parasitic organisms, virtually all of which are immunogenic to some degree. Other classes of antigen are proteins foreign to the animal, and certain carbohydrates, lipids, and nucleic acids. Antibodies can also be produced against many synthetic polypeptides and against a large variety of molecules called HAPTENS. Haptens are substances that will not induce antibody formation unless they are attached (conjugated) to a CARRIER molecule, such as a foreign protein. Antibodies induced by such a conjugate will react with the free hapten molecule, with the hapten–protein conjugate used to immunize the animal, or with the hapten conjugated to another protein. A great variety of substances of low molecular weight act as haptens.

Most pathogens enter the body by way of the respiratory or digestive systems. In experimental immunology, antigens are, however, usually injected into an animal by an intravenous, intramuscular, or subcutaneous route. The production of antibodies can be increased by injecting the antigen subcutaneously or intramuscularly in an emulsion containing an ADJUVANT and the antigen. Adjuvants are preparations that enhance the immunogenicity of an antigen; in general they permit prolonged slow release of the antigen and tend to induce an influx of leukocytes (white blood cells) to the site of inoculation of the antigen–adjuvant mixture. Commonly used adjuvants are Freund's adjuvant[1] or alum.

When antibodies are formed in response to particles such as viruses, bacteria, or other cells, the antibodies of primary interest are those formed against components on the particle surface, although antibodies are also produced against molecules present inside cells. The antibodies that react with the intact particles are those directed against surface antigens. Most antiviral antibodies are directed against the protein coat of the virus.

The region of an antigen that actually interacts with an antibody is called the ANTIGENIC DETERMINANT or EPITOPE. Its size bears no

---

[1] Freund's adjuvant is a water-in-oil emulsion containing killed mycobacteria (generally *M. tuberculosis*) and a detergent (the emulsifying agent).

relationship to the overall size of the antigen. The COMBINING SITES of antibodies that react with bacteria are no larger than the combining sites of antibodies that interact with macromolecules or with haptens. Roughly speaking, the effective size of an antibody combining site (and, therefore, of an antigenic determinant) may correspond in size to three to seven glucose molecules. Thus, when an antibody molecule combines with a bacterium, the molecule occupies a very small fraction of the total surface of the bacterial cell. This property accounts in part for our ability to prepare vaccines. Bacteria or viruses can be modified so that they are no longer infectious while leaving many antigenic determinants intact. Those determinants that remain intact can stimulate the production of antibodies that will recognize and combine with the *unmodified* pathogen in a future encounter.

Substances that are native to the animal are normally not immunogenic. For example, if one injects mouse gamma globulin into a mouse, antibodies will not be produced. Animals are thus TOLERANT of their own constituents. Exceptions are constituents that are shielded from the immune system in the animal by virtue of the fact that they do not come into direct contact with cells involved in antibody production. For example, antibodies can be induced within an individual animal against certain proteins from its own sperm or from parts of its own central nervous system. AUTOIMMUNE DISEASES are characterized by the production of antibodies against the body's own constituents, to which the individual is normally tolerant. The potential to produce anti-self antibodies thus exists; and when it takes place, a pathological condition often results. An example is autoimmune hemolytic anemia, which is caused by the production of antibodies to one's own erythrocytes (red blood cells).

THE ANTIBODY RESPONSE

Within 3 or 4 days after inoculation of an antigen, leukocytes secreting antibody will be present in the spleen, lymph nodes, and bone marrow. The antibody-secreting cells are PLASMA CELLS, and cells that are intermediate in their stage of differentiation between the B lymphocyte and the plasma cell. Within a week or two, antibody will ordinarily be present in detectable amounts in the blood. The methods used for detecting and quantitatively assaying antibodies are discussed in Chapter 9. After repeated immunization, the concentration of antibody in the blood is highly variable but may exceed 1 mg/ml. After a second challenge (inoculation) with antigen, antibody is produced more rapidly and attains a higher concentration. The responses to the first or subsequent challenge with antigen are referred to as PRIMARY or SECONDARY RESPONSES, respectively. The secondary response is more intense because the initial inoculation of antigen leads to multiplication of responsive cells, which may persist for a long time in the animal.

Upon standing in a test tube, a sample of blood clots spontaneously, trapping the cellular elements in a fibrin network. The clear fluid obtained after removal of the clot by centrifugation is referred to as SERUM. The antibodies, as well as over 50 other proteins, are present in the serum fraction. The protein that is present in the highest concentration is serum albumin, which constitutes about 60% of the protein by weight.

As indicated earlier, antibodies are protein molecules; they have molecular weights ranging from 145,000 to 950,000. More precisely, they are glycoproteins, containing 3 to 12% carbohydrate. The carbohydrate generally plays no significant role in determining the antigen-binding specificity of the antibody, but it is important because of its effect on the structure of the molecule and its transport within the cell.

An important feature of all antibody molecules is the presence of at least two antigen-binding sites per molecule. This permits the antibody to form a crosslinked network, or lattice, upon interaction with the antigen (Figure 1). The antigen, in turn, must have at least two antigenic determinants, or epitopes, per molecule to permit extensive crosslinking. If the antigen is a protein or a large carbohydrate molecule, it will precipitate upon interaction with the antibody as a consequence of crosslinking and aggregation. This phenomenon is called the PRECIPITIN REACTION. Similar crosslinking reactions, followed by precipitation, occur with bacterial or viral antigens; for such particulate antigens, the process is called AGGLUTINATION.

As already mentioned, the effective size of the combining site of an antibody, which is complementary to an epitope of the antigen, is relatively small, constituting only a few percent of the total surface area of an antibody molecule. Each of the combining sites of an individual antibody molecule has precisely the same structure and antigen-binding specificity.

Antibodies confer immunity through several mechanisms. One is OPSONIZATION, or enhancement of PHAGOCYTOSIS (engulfment by white blood cells). Bacteria or viruses that are complexed with antibodies are more readily engulfed by phagocytic cells. In addition, antibodies, acting together with a group of serum proteins called COMPLEMENT, can LYSE (rupture) various gram-negative bacteria and certain parasites. Viruses can be inactivated when antibodies occupy sites on the viral surface that are critical for penetration of the virus into its host cell. There is also evidence that antibodies can, together with complement, destroy virus-infected cells and in this way limit the spread of

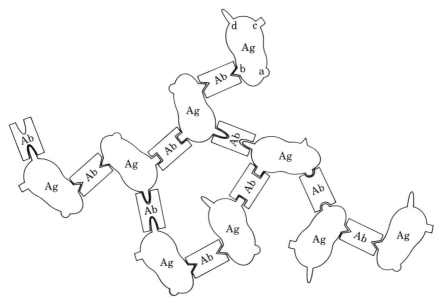

FIGURE 1. Mechanism of crosslinking of a soluble antigen (Ag) by antibody. The antigen is represented as having four different determinants (epitopes), labeled a, b, c, and d. The network, or lattice, can grow indefinitely, eventually resulting in precipitation. Note that for crosslinking to occur, the antibody and antigen must each have at least two combining sites.

infection. Cellular immunity is, however, probably more significant than the humoral response in preventing the spread of viral infections. Both humoral and cellular responses are important in inactivating viruses before they penetrate cells.

SUGGESTED ADDITIONAL READING

Benacerraf, B. and Unanue, E. R. (1979). *Textbook of Immunology.* Baltimore, Williams and Wilkins.

Burnet, F. M. (1959). *The Clonal Selection Theory of Acquired Immunity.* Cambridge, Cambridge University Press.

Golub, E. S. (1981). *The Cellular Basis of the Immune Response,* 2nd ed. Sunderland, MA, Sinauer Associates.

Gowans, J. L. (1971). Immunobiology of the small lymphocyte. In R. A. Good and D. W. Fisher, Eds., *Immunobiology.* Sunderland, MA, Sinauer Associates.

Jerne, N. H. (1955). The natural selection theory of antibody formation. *Proc. Natl. Acad. Sci. USA 41,* 849.

2

GENERAL STRUCTURAL PROPERTIES
OF ANTIBODIES

OVERVIEW

Serum proteins with antibody activity are collectively called immunoglobulins. Most immunoglobulins are present in a fraction of serum designated as gamma globulin. Despite their similarity with respect to physical and chemical properties, the immunoglobulins are very heterogeneous; the various levels at which this heterogeneity is expressed are discussed. A four-chain structure, which is made up of two heavy (H) chains and two light (L) chains, is common to all immunoglobulins; however, some immunoglobulins are polymers of the four-chain monomeric unit. An antigen-binding site is made up of amino acids from one H chain and one L chain. Thus, the four-chain monomer possesses two combining sites. Bivalence or multivalence confers important biological properties. Each H chain and each L chain consists of a variable (V) and a constant (C) part. The V regions are responsible for the diversity of antibody specificities. The C regions are invariant for a given class of H chain or type of L chain, except for minor genetic polymorphisms. The amino acid sequence of the C region of the H chain determines the class of the immunoglobulin: there are five classes in mammals. Within each V region are three clusters of hypervariable amino acids that contribute directly to the formation of the combining site. Mammals possess two types of L chain, called κ and λ, which can combine with H chains of any class.

Both H and L chains are made up of domains, each domain containing 110–120 amino acid residues. Each domain also has an intrachain disulfide bond, spanning 55–65 amino acid residues. Each L chain has two domains (V and C). Each H chain has one V domain and three or four C domains, depending on its class. There is evidence that a primordial gene encoded a single domain and that this gene

7

subsequently underwent replication, giving rise to the larger polypeptide chains.

Each L chain is linked to an H chain by strong noncovalent forces and, in most immunoglobulins, by an interchain disulfide bond. Similar forces are involved in holding together pairs of H chains. An IgG molecule can be cleaved into large fragments by certain proteolytic enzymes. Papain liberates two large monovalent fragments and a third fragment that in some species is crystallizable. Properties of these fragments and of fragments produced by the enzyme pepsin and their relationship to the four-chain structure are described.

* * *

This chapter provides a general discussion of antibody structure. The chapter contains a considerable amount of factual information and forms the basis for our subsequent discussion of structure and genetic control of immunoglobulins. Many of the concepts introduced will be reinforced in Chapters 4 through 8.

SERUM GLOBULINS

Antibodies are GLOBULINS (proteins insoluble in distilled water or at high salt concentrations). Thus, a fraction containing all of the antibodies can be separated by precipitation of serum with a high concentration of ammonium sulfate or sodium sulfate. Such a precipitate will also contain serum globulins other than antibodies. Further purification of the antibody-containing fraction can be achieved by electrophoresis, ion-exchange chromatography, or both. It is possible by such means to obtain a fraction of serum that contains most of the antibodies—of all specificities—with only slight contamination by other serum proteins. Those serum proteins that possess antibody activity are referred to collectively as IMMUNOGLOBULINS. (Methods for isolating antibodies of a particular specificity will be discussed in Chapter 9.)

Four major groups of proteins can be separated by electrophoresis at slightly alkaline pH. The albumins migrate most rapidly to the anode, followed by the α-, β-, and γ-globulins. Most of the antibodies are present in the slowest moving γ-GLOBULIN fraction, although some migrate more rapidly, i.e., with the β-globulins.

"NORMAL" IMMUNOGLOBULINS

Animals that have not been actively immunized nonetheless contain substantial concentrations of immunoglobulins in their sera.

These result in part from the presence of immunogenic substances in bacterial flora of the intestines, in food, and in inhaled particles. Germ-free animals, which are maintained under sterile conditions from the time of birth, have greatly reduced concentrations of NORMAL IMMU-NOGLOBULINS. There is also evidence that, when an animal is exposed to an antigen, some immunoglobulins are produced that are not specific for that antigen; this is attributed to a generalized proliferation and differentiation of B cells during an immune response. This would also contribute to the "normal" immunoglobulin population.

HETEROGENEITY OF ANTIBODIES

The number of different antibodies that can be made by an individual animal is extremely large. It is conservatively estimated that in the mouse the number exceeds 10^6, and it probably exceeds 10^7; it may be much greater if, as it now appears, random mutations occur in immunoglobulin genes during the lifetime of the animal (Chapter 6). There are several levels at which this heterogeneity is expressed.

1. *Variety of antigens.* A corollary of the specificity of antibodies is that the number of different antibodies must be very large, since antibodies can be prepared that are specific for virtually any type of bacterium, virus, foreign protein, or hapten group.

2. *Multiple, unrelated epitopes on individual antigens.* This can be illustrated by considering a typical globular protein such as myoglobin. Despite the relatively low molecular weight of the molecule (~17,000), it has several distinct antigenic determinants or epitopes, i.e., antibodies reactive with one determinant on the surface of the molecule do not react with another determinant. A particle such as a red blood cell has many different antigens on its surface, each of which has multiple epitopes.

3. *Heterogeneity of antibodies directed against a single epitope.* Informative data on this question have come from studies of antibodies to haptens. Rabbit antibodies to a single hapten, the dinitrophenyl group, have been shown to possess binding affinities (K_A) ranging from 1×10^5 to 1×10^8 M^{-1}. Another type of evidence is derived from amino acid sequence analyses; antibodies to a single hapten can possess a large number of different amino acid sequences. Subpopulations of antibodies to a given hapten, made in an individual animal, can also be distinguished by virtue of the different antigenic determinants that are present on the *antibodies.* Such antigenic determinants, associated with the region of the antigen-binding site on the antibody, are referred to as IDIOTYPIC DETERMINANTS (Chapter 8).

4. *Heterogeneity unrelated to antibody specificity.* Most species of vertebrates possess more than one class of antibody (IgM, IgG, etc.), whose characteristics are discussed later. Within each class one can find antibodies of virtually all specificities. The class of an antibody is determined by structures unrelated to the antigen-binding site. Another level of heterogeneity is associated with genetically transmitted variants of immunoglobulins (ALLOTYPES, Chapter 7). These variations in structure are also, in general, unrelated to antigen-binding specificity.

THE FOUR-CHAIN STRUCTURE

Common to the immunoglobulins of vertebrates from the shark to the human is a four-chain structure consisting of two identical L chains and two identical H chains (Figure 1). The identity of each pair of chains reflects the fact that a B cell secretes the protein product of only one chromosome for the L chain and one for the H chain, despite the fact that each type of chain is controlled by genes on a pair of chromosomes.[1] This effect is referred to as ALLELIC EXCLUSION. The control mechanism that prevents expression of the gene product of one chromosome of each pair is not yet known. Each antibody combining site is lined with amino acid side chains from one H chain and one L chain. There are two combining sites in each four-chain monomeric unit, and the minimum valence of an antibody is therefore two. In an individual four-chain monomer, the two combining sites are identical. This is a consequence of the fact that each antibody-producing cell synthesizes only a single species of L chain and a single species of H chain. The identical specificity of the combining sites means that the *exact* configuration of the combining site is predetermined by the structures of the H and L chains; when a given H chain combines with a given L chain, the two chains always combine through noncovalent bonds to give precisely the same three-dimensional structure.

Some immunoglobulin classes have more than one four-chain monomer per molecule, e.g., IgM in most species has five four-chain monomeric units and a valence of 10. Because identical H chain–L chain pairs form each of the combining sites, the specificities of the 10 combining sites in an individual molecule are identical.

The molecular weight of all L chains, throughout the vertebrate kingdom, is approximately 23,000. Two types of L chain, designated kappa (κ) and lambda (λ), are found in mammalian immunoglobulins.

---

[1] mRNA and the protein products from genes on both chromosomes of a pair are frequently produced. However, only one species of L chain and one species of H chain are assembled into immunoglobulin and secreted.

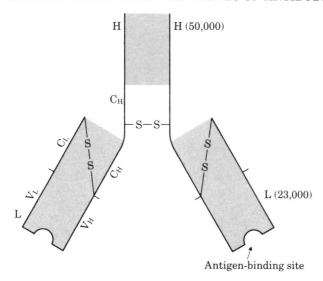

FIGURE 1. A diagrammatic sketch of the structure of rabbit IgG. In an individual molecule, the two H chains are identical to one another, as are the two L chains. An IgG molecule can contain two κ or two λ chains. The shaded areas represent regions that are held together by noncovalent bonds. Note that the variable regions of the L and H chains (V_L and V_H) are approximately equal in size, whereas the constant region of the H chain (C_H) is about three times as large as C_L.

κ and λ chains have similar molecular weights and similar three-dimensional structures but differ considerably in their amino acid sequences. The similarities suggest that genes controlling the two types of chains are derived from a common ancestral gene, which underwent replication and subsequent divergent evolution. The ratio of κ to λ chains varies among species, e.g., the ratio is approximately 6 to 4 in humans, 97 to 3 in mice, and 2 to 98 in horses.

H chains and L chains of immunoglobulins all contain a VARIABLE REGION and a CONSTANT REGION, which are encoded by separate gene segments. These structures will be considered in detail in later chapters.

In humans there are five major classes of H chains, which define five CLASSES OF IMMUNOGLOBULINS: IgG, IgM, IgA, IgD, and IgE. The H chains of the five classes are designated γ, μ, α, δ, and ε, respectively. The class of an immunoglobulin is defined by the constant region of its H chain. A given H chain can, in general, combine equally well with κ or λ light chains, and each class contains molecules with either type of L chain. H chains of the five classes differ from one another in amino acid sequence and in length, ranging in molecular weight from about 50,000 to 75,000. They also vary with respect to carbohydrate content. (Most L chains contain no carbohydrate.) In addition to possessing different H chains, the classes differ in their overall structure. The existence of several classes of immunoglobulins is of benefit to the animal because each class has certain biological functions; these functions are a direct consequence of the unique amino acid sequences associated with the H chains. For example, IgG can pass through the placenta of mammals into the embryo, whereas other classes cannot, and IgE is responsible for allergic reactions. Note, however, that all classes have essentially the same repertoire of antigen-binding specificities.

SIGNIFICANCE OF BIVALENCE OR MULTIVALENCE OF IMMUNOGLOBULINS

It is evident that all immunoglobulins have at least two combining sites per molecule, i.e., each is at least bivalent. We have already discussed the dependence of crosslinking of antigens on the bivalence or multivalence of the antibody. Crosslinking is of physiological importance because it enhances the engulfment of antigen by phagocytic leukocytes. It is also involved in activation of the complement system (Chapter 11). In addition, crosslinking may be required for the triggering of antibody-producing cells (B cells) by antigen. Initiation of the humoral response requires an encounter between antigen and a receptor on B cells. These receptors are cell surface immunoglobulins that are identical in specificity to the immunoglobulins that will eventually be secreted by progeny of the stimulated B cells. When antigen is presented to a resting B cell under appropriate conditions, it stimulates the cell to divide and differentiate, a process that eventually yields antibody-producing cells. The initial triggering by antigen is believed to require crosslinking and aggregation of the receptor immunoglobulins; this, in turn, is dependent on bivalence or multivalence of the receptors.

Another, more subtle role of multivalence relates to the avidity with which an antibody can bind certain types of antigens. A particulate antigen (such as a red blood cell, bacterium, or virus) has repeating antigenic determinants on its surface. An antibody molecule (say, IgG) may interact with a single particle in a manner such that both of its combining sites are bound to epitopes on that particle (rather than to epitopes on two adjacent particles). This is sometimes referred to as MONOGAMOUS BINDING. When this type of binding occurs, the effective energy of interaction, or AVIDITY, is greatly increased, as

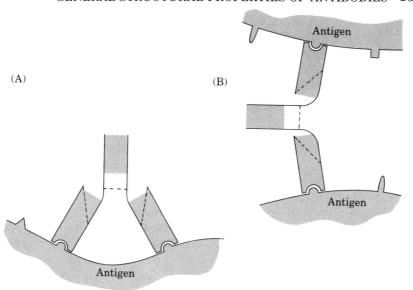

(A)

(B)

FIGURE 2. Panel A illustrates "monogamous binding," i.e., both combining sites of an antibody molecule are attached to the same particle (such as a virus or a bacterium). In Panel B a single antibody molecule links two different antigen particles. Monogamous binding greatly increases the avidity of the interaction. Note that the antibody molecule is flexible; the angles between the two Fab fragments are different in the two sketches.

compared to that associated with monovalent attachments to two particles. This mechanism has been shown to be physiologically important in the neutralization of viruses by antibodies of relatively low binding affinity (Figure 2).

SUBCLASSES OF IMMUNOGLOBULINS

Human IgG occurs as four major subclasses: IgG1, IgG2, IgG3, and IgG4. Subclasses, as well as classes of immunoglobulin, are distinguished by the amino acid sequences of the constant regions of the H chains. The term "subclass" is used because different subclasses resemble one another closely. For example, the amino acid sequences of the H chains of human IgM and IgG show only about 30% identity, whereas the percentage of positions of the sequences that are identical in any pair of the four subclasses of IgG exceeds 90%. Human IgA occurs as two subclasses: IgA1 and IgA2. So far there is no clear evidence for subclasses of human IgM, IgD, or IgE. In practice, classes and subclasses are usually distinguished through their antigenic determinants, i.e., antibody molecules, being proteins, can act as antigens, and each class has its unique determinants.

The existence of subclasses in the various species of vertebrates is variable and unpredictable. Our knowledge is limited because of the difficulty of identifying minor variations unless large amounts of homogeneous immunoglobulins are available. In the mouse, there are four subclasses of IgG; in the rabbit, only two, one of which is present at very low concentrations. The horse has four or five (the number is controversial) known subclasses of IgG. On the basis of the available data, one can generalize that, in mammals, subclasses are most likely to be found in IgG.

A widely accepted explanation for the existence of subclasses is that a gene controlling the C region of the H chain of, for example, human IgG underwent replication, eventually giving rise to four copies. Each of the copies then evolved independently, yielding the four subclasses. The close resemblances among the four subclasses of human IgG are thought to reflect relatively recent replication and divergence of the genes, going back perhaps 1×10^7 years (as compared to $\sim 1.8 \times 10^8$ years for the time of emergence of mammals). By contrast, IgM and IgG are believed to have diverged from a common ancestral gene over 2×10^8 years ago.

IDENTIFICATION OF CLASSES AND SUBCLASSES BY SEROLOGICAL METHODS

As indicated earlier, classes and subclasses are defined by the amino acid sequences of the constant regions of the H chains. There are also certain obvious structural distinctions among the classes, e.g., the pentameric structure of IgM. Classes and subclasses can also be identified by immunological methods, and these were, in fact, widely used and effective before knowledge of amino acid sequences became available. One can, for example, inject purified human IgM into a rabbit and obtain rabbit anti-IgM. The rabbit antiserum will, however, also react with all other classes of human immunoglobulins because all of the classes share the same repertoire of L chains. The rabbit antiserum may be rendered specific for IgM by the following procedure.

Prepare an IgG fraction from human serum and conjugate it covalently to an insoluble support such as Sepharose beads. Make a slurry of the beads, pour them into a column, and wash the column. Then slowly apply the rabbit anti-IgM antiserum to the column. Those antibodies that are reactive with human IgG will adhere to the beads; the antibodies that pass through will react with human IgM but not with human IgG. They will also fail to react with human IgA, IgD, and IgE; because the L chains of all classes are similar, the IgG on the column will adsorb all the antibodies to L chains. Therefore, the treated antiserum is specific for human IgM. Analogous procedures can be used to prepare antiserum specific for human IgG, IgA, etc. To obtain specific anti-IgG, one immunizes a rabbit with IgG and adsorbs the antiserum with immobilized IgM, IgA, or, preferably, both.

The preparation of antisera specific for *subclasses* can pose a more difficult problem. Antisera specific for certain subclasses are readily obtained, others only with difficulty. The problem arises because of the similarity of subclasses. Antibodies against, say, human IgG2 may be almost completely cross-reactive with IgG1. If anti-IgG2 is adsorbed with immobilized IgG1, virtually all the antibodies in some antisera may be retained on the column. In preparing antisera to individual subclasses, the species of animal immunized may be critical. For example, primates are more likely than rabbits to "recognize" the small antigenic differences between human IgG1 and IgG2. (It is a general rule that the species of animal producing antibody against an antigen of vertebrate origin determines the spectrum of antibodies that can be produced against the antigen.) With the advent of monoclonal antibodies (Chapter 10), the availability of antibodies to individual subclasses is improving.

GENERAL STRUCTURAL FEATURES OF LIGHT AND HEAVY CHAINS

The diagram in Figure 3 shows some of the structural properties of a human κ chain. The λ chain is very similar in size and shares most important structural features with κ chains; however, the κ and λ chain amino acid sequences differ markedly. By convention, the amino-terminus (N-terminus) is shown on the left and the carboxy-terminus (C-terminus) on the right; numbering is from left to right. The number of amino acids in an L chain varies from about 212 to 220.

The N-terminal half of the L chain is designated as the variable, or V, region and the C-terminal half is referred to as the constant, or C, region. Within a species, amino acid sequences of the C region are essentially constant for a given type of chain, κ or λ. (Minor inherited variations will be considered later.) In contrast, sequences in the V region are highly variable. Within the V region of the κ chain, a few amino acids are conserved, showing little or no variability. At other positions, occasional amino acid substitutions are observed, and a third group of positions is extremely variable. The latter are referred to as the HYPERVARIABLE or COMPLEMENTARITY-DETERMINING REGIONS

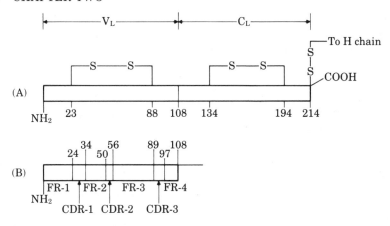

FIGURE 3. Diagrammatic sketch of a human κ chain (A). Numbering is from the N-terminus on the left to the C-terminus on the right. Note the intrachain disulfide bond (S–S) spanning about the same number of amino acid residues in the V_L and C_L domains. Panel B shows the locations of the complementarity-determining regions (CDR) in the V_L domain. Segments outside the CDR are the framework segments (FR).

(CDR); they occur as three clusters in the V region: CDR-1, CDR-2, and CDR-3.

Those amino acids in the V region that are highly conserved are involved in interactions with the H chain or are important in the maintenance of the correct three-dimensional structure of the L chain itself. They are found in the interior of the molecule. Such amino acids have been conserved during evolution because of their critical structural role. Amino acids in the CDR are involved in the formation of the antigen-binding site. The three CDR are brought into close proximity when the L chain folds to form its final three-dimensional structure. An H chain similarly has three CDR; and in the antibody molecule, the six CDR of the two chains are in close proximity. The antigen-binding region of the antibody contains a pocket that is lined with amino acid side chains from the CDR of both the H and the L chains. Most amino acids of the CDR are on the surface of the molecule, i.e., exposed to the aqueous medium.

Figure 4 is a sketch of an H chain of human IgG (IgG1 subclass). The V region is about the same size as the V region of an L chain (about 118 amino acid residues). However, the C region contains approximately 330 amino acids, making it about three times as large as that of an L chain.

An interesting structural feature of both L and H chains is the

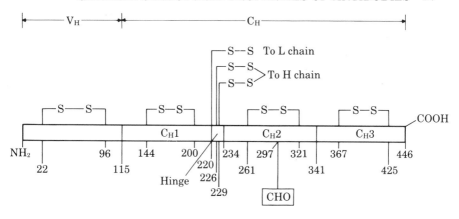

FIGURE 4. Diagrammatic sketch of an H chain of human IgG (IgG1 subclass). Note the presence of four domains, each containing an intrachain disulfide bond (S–S) spanning approximately 60 amino acid residues. The symbol CHO stands for carbohydrate. The V region of the H chain (V_H) resembles V_L in having three hypervariable CDR (not shown).

presence of intrachain disulfide bonds at regularly spaced intervals (Figures 3 and 4). This, and other considerations discussed below, led to the recognition of DOMAINS, which each contain 110–120 amino acids and possess an intrachain disulfide bond. Thus, an L chain possesses two domains: one variable (V) and one constant (C); an IgG heavy chain has one V domain and three C domains. The concept of domains is based on the following facts:

1. Invariably, a domain has an intrachain disulfide bond, spanning about 55–70 amino acid residues. (For example, the intrachain bond in the V_κ domain joins cysteine residues at positions 23 and 88.)

2. Each domain has a similar three-dimensional structure, characteristic of all immunoglobulins. The boundaries of the domains are clearly visible in X-ray crystallographic models (Chapter 5).

3. One can align the amino acids in the C-region domains of an H chain and show that there is a significant degree of HOMOLOGY or relatedness of sequences among the individual domains.

4. The segments of the molecule exhibiting the above properties are similar in size, each containing 110–120 amino acid residues. A comparison of sequences for the three C domains of human IgG1 is shown in Figure 5. Three rows of sequences represent the three C region domains, designated C_H1, C_H2, and C_H3. They are vertically

```
                              120                                    130
CH1 (Residues 119—220)  Ser Thr Lys Gly Pro Ser Val Phe Pro Leu Ala Pro Ser Ser Lys Ser

CH2 (Residues 234—341)  Leu Leu Gly Gly Pro Ser Val Phe Leu Phe Pro Pro Lys Pro Lys Asp

CH3 (Residues 342—446)  Gln Pro Arg Glu Pro Gln Val Tyr Thr Leu Pro Pro Ser Arg Glu Glu


                              140                                    150
  -   -  Thr Ser Gly Gly Thr Ala Ala Leu Gly Cys Leu Val Lys Asp Tyr Phe Pro Glu Pro Val

Thr Leu Met Ile Ser Arg Thr Pro Glu Val Thr Cys Val Val Val Asp Val Ser His Glu Asp Pro

  -   -  Met Thr Lys Asn Gln Val Ser Leu Thr Cys Leu Val Lys Gly Phe Tyr Pro Ser Asp Ile


                              160                                    170
Thr Val  -   -  Ser Trp Asn Ser  -  Gly Ala Leu Thr Ser Gly  -  Val His Thr Phe Pro Ala

Gln Val Lys Phe Asn Trp Tyr Val Asp Gly  -  Val Gln Val His Asn Ala Lys Thr Lys Pro Arg

Ala Val  -   -  Glu Trp Glu Ser Asn Asp  -  Gly Glu Pro Glu Asn Tyr Lys Thr Thr Pro Pro


                              180                                    190
Val Leu Gln Ser Ser Gly Leu Tyr Ser Leu Ser Ser Val Val Thr Val Pro Ser Ser Ser Leu Gly

Glu Gln Gln Tyr Asp Ser Thr Tyr Arg Val Val Ser Val Leu Thr Val Leu His Gln Asn Trp Leu

Val Leu Asp Ser Asp Gly Ser Phe Phe Leu Tyr Ser Lys Leu Thr Val Asp Lys Ser Arg Trp Gln


                              200                                    210
Thr Gln  -  Thr Tyr Ile Cys Asn Val Asn His Lys Pro Ser Asn Thr Lys Val  -  Asp Lys Arg

Asp Gly Lys Glu Tyr Lys Cys Lys Val Ser Asn Lys Ala Leu Pro Ala Pro Ile  -  Glu Lys Thr

Glu Gly Asn Val Phe Ser Cys Ser Val Met His Glu Ala Leu His Asn His Tyr Thr Gln Lys Ser


                              220
Val  -   -  Glu Pro Lys Ser Cys

Ile Ser Lys Ala Lys Gly

Leu Ser Leu Ser Pro Gly
```

FIGURE 5. Amino acid sequences of human IgG1, aligned so as to maximize homologies (number of positions of identity) among the chain segments. Positions 221–233 constitute the hinge region, which does not show homology of sequence to other portions of the chain. The hyphens are gaps that are artificially inserted to improve the degree of homology. (From Edelman et al., 1969). Abbreviations are defined in Appendix I.

aligned so as to exhibit maximum homology of sequences; the hyphens represent gaps artificially introduced for this purpose. With the arrangement shown, any pair of sequences exhibits approximately 30 to 33% homology. To maximize homology, positions 221 to 233 were omitted. These 13 amino acids constitute the HINGE REGION of the molecule, which serves a special function, discussed below, and which is not related in sequence to the C_H domains.

The existence of domains with related sequences led to the hypothesis that there existed a primitive gene coding for about 115 amino acids. During evolution this gene is presumed to have undergone replication. The replicated genes then evolved independently, but their common origin is still reflected by the similarities in their sequences. There is sufficient similarity between L and H chain sequences to indicate that a single primordial gene was the precursor for both types of chain and, therefore, for all existing immunoglobulin genes. Support for these views has come from studies of the organization of the genes in chromosomes (Chapter 6).

BIOLOGICAL ACTIVITIES ASSOCIATED WITH DOMAINS ("EFFECTOR FUNCTIONS")

The major function of the variable domains of L and H chains (V_L and V_H) is obvious; they are responsible for the antigen-binding specificity of the antibody molecule. However, the C domains also mediate important biological functions. For example, the ability to interact with complement is associated with the C_H2 domain of IgG; the capacity to interact with macrophages and neutrophils is associated with C_H3. Such specialized activities, associated with all molecules of a given class, are referred to as EFFECTOR FUNCTIONS of the antibody. They are discussed in more detail in Chapter 4.

STRUCTURAL ROLES OF INTERCHAIN AND INTRACHAIN DISULFIDE BONDS

The heavy and light chains of immunoglobulins are held together by strong noncovalent forces. In addition, in most immunoglobulins, each H chain is linked to an L chain by an interchain disulfide bond. One or more disulfide bonds as well as noncovalent bonds also join the two H chains in a four-chain unit (Figure 1).

To physically separate the H chains from the L chains, one first reduces the interchain disulfide bonds with a reagent such as 2-mercaptoethanol, then alkylates free SH groups with iodocetamide or iodoacetate to prevent reoxidation. In the equation below, P_1 represents the H chain, P_2 the L chain, and RSH the reducing agent (a mercaptan).

$$P_1{-}S{-}S{-}P_2 + 2\,RSH \rightarrow P_1{-}SH + P_2{-}SH + R{-}S{-}S{-}R$$

$$P_1{-}SH + P_2{-}SH + 2\,I{-}CH_2{-}\overset{\displaystyle O}{\overset{\|}{C}}{-}NH_2 \rightarrow$$

$$P_1{-}S{-}CH_2{-}\overset{\displaystyle O}{\overset{\|}{C}}{-}NH_2 + P_2{-}S{-}CH_2{-}\overset{\displaystyle O}{\overset{\|}{C}}{-}NH_2 + 2\,I^- + 2\,H^+$$

After the reduction and alkylation, the H and L chains (P_1 and P_2) are still strongly bound to one another by noncovalent bonds. To separate the chains, the protein is exposed to a reagent that disrupts noncovalent bonds in proteins. Such a reagent may be 8 M urea, 5 M guanidine, or 1 M propionic acid; the latter is favored when one wishes to minimize denaturation. The H and L chains will now separate and can be isolated by gel filtration in the dissociating solvent, e.g., 1 M propionic acid. The H chains, being larger, emerge from the gel filtration column first. (Gel filtration separates macromolecules according to size.)

*Intra*chain disulfide bonds play a major role in maintaining the internal stability of the folded chain structure. We have already seen that each domain contains an intrachain disulfide bond. Such bonds are invariably found in the interior of the molecule. Together with hydrophobic bonds, they stabilize the final folded structure.

Because of their exposed location, interchain disulfide bonds are much more easily reduced than most intrachain bonds. By using a relatively low concentration of reducing agent, under nondenaturing conditions, it is possible to selectively reduce the interchain bonds of an immunoglobulin. It is therefore possible to isolate H and L chains with their intrachain disulfide bonds virtually intact.

CARBOHYDRATE IN IMMUNOGLOBULINS

All immunoglobulins contain carbohydrate—in amounts varying from 3 to 12% by weight. Nearly all of the carbohydrate is associated with the C regions of H chains, although occasionally some is found in the V_H or V_L domain. Carbohydrate is covalently bound to an asparagine or, occasionally, to a serine or threonine side chain. An enzyme, *N*-acetylglucosamine-asparagine transglycosylase, catalyzes the attachment of an amino sugar to asparagine. The asparagine is frequently part of a triplet of amino acids in which asparagine is the first and serine or threonine the third amino acid; the second amino acid is variable. The points at which such a sequence occurs in the C region represent points of attachment of the *N*-acetylglucosamine.

Additional sugars are attached by a series of transglycosylase enzymes. The construction of the oligosaccharide is not absolutely predetermined, and one therefore sees some microheterogeneity with respect to the exact composition and structure of the carbohydrate side chains, even at the same position in the same class of heavy chain. Two typical examples of carbohydrate side chains found in immunoglobulins are shown in Figure 6. The point of attachment of carbohydrate (CHO) in human IgG1 is indicated in Figure 4.

Occasionally carbohydrate is found in a V_H or V_L region. Because of the variability of amino acid sequence, the triplet, asparagine, ——, serine/threonine sometimes appears in a V region. When this happens, it can represent a locus for initiation of carbohydrate growth by the transglycosylase enzyme.

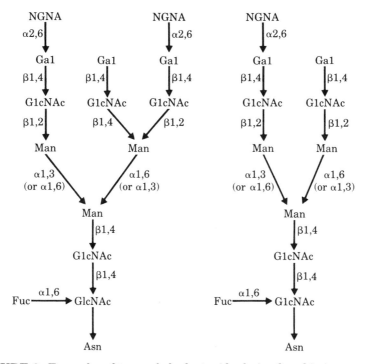

FIGURE 6. Examples of two carbohydrate side chains found in immunoglobulins. The two branched chains shown are present at two different positions in the C_H region of a mouse IgM myeloma protein. Note that the point of attachment in each case is an asparagine side chain (Asn) of the IgM molecule. The symbols used are GlcNAc, N-acetylglucosamine; Man, mannose; Gal, galactose; NGNA, N-glycolylneuraminic acid; Fuc, fucose. (From Brenckle and Kornfeld, 1980.)

Biological functions that have been ascribed to the carbohydrate include (1) increasing the solubility of immunoglobulins; (2) conferring protection against catabolic degradation; and (3) facilitating secretion from the antibody-producing cell. Mouse IgM, IgA, and IgE are not secreted if carbohydrate synthesis within the cell is inhibited; there is no inhibition of the secretion of IgG. A possible role of carbohydrate in the interaction with complement has also been suggested.

THE HINGE REGION

The H chains of IgG, IgA, or IgD of various species possess a flexible stretch of amino acids that is located between the C_H1 and C_H2 domains and that confers certain unique properties to the molecule. In human IgG1, this HINGE REGION comprises residues 221 to 233. The amino acid sequence of this region is not homologous in sequence to that of the rest of the molecule; when aligning sequences of the H chain domains for estimation of their degree of relatedness, the hinge region must be omitted from the comparison. This region has the following properties.

1. It is flexible and is believed to account for the ability of an IgG molecule to assume a horseshoe-shaped, as well as a linear configuration. This permits an antibody to become attached to a single particle (e.g., a bacterium) through both of its combining sites or, alternatively, to stretch out to its full length to join two particles (Figure 2).

2. The hinge region contains the interchain disulfide bonds that link the two heavy chains of IgG, IgA, or IgD. These disulfide bonds, being in a loosely folded exposed segment of the molecule, are particularly susceptible to reduction or oxidation.

3. Because of its exposed location and loosely folded structure, the hinge region is readily attacked by various proteolytic enzymes. Since the rest of the molecule is relatively resistant to proteolysis, the attack by the enzyme at the hinge region liberates large fragments. Such cleavages will be discussed in the next section.

CLEAVAGE OF ANTIBODIES INTO LARGE FRAGMENTS BY PROTEOLYTIC ENZYMES

Proteolytic enzymes are capable of cleaving many polypeptide bonds in an immunoglobulin molecule, provided the molecule is first denatured. However, native immunoglobulin, like many other globu-

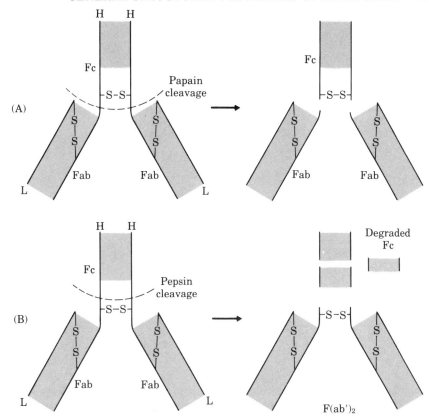

FIGURE 7. Location of cleavages in rabbit IgG by the enzymes papain (A) and pepsin (B). Note that the Fc fragment contains amino acids derived only from the constant regions of the heavy chains. Each Fab fragment contains one complete L chain and approximately half of an H chain, and each fragment contains one of the antigen-binding sites of the molecule. The F(ab')₂ fragment produced by pepsin is bivalent; the Fc segment is partially degraded. If the disulfide bond between the two heavy chains in F(ab')₂ is subsequently reduced, two monovalent Fab' fragments are released.

lar proteins, is quite resistant to proteolysis. There are, however, restricted regions in immunoglobulins that are accessible to such enzymes. Rodney R. Porter, a scientist at the National Institute for Medical Research in London, discovered in 1958 that papain cleaves rabbit IgG into three large fragments, each having a molecular weight of 45,000–50,000 (Figure 7). Cleavage occurs in the hinge region of the molecule. Two of the fragments are identical and each contains

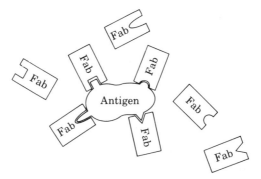

FIGURE 8. Inhibition of precipitation by Fab fragments. Fab fragments can combine with the antigen, covering its epitopes. If a large excess of Fab is present, it will compete successfully for the epitopes and block access of undegraded bivalent antibody molecules. Because Fab fragments are monovalent, they cannot form a crosslinked network; they will, therefore, inhibit precipitation by bivalent antibody.

one of the antigen-binding sites of the molecule, i.e., each fragment is monovalent. These fragments are designated Fab (ab for antigen-binding). An Fab fragment contains a complete L chain and the V_H and C_H1 regions—or about half of one H chain. Being monovalent, Fab fragments cannot form crosslinked networks with antigen and are therefore incapable of forming precipitates or agglutinates. Moreover, Fab fragments can inhibit precipitation by occupying the epitopes of the antigen, thus denying access to untreated, bivalent antibody (Figure 8). The demonstration that the two Fab fragments of an individual molecule are identical provided strong evidence for the symmetry of the IgG molecule. This symmetry reflects the fact that all the L chains, or H chains, produced by a single plasma cell are identical.

The third fragment released by papain was designated Fc because it crystallizes spontaneously from a papain digest of rabbit IgG in cold neutral buffer. The Fc fragment contains the C-terminal halves of both H chains (the C_H2 and the C_H3 domains), which are held together by strong noncovalent forces and by an interchain disulfide bond. This disulfide bond is cleaved when a high enough concentration of reducing agent is used, but the Fc fragment remains intact, stabilized by noncovalent forces acting between the two H chains. The fact that fragment Fc crystallizes readily, even when derived from a heterogeneous antibody preparation, provided the first evidence for the constancy of amino acid sequence in that portion of the H chain. (Crystallizability implies homogeneity.) Porter's studies, together with the demonstration by Gerald M. Edelman at The Rockefeller University that the molecule contains H and L chains, provided our first deep insights into the structure of immunoglobulins. The two investigators shared a Nobel Prize in 1972. Between 1958 and 1975, the intensive efforts of many laboratories resulted in virtually complete elucidation of the molecular structure.

Another proteolytic enzyme that is frequently used for the limited cleavage of immunoglobulins is pepsin, an enzyme that is effective at a pH below 4.5. The site of cleavage of rabbit IgG by pepsin is very close to that of papain, but the result is strikingly different. Pepsin splits the two heavy chains on the C-terminal side of the disulfide bond that joins the two H chains (Figure 7). As a result, the Fc fragment is removed; it is also partially degraded and will not crystallize. The two Fab fragments are still joined, however, by the disulfide bond. This large residual fragment, designated $F(ab')_2$, has two combining sites and exhibits the precipitating properties of a bivalent antibody (in contrast to the monovalent fragments liberated by papain, which inhibit precipitation). In $F(ab')_2$ the two monovalent Fab' fragments are not held together by noncovalent bonds. The only bond that links them is the disulfide bond. This is easily reduced, splitting the bivalent molecule into two monovalent fragments, designated Fab'. Interestingly, it is possible, by oxidation, to reconstitute the disulfide bond that links the Fab' fragments, once again creating a bivalent molecule.

This property of reoxidation can be utilized to create artificially an antibody molecule with two combining sites having different antigen-binding specificities, i.e., a hybrid molecule. Such molecules do not occur naturally. The starting material consists of two purified antibodies of different specificity (anti-A and anti-B). $F(ab')_2$ fragments are prepared from each by peptic digestion and freed of Fc components by gel filtration. Both $F(ab')_2$ fragments are then reduced to Fab' and the reducing agent is removed. The two Fab' preparations are mixed and allowed to reoxidize (Figure 9). Three products are formed, des-

$$A-S-S-A + 2\ RSH \longrightarrow 2\ ASH + R-S-S-R$$

$$B-S-S-B + 2\ RSH \longrightarrow 2\ BSH + R-S-S-R$$

$$4A-SH + 4B-SH + 2O_2 \longrightarrow A-S-S-A + B-S-S-B + 2A-S-S-B + 4H_2O$$

FIGURE 9. Mechanism of formation of hybrid antibodies. A-S-S-A and B-S-S-B represent the $F(ab')_2$ fragments of anti-A and anti-B IgG, respectively. RSH is a mercaptan (e.g., mercaptoethanol), which is a reducing agent. After reduction, the mercaptan is removed by gel filtration, the fragments are mixed and allowed to reoxidize. Approximately 50% of the product is A-S-S-B, a hybrid antibody molecule.

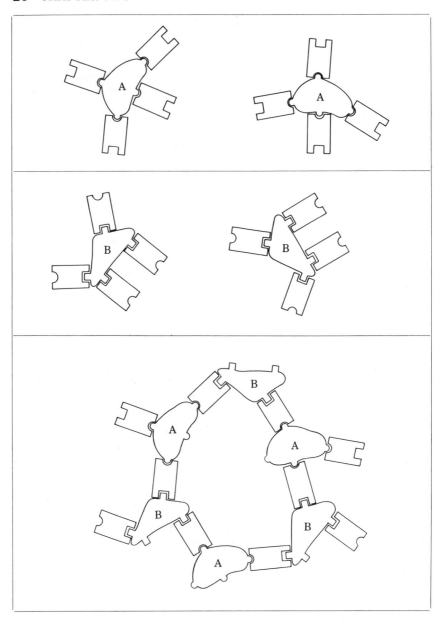

FIGURE 10. Interaction of hybrid (anti-A–anti-B) antibody molecules with antigen A, antigen B, or a mixture of A and B. The hybrid antibody is monovalent with respect to either antigen and cannot induce crosslinking. It can, however, form a crosslinked network with a mixture of the two antigens and precipitate them.

ignated A-S-S-A, B-S-S-B, and A-S-S-B, where A and B refer to the Fab' fragments of anti-A and anti-B, respectively. The hybrid molecules, A-S-S-B, can be isolated by successive adsorption to and elution from immobilized antigen A and antigen B. The hybrid molecules will inhibit the precipitation of A with anti-A or of B with anti-B because they are monovalent with respect to either antigen. However, a mixture of antigen A and antigen B will form an aggregate with the hybrid antibody (Figures 10 and 11).

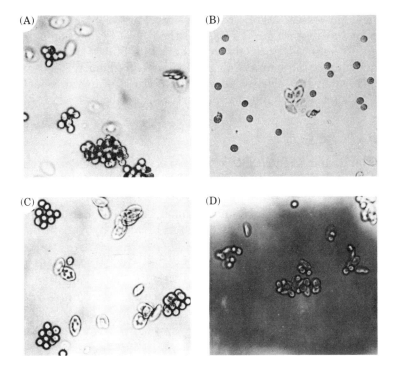

FIGURE 11. Agglutination reactions produced by F(ab')₂ fragments and human red blood cells (round discs) or chicken red blood cells (larger, nucleated, and oval-shaped). The human red blood cells were coated with hen ovalbumin and the chicken red blood cells with bovine γ-globulin (BGG). The following rabbit F(ab')₂ fragments were present in the mixtures: A, anti-ovalbumin; B, anti-BGG; C, a mixture of anti-ovalbumin and anti-BGG; D, a hybrid preparation of anti-ovalbumin and anti-BGG. Note that the anti-ovalbumin agglutinates only the coated human red blood cells; the anti-BGG agglutinates only the coated chicken cells; the mixture of two antibodies agglutinates both cell types but they form separate aggregates; the hybrid antibody produces mixed aggregates of the two cell types (Fudenberg et al., 1964).

Such hybrid antibodies have been used, for example, to visualize antigens on cell surfaces. The experiments make use of hybrid antibodies with one combining site directed against a cell surface antigen and the other against ferritin, an electron-dense protein. The hybrid antibody binds to antigens on the cell surface; if ferritin is then added, it will combine with the other, free combining site of the antibody. The high electron density of ferritin makes it visible in the electron microscope, thus identifying the locations of the cell surface antigens.

Perhaps the most significant application of $F(ab')_2$ fragments, however, has been in studies of the role of the Fc fragment in various biological processes. $F(ab')_2$ has the properties of bivalent antibody except for the absence of Fc. To assess the role of Fc, one compares the activity of the intact antibody with that of its $F(ab')_2$ fragment.

Monovalent fragments, Fab or Fab', are frequently used experimentally when it is desired to eliminate crosslinking as a factor in investigations of the biological properties of antibodies.

LITERATURE CITED

Brenckle, R. and Kornfeld, R. (1980). Structure of the oligosaccharides of mouse IgM secreted by the MOPC 104E plasmacytoma. *Arch. Biochem. Biophys. 201,* 160.

Drews, G., Fudenberg, H. H. and Nisonoff, A. (1964). Serological demonstration of dual specificity of rabbit bivalent hybrid antibody. *J. Exp. Med. 119,* 151.

Edelman, G. M., Cunningham, B. A., Gall, W. E., Gottlieb, P. D., Rutishauser, U. and Waxdal, M. J. (1969). The covalent structure of an entire γG immunoglobulin molecule. *Proc. Natl. Acad. Sci. USA 63,* 78.

SUGGESTED ADDITIONAL READING

Edelman, G. M. (1970). The structure and function of antibodies. *Sci, Amer. 123,* 3.

Kabat, E. A. (1976). *Structural Concepts in Immunology and Immunochemistry,* 2nd ed. New York, Holt, Rinehart & Winston.

Litman, G. and Good, R., Eds. (1980). *Comprehensive Immunology.* Vol. V. *Immunoglobulins.* New York, Plenum Press.

Porter, R. R. (1973). Structural studies of immunoglobulins. *Science 180,* 713.

3

SPECIFICITIES, AFFINITIES, AND REACTION RATES OF ANTIHAPTEN ANTIBODIES

OVERVIEW

Investigations of haptens (i.e., substances that are not immunogenic unless attached to a suitable carrier) are responsible in large part for our understanding of the fine specificity of antibodies, the forces involved in antigen–antibody interactions, and the energetics and rates of such interactions. Most haptens are small molecules of known structure; the effects of small variations in structure on interactions with antibody can therefore be investigated. A large amount of data has been obtained by measuring the capacities of various haptens that are related in structure to inhibit precipitation reactions of a given antihapten antibody. Such measurements yield relative binding affinities for a series of haptens. The actual affinities can be obtained by direct binding measurements—using methods such as equilibrium dialysis, described in this chapter. From such measurements one can determine the valence of the antibody molecule as well as the average affinity of a population of antibodies specific for a given hapten. Typical binding affinities for antibody–hapten interactions range from 1×10^5 to 1×10^9 liters/mole (M^{-1}). Antibodies directed against an individual hapten are heterogeneous with respect to binding affinity.

Direct measurements of the *rates* of antibody–hapten interactions have shown that velocity constants are very high, being limited principally by rates of diffusion. This indicates that activation energies for the binding interactions are small. Rates of interaction of macromolecular antigens with antibodies are lower than those of haptens because of the effect of size on diffusion rate. The affinity of an antibody is largely determined by the rate at which the ligand dissociates from the combining site.

*   *   *

29

FIGURE 1. Two widely used methods for conjugation of haptens to protein. ▶
(A) An aniline ($C_6H_5NH_2$) derivative is treated with nitrous acid to produce
a diazonium salt. The diazonium salt reacts with a tyrosine (shown in the
figure), a histidine, or a lysine side chain of a protein to form a stable derivative. (B) Dinitrobenzenesulfonate is conjugated at alkaline pH to a lysine
side chain of a protein.

ANTIBODIES TO HAPTENS

The versatility of the immune response is well illustrated by the
ability of an animal to produce antibodies against an almost unlimited
array of small molecules, or HAPTENS.[1] As noted earlier, haptens are
molecules, often of low molecular weight, that will not induce antibody
formation when inoculated alone, but will do so if conjugated to a
suitable carrier such as a protein molecule. Almost any small molecule
that has a reasonably rigid structure can act as a hapten. Such molecules include benzene or almost any benzene derivative, small carbohydrates, virtually any hormone of low molecular weight, etc. An
interesting phenomenon is observed if one inoculates an iodinated
protein. The antibodies formed will react with other iodinated proteins
that have never been injected into the animal. Such cross-reactions
have been shown to be due to the recognition of iodotyrosine and
iodohistidine by the antibodies. When a protein is treated with iodine,
the tyrosine and histidine side chains are iodinated and are recognized
as "foreign" by the immune system. Even when a larger hapten group
(e.g., a benzene derivative) is conjugated to a protein and used in
immunization, the antibodies formed may interact not only with the
hapten but also with a structure made up of the hapten and the amino
acid side chain to which it is conjugated.

Much of what we know about the fine specificity of antibodies has
come from studies of haptens because we know the exact structure of
a hapten molecule, whereas our knowledge of the precise structures
of epitopes of proteins, bacteria, and viruses is much more limited. For
immunization, haptens are attached to proteins through the side
chains of amino acids. Two examples of chemical procedures for preparing such hapten–protein conjugates are shown in Figure 1. Almost
any protein can be used; however, it is disadvantageous to use, for
example, a rabbit protein as carrier if a rabbit is to be immunized;
better responses to the hapten are achieved if the carrier is a molecule
that is recognized as foreign by the immunized animal. A typical
conjugate may have 10 to 20 hapten molecules per molecule of protein
of molecular weight 100,000.

---

[1] From the Greek *haptein,* to grasp or fasten.

(A)

(B)

Suppose hen ovalbumin conjugated with dinitrobenzene is injected into a rabbit. Because much of the protein's surface is unaltered, the rabbit will make antibodies that react with native (unconjugated) ovalbumin. In addition, other antibodies will be formed that react with the hapten dinitrobenzene. Evidence that antihapten antibodies are present in the rabbit's serum includes the following:

1. The antibodies will form a precipitate with dinitrobenzene conjugated to a protein (protein B) other than ovalbumin; because protein B was never injected into the rabbit, the reaction must involve the hapten.

2. Dinitrophenol and closely related molecules will inhibit the precipitation of such antibodies with dinitrobenzene conjugated to protein B. (Dinitrophenol is used because dinitrobenzene is insoluble in water.) The mechanism by which free haptens inhibit the precipitation is illustrated in Figure 2. Note that the free hapten cannot form a precipitate because it cannot crosslink the antibodies. However, it can occupy the combining sites of an antibody molecule and prevent the antibody from interacting with the hapten–protein B conjugate. If the free hapten is present in large excess, precipitation can be inhibited virtually completely through such competition.

3. The antibody can be shown to bind free hapten. We inferred

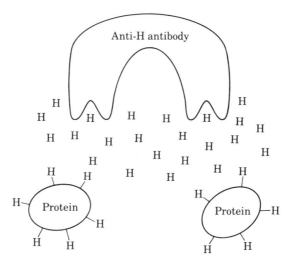

FIGURE 2. Mechanism of inhibition by free hapten molecules of the precipitation of an anti-hapten antibody with a protein–hapten conjugate. The large excess of free hapten competes effectively with the protein–hapten conjugate for the combining sites of the anti-hapten antibody.

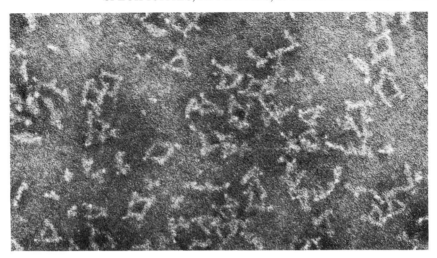

FIGURE 3. Electron micrograph of a mixture of specifically purified rabbit anti-2,4-dinitrophenyl antibody and a bivalent hapten (see text). The length of a typical linear segment in one of the many closed structures is about 120 Å. (From Valentine and Green, 1967.)

that binding took place from the ability of free hapten to block precipitation. However, it can also be demonstrated by a direct method such as equilibrium dialysis—a process described later in this chapter.

As indicated earlier, free hapten is effectively monovalent and therefore cannot crosslink antibodies to form a precipitate. An interesting study of bivalent haptens was carried out by R. C. Valentine and N. M. Green (1967), who prepared the following group of bivalent hapten molecules. (The symbol X represents dinitrobenzene.)

$$X—CH_2—X$$
$$X—CH_2—CH_2—X$$
$$X—CH_2—CH_2—CH_2—X, \text{ et cetera}$$

They found that crosslinking did not occur unless the number of CH_2 groups exceeded eight. One can think of the CH_2 grouping as a spacer; the spacer must be at least eight units in length in order to allow two antibody molecules to be joined. This would be expected if the depth of the antibody combining site corresponds to the length of four CH_2 groups plus one dinitrobenzene group (approximately 13 Å).

They also made the interesting observation that the bivalent haptens could join antibody molecules together but did not yield precipitates. When examined by electron microscopy, closed figures with three, four, or five sides were seen. Such molecular complexes are too small to precipitate. An electron micrograph that they obtained is shown in Figure 3 and the interpretation is illustrated schematically in Figure 4. The relative size of the bivalent hapten, as compared to the antibody, is necessarily greatly exaggerated in the latter figure; the antibody molecule, but not the hapten, is seen in the electron micrograph. Experiments such as these have demonstrated that an antigen molecule should be at least trivalent to be effective as a precipitating agent, although precipitation by bivalent antigen has occasionally been observed.

BINDING AFFINITIES OF ANTIBODIES

The antibody–hapten interaction is reversible; the BINDING AFFINITY of an antibody can therefore be expressed in terms of the equilibrium constant for the interaction (the ASSOCIATION CONSTANT K_A).

$$Ab + H \rightleftharpoons AbH$$
$$K_A = [AbH]/[Ab][H]$$

The equation applies when equilibrium is attained. [AbH] is the molar concentration of antibody combining sites that are occupied by hapten; [Ab] is the concentration of unoccupied combining sites; and [H] is the concentration of hapten that remains unbound at equilibrium. Typical association constants for antibody–hapten interactions are in the range of 1×10^5 to 1×10^9 liters/mole (M^{-1}), although these values do not represent extreme limits.

One can grasp the significance of K_A by considering the situation in which an antibody of the IgG class interacts in solution with a hapten that is present at a low concentration relative to that of the antibody. If K_A is 1×10^5 M^{-1}, the antibody will bind half of the hapten present when the total concentration of antibody combining sites is 1×10^{-5} M (0.75 mg/ml of IgG). If the concentration of antibody combining sites is only 1×10^{-7} M, it will bind only about 1% of the antigen. In contrast, an antibody with $K_A = 1 \times 10^9$ M^{-1} will bind 99% of the hapten present even when the antibody concentration is only 1×10^{-7} M. (We have simplified the calculations by assuming a concentration of hapten that is low relative to that of the antibody; similar conclusions are reached for higher hapten concentrations.)

The binding affinity of an antibody is biologically significant because it determines the minimal concentrations of antigen and of antibody at which an effective interaction can take place. For example, when an infectious agent such as a virus invades the body, it may be present at a very low concentration. An antibody present at low concentration will interact effectively with the virus only if its binding

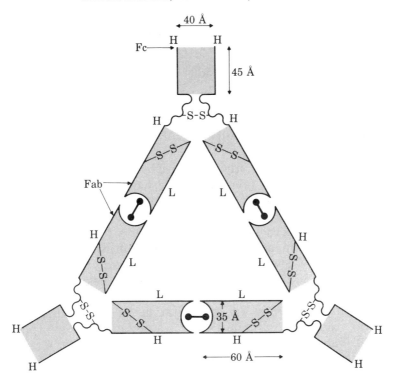

FIGURE 4. Schematic diagram of a trimer of anti-dinitrophenyl antibody and bivalent hapten (●——●), based on the electron micrograph shown in Figure 3. The sum of the lengths of two Fab fragments, linked by hapten, is approximately 120 Å. The widths of the Fab and Fc fragments are approximately 35 and 40 Å, respectively. (From Valentine and Green, 1967.)

affinity is sufficiently high. In general, binding affinities tend to increase with prolonged immunization, and the increase appears to occur mainly after a switch from IgM to IgG production (Chapter 6). The use of low, rather than high, doses of antigen also tends to promote the production of antibodies of high affinity.

Antibodies of high affinity are of importance in radioimmune or ELISA assays (Chapter 9). The lower limit of concentration at which antigen or hapten can be detected in such an assay is dependent on the affinity of the antibody used.

As indicated earlier, antibodies to a single antigenic determinant or to a hapten group are heterogeneous. One manifestation of this heterogeneity is in the binding affinities for an antibody–hapten reaction, i.e., antibodies from an individual animal may bind a given hapten with a wide range of affinities.

SPECIFICITY OF ANTIHAPTEN ANTIBODIES AND BINDING AFFINITIES IN ANTIBODY–HAPTEN INTERACTIONS

One may ask whether antibodies will react exclusively with the hapten used for immunization. The answer is no; reactions (designated cross-reactions) with related haptens can be demonstrated. A hapten that is structurally unrelated will not, however, interact with the antibody. In this section we will deal with the nature of cross-reactions that are observed.

One convenient way to study specificity of the antibody is to make use of the inhibition of precipitation by haptens. We have already discussed the mechanism of inhibition; free hapten competes with the protein–hapten conjugate for occupancy of antibody combining sites (Figure 2). Because competition is involved, a free hapten of high affinity will compete more effectively for the antibody combining site than a hapten of lower affinity, i.e., a lower concentration of the hapten of high affinity is required to cause a given degree of inhibition of precipitation. One can obtain an estimate of relative binding affinities (K_{rel}) by comparing the concentrations of various haptens required to cause 50% inhibition of precipitation, using constant amounts of antibody and of protein–hapten conjugate. If the required concentration of hapten X is tenfold higher than the required concentration of hapten Y, the latter is considered to have an affinity (K_{rel}) about 10 times greater than that of X.[2]

Tables 1 and 2 present relative affinities for haptens reacting with antibodies to the p-phenylazobenzoate group. The immunogen is

where H is

Table 1 lists some compounds that fail to inhibit the precipitation, i.e., have a very low K_{rel}. Benzoate, which is a good inhibitor, is arbitrarily assigned a value for K_{rel} of 1.0. Acetate (which has a carboxylate group

---

[2] Because antibodies are heterogeneous with respect to their binding affinities, the K values obtained are an approximation of an average value for the population of antibodies.

TABLE 1. Interactions of haptens with rabbit antibodies to the p-phenylazobenzoate group.[a]

Hapten	Relative K value
Benzoate	1.0^b
Acetate	<0.01
Phenol	<0.01
Phenylacetate	<0.01
Benzenesulfonate	<0.01
p-Aminobenzenearsonate	<0.01

From Nisonoff and Pressman (1957).

[a] $-N=N-\langle\bigcirc\rangle-N=N-\langle\bigcirc\rangle-\overset{\overset{O}{\parallel}}{C}-O^-$

[b] The K value for benzoate arbitrarily has been assigned the value of 1.0 and all other values have been calculated relative to this assigned value.

but lacks a benzene ring) fails to inhibit, as does phenol (which possesses the benzene ring but lacks the carboxylate group). Thus, both the benzene ring and the carboxylate group are important to the interaction. Benzenesulfonate and p-aminobenzenearsonate (which have benzene rings and, like carboxylate, have negatively charged groups) are very poor inhibitors; the sulfonate and arsonate groups are evidently too large to fit into the antibody combining site. Phenylacetate

$$\langle\bigcirc\rangle-CH_2-COO^-$$

is also a very poor inhibitor. The extra CH_2 group obviously prevents the accommodation of the hapten by the antibody; this again demonstrates the sensitivity of the interaction to small changes in size or shape of the hapten.

Table 2 shows that the presence of a second benzene ring and an azo group markedly enhance the affinity, as compared to that of benzoate. This is not surprising since the immunogen possessed two benzene rings joined by an azo linkage.

Table 2 also demonstrates that substitutions in the meta and, especially, in the ortho position of benzoate lower the binding affinity; however, meta-substituted benzoate derivatives still combine quite

TABLE 2. Interactions of benzoate derivatives with rabbit antibodies to the p-phenylazobenzoate group.

Hapten (benzoate derivative)	Relative K Value
Unsubstituted benzoate	1.0^a
p-Phenylazo-	67
p,p'-Hydroxyphenylazo-	111
o-Chloro-	0.11
o-Methyl-	0.03
o-Iodo-	0.013
m-Chloro-	0.43
m-Methyl-	0.21
m-Iodo-	0.29
p-Chloro-	5.3
p-Methyl-	1.8
p-Iodo-	9.0

^{a} K for benzoate arbitrarily was assigned a value of 1.0, and all other values were calculated relative to this assigned value.

well with the antibody. The reductions in binding affinity associated with meta and, particularly, with ortho substitutions are consistent with a close fit of the antibody around the benzoate group; thus, meta and ortho substituents interfere sterically with binding to the antibody. Substitutions in the para position are, however, well tolerated. This is explained by the fact that the immunogen has an azo group (N=N) in the para position. The antibodies formed must accommodate this azo group and therefore can accommodate other groups in the same position.

In other experiments it was shown that two-ring haptens are stronger inhibitors than benzoate, even in experiments where the immunogen (the substance used for immunization) has only *one* benzene ring instead of two, i.e.,

$$\text{Protein} - (N{=}N - \langle \bigcirc \rangle - COO^-)_n$$

This is explained by the fact that most of the hapten groups of the immunogen are attached to tyrosine side chains in the protein carrier. The antibodies formed interact with the tyrosine (which has a benzene ring) in addition to the azobenzoate group and therefore react with higher affinity with two-ring haptens as compared to haptens having a single benzene ring.

From studies such as these, the following generalizations have emerged; these have largely been confirmed by recent X-ray crystallographic analyses (Chapter 5).

1. The antibody-combining site is closely complementary to the hapten. Very small alterations in the hapten molecule can markedly affect the antibody–hapten interaction.

2. There is considerable variation among antibody molecules with respect to the size and shape of the antigen-binding site. The dimensions of most sites, however, correspond roughly in size to the dimensions of three to seven glucose molecules.

3. Antibody interactions are mediated by several types of noncovalent bonds: hydrogen bonds, positive–negative charge interactions, hydrophobic interactions, and van der Waal's interactions. Hydrophobic interactions are based on the strong tendency of nonpolar regions of molecules to associate with one another in an aqueous medium; the association reduces the hydrophobic area exposed to water. van der Waal's interactions take place between any pair of atoms that are in close and correct proximity; the strength of the interaction is critically dependent on the distance of separation.

4. For a large hapten, that portion of the hapten molecule that protrudes farthest from the carrier is generally most significant in terms of energy of interaction with the antibody. For example, for the protein–hapten conjugate

ring 1 contributes more to the energy of interaction with antibody than ring 2. Furthermore, the "fit" of antibody around the first ring is closer than that around the second. The protruding portion of the hapten (ring 1 in the example) is referred to as an IMMUNODOMINANT GROUP.

The data we have discussed in this section were expressed as binding affinities relative to that of the hapten, benzoate, which was arbitrarily assigned a K_{rel} value of 1.0. Actual binding affinities can be obtained by direct binding measurements (discussed in the next section). Because induced antibody populations are heterogeneous, the K

value obtained will be some type of weighted average of the K values of the antibodies present in the serum. As we have indicated, this is also true of the K_{rel} values obtained by measurements of hapten inhibition of precipitation.

EQUILIBRIUM DIALYSIS

This is the most commonly used method for directly measuring the binding of a hapten to antibody. It is based on the fact that the antibody–hapten interaction, which is mediated by noncovalent bonds, is reversible. The principle can be illustrated as follows (Figure 5). Assume that a small dialysis sac (capacity approximately 1 ml) is filled with neutral buffer, sealed, then immersed in a solution containing a hapten dissolved in the same buffer. The sac is permeable to small molecules but not to large molecules such as antibodies. Hapten will diffuse into the sac, and, when equilibrium is attained, the concentration of hapten will be the same inside and outside the sac. Next, assume that the sac contains antibody to that hapten. Hapten bound to the antibody is not free to diffuse. At equilibrium, the total concentration of hapten inside the bag will consist of free hapten (diffusible) and bound hapten (nondiffusible). The free, or diffusible, hapten concentration will equal the hapten concentration outside the bag. Therefore, the *total* hapten concentration inside will be greater than the hapten concentration outside the bag: the difference is the concentration bound. One can then set up a series of flasks that have a constant concentration of antibody inside, and increasing concentrations of hapten outside the sac. The concentration bound at

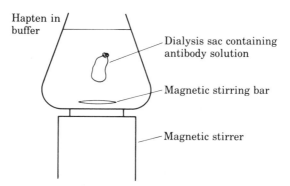

Hapten in buffer

Dialysis sac containing antibody solution

Magnetic stirring bar

Magnetic stirrer

FIGURE 5. Equilibrium dialysis. The closed sac, made of dialysis membrane, is filled with a solution containing anti-hapten antibody. The outer solution contains hapten. The hapten diffuses into the sac until equilibrium is attained.

equilibrium can then be determined as a function of the concentration of free hapten. The concentration bound will increase with increasing free hapten concentration and will reach a plateau as the antibody becomes saturated with hapten. From such data one can calculate the association constant for the interaction. If the antibodies are heterogeneous, an average K_A can be evaluated.[3] The association constant K_A for a homogeneous antibody is equal to the reciprocal of the free hapten concentration at which half the combining sites of the antibodies in the sac are occupied by hapten. K_A is expressed as liters/mole (M^{-1}).

Equilibrium dialysis can also be used to determine the number of combining sites per molecule (valence of an antibody) if purified antibody is available or if the antibody concentration is accurately known. As indicated earlier, the concentration of bound hapten increases as the free hapten concentration is increased, with the antibody concentration held constant. The maximum concentration of hapten that can be bound is equal to the concentration of antibody combining sites. One evaluates, by extrapolation, the maximum molar concentration of hapten that can be bound and divides by the molar concentration of antibody present to obtain the valence. This presupposes a knowledge of the molecular weight of the antibody, as well as of its concentration.

Equilibrium dialysis can also provide information as to the degree of heterogeneity of a population of antibodies specific for a given hapten. Such information is derived from a mathematical analysis of data relating concentration of hapten bound to the free hapten concentration (Nisonoff et al., 1975).

RATES OF ANTIGEN–ANTIBODY REACTIONS

As indicated earlier, it may take from 1 to 48 hours for antigen–antibody complexes to settle out as a precipitate. This might suggest that the interaction is rather slow. In fact, the initial binding of antigen to antibody usually takes place very rapidly; the growth of complexes to a large size and the sedimentation of the complexes are the rate-limiting processes in precipitation. A typical second-order velocity constant for the interaction of a small hapten (e.g., benzoate or dinitrophenol) with antibody exceeds 1×10^7 liters $\cdot$ mole$^{-1} \cdot$ sec^{-1}. Suppose that the antibody concentration in serum is 0.1 mg/ml (a rather low value for an immunized animal). This corresponds to a molar concentration (for IgG) of about 7×10^{-7} M, or 1.4×10^{-6} M

---

[3] The mathematical methods used are described elsewhere (Nisonoff et al., 1975; Werblin and Siskind, 1972).

with respect to concentration of combining sites, because the antibody is bivalent. If hapten is added at the same concentration, 1.4×10^{-6} M, and the forward, second-order velocity constant k_{12} is 1×10^7 liters $\cdot$ mole$^{-1} \cdot$ sec^{-1}, the reaction will be half complete in 0.07 seconds.

Forward velocity constants of antigen–antibody reactions are so high that they appear to be limited principally by rates of diffusion. This indicates that activation energies for the interactions are small. Because of their lower rates of diffusion, values of k_{12} for protein antigens are lower than those for haptens. For a protein such as ovalbumin, with a molecular weight of 44,000, the velocity constant might be two orders of magnitude lower than that of a typical hapten. If, in the example cited above, one assumes a velocity constant 100 times lower, the time required for 50% of the sites to be engaged with the antigen will increase to 7 seconds.

In the above calculations, the reverse reaction (dissociation of antigen from the antibody) has been neglected. This does not introduce a serious error because reverse rate constants are very low relative to forward rate constants.

The equilibrium constant for the association (K_A) is equal to k_{12}/k_{21}, where k_{21} is the velocity constant for the reverse reaction. Because k_{12} does not vary markedly (for antigens of comparable size), K_A is largely determined by the rate of the reverse reaction, i.e., the binding affinity is principally a function of the rate at which the antigen and antibody dissociate.

LITERATURE CITED

Nisonoff, A. and Pressman, D. (1957). Closeness of fit and forces involved in the reactions of antibody homologous to the p-(p'-azophenylazo)-benzoate ion group. *J. Amer. Chem. Soc. 79*, 1616.

Nisonoff, A., Hopper, J. E. and Spring, S. B. (1975). *The Antibody Molecule*. New York, Academic Press.

Valentine, R. C. and Green, N. M. (1967). Electron microscopy of an antibody–hapten complex. *J. Mol. Biol. 27*, 615.

Werblin, T. P. and Siskind, G. W. (1972). Distribution of antibody affinities: technique of measurement. *Immunochemistry 9*, 987.

SUGGESTED ADDITIONAL READING

Eisen, H. N. (1964). Equilibrium dialysis for measurement of antibody-hapten affinities. *Methods in Med. Res. 10*, 16.

Karush, F. (1976). Multivalent binding and functional affinity. *Contemp. Top. Mol. Immunol. 5*, 217.

Landsteiner, K. (1945). *The Specificity of Serological Reactions*. Cambridge, Harvard University Press.

Pressman, D. and Grossberg, A. L. (1968). *The Structural Basis of Antibody Specificity*. Menlo Park, CA, W. A. Benjamin.

Sela, M. (1966). Immunological studies with synthetic polypeptides. *Adv. Immunol. 5*, 29.

4

PROPERTIES AND EVOLUTION OF
CLASSES OF ANTIBODIES

OVERVIEW

There are five classes of human immunoglobulin: IgG, IgM, IgA, IgD, and IgE. The classes differ in their C_H regions but share the same repertoire of V_H regions and L chains. There are four subclasses of IgG and two of IgA. Subclasses also differ with respect to C_H sequences, but the differences are small, reflecting relatively recent evolutionary divergence. IgM is a disulfide-linked pentamer of the basic four-chain unit and contains an additional small polypeptide (J chain). IgA exists in serum principally as the four-chain monomer, but IgA in secretory fluids (tears, saliva, etc.) is a dimer that also contains a J chain and another polypeptide, secretory component (SC). Each class and subclass has certain unique biological functions, e.g., IgE is responsible for allergic reactions and IgD is important as a receptor on B-cell membranes. Some biological functions have been localized to individual domains in C_H regions.

Immunoglobulins of all classes of vertebrate, from fish to mammals, contain the four-chain unit. L chains with an approximate molecular weight of 23,000 are present in all immunoglobulins. IgM was the first immunoglobulin to appear during evolution and is present in all classes of vertebrates. An immunoglobulin of lower molecular weight than IgM (LMIg) first appears in the lungfish and is found in most or all higher species. Because of evolutionary changes, it is very difficult to establish relationships among the LMIg of different classes of vertebrate.

*   *   *

We have seen that the class and subclass of an immunoglobulin is defined by the amino acid sequence of its C_H region. Each class and

45

subclass that is characteristic of a species is referred to as an ISOTYPE. In the species studied there is one C_H gene, or occasionally two, for each class and subclass of immunoglobulins. In some cases minor variations in DNA sequence are observed among the individual members of a species; these are transmitted to offspring, are reflected in amino acid sequences, and are called allotypic differences (Chapter 7). Because the various classes share the same repertoire of V_H regions and L chains, they can also express the same range of antigen-binding specificities. As would be expected, then, the biological properties that are unique for each class are associated with C_H domains. Such unique biological functions would explain the development and preservation of the various classes during evolution. In this chapter we will discuss some of the properties associated with classes and subclasses of human immunoglobulins and present information on the association of biological properties with C_H domains. This will be followed by a discussion of the evolution of the immunoglobulins.

Table 1 lists various properties of the classes and subclasses. Note that there are four subclasses of human IgG (IgG1, IgG2, IgG3, IgG4) and two of IgA (IgA1, IgA2). The designations of the corresponding heavy chains (γ_1, γ_2, etc.) are indicated in the table. In normal human serum, IgG constitutes about 70% of the total immunoglobulin. The concentrations of IgD and, particularly, of IgE are very low.[1]

Each H chain is linked to an L chain by a single disulfide bond (with the exception noted later). The number of bonds joining pairs of H chains is variable, ranging from 2 for γ_1 and γ_4 to 10 or 11 for γ_3. These inter-heavy chain bonds are present in the hinge region of IgG. The large number of bonds in IgG3 is associated with a large hinge region, which contains 62 amino acid residues. It is approximately four times as long as that of the other IgG subclasses. This is attributed to quadruplication—during evolution—of a separate gene segment encoding the hinge region.

The disulfide bond joining an H and an L chain originates at, or next to, the C-terminus of the L chain and in the hinge region of the H chain (of IgG1) or near the beginning of the C_H1 domain (of the other subclasses). This is illustrated diagrammatically in Table 1. The structure of IgA molecules expressing the $A_2m(1)$ allotype (Chapter 7) is unusual in that the L chains are disulfide-bonded to one another rather than to H chains. In a suitable dissociating solvent, such as 5 M guanidine, the L chains can therefore be separated from H chains without prior reduction of disulfide bonds. This structural feature has

---

[1] The classes of antibodies in the mouse are, for comparison, designated IgM, IgG$_1$, IgG$_{2a}$, IgG$_{2b}$, IgG$_3$, IgA, IgD, and IgE. Note that subscripts are used for subclasses in the mouse but not in the human.

TABLE 1. Properties of human immunoglobulins.

Isotype	Chain structure	H chain designation	Mol. wt. ($\times 10^{-3}$)	No. of domains in H chain	Mol. wt. of H chain ($\times 10^{-3}$)	Percentage of carbohydrate	Normal serum conc. (mg/ml)[b]	Half-life (days)
IgG1		γ_1	146	4	51	2–3	9	21 ± 5
IgG2		γ_2	146	4	51	2–3	3	20 ± 2
IgG3		γ_3	165	4	60	2–3	1	7 ± 1
IgG4		γ_4	146	4	51	2–3	0.5	21 ± 2.5
IgM	+ J	μ	970	5	72	9–12	1.2	5
IgA1		α_1	160	4	58	7–11	2.0	6
IgA2 A2m(1)		α_2	160	4	58	7–11	0.5	?
A2m(2)		α_2	160	4	58	7–11		6
sIgA	+ J + SC	α_1 or α_2	405	4	58	7–11	0–0.05	—
IgD		δ	170	4	63	10–12	0.06	3
IgE		ϵ	188–196	5	72–76	12	0.0002	2.5–4

[a] 10 or 11 S-S bonds link the H chains.

[b] There is considerable individual variation in these values.

TABLE 2. Biological properties (effector functions) of subclasses of human IgG and their domains.

Property	IgG1	IgG2	IgG3	IgG4	Domain(s) involved
Binding to C1q component of complement	+	+	+	−	C_H2
Activation of alternate pathway of complement fixation by the aggregated IgG	+	+	+	+	C_H1
Passage through placenta	+	+	+	+	C_H2 and/or C_H3
Binding to receptors on monocytes	+	−	+	−	C_H2 and C_H3
Binding to receptors on granulocytes	+	+	+	+	C_H2 and C_H3
Passive cutaneous anaphylaxis in guinea pigs	+	−	+	+	?
Binding to Protein A of *Staphylococcus aureus*	+	+	−	+	C_H2 and C_H3

also been found in IgA of the BALB/c strain of mice, but not in the NZB strain.[2]

IgM and three of the four subclasses of IgG are capable of activating the complement system through the conventional pathway (Chapter 11). IgG4, IgA, and IgE are inactive in this respect but, when aggregated, can activate the alternate pathway, which starts with the C3 component. The binding of IgG1 or IgG3 to Fc receptors on mononuclear phagocytic cells results in enhancement of phagocytosis, or opsonization, of bacteria, viruses, or parasites complexed with antibodies of these subclasses. As indicated in Table 2, only IgG is transmitted through the placenta from the mother to offspring. Such antibodies are essential for the newborn child, whose capacity to produce antibodies is negligible at birth and increases gradually during the first year of life.

[2] Data on this structural feature are available for these two inbred strains because myeloma can be induced in them but not in most other strains of mice; many BALB/c and NZB myeloma proteins have therefore been studied. With the advent of hybridomas, such data can now be obtained for other strains of mice by studying monoclonal antibodies (Chapter 10).

In Chapter 2 we considered many of the structural properties of IgG. In the following sections, some of the special properties of human IgM, IgA, IgE, and IgD will be discussed.

IgM

Sketches illustrating the structure of IgM are shown in Figure 1, A and B. Each of the heavy (μ) chains consists of five domains: one V_H and four C_μ. At the C-terminal end of the μ chain is an extra "tail" of 19 amino acids, whose sequence is unrelated to that of the rest of the molecule; it is not considered part of a domain. The tail contains a cysteine residue that forms a disulfide bond either with another μ chain in the same four-chain subunit or with a J chain. The IgM molecule is a pentamer of four-chain units and thus has ten antigen-binding sites. The sedimentation coefficient of the pentameric molecule is 19 S, whereas that of the monomeric four-chain unit is 7.5 S. Within a four-chain monomeric unit, the two μ chains are linked by two interchain disulfide bonds. In the pentameric structure, each four-chain unit is joined to an adjacent unit by a single disulfide bond joining two μ chains. If the molecule is subjected to mild reduction at neutral pH, it dissociates readily into five four-chain units. Thus, the four-chain monomers are linked to one another only by the disulfide bond and not by noncovalent interactions. In contrast to IgG, IgA, and IgD, there is no clearly defined hinge region in IgM.

Each molecule of IgM also contains one J chain, which has a molecular weight of 15,000 and is disulfide-bonded to two μ chains of the same four-chain monomer, next to their C-terminal ends. The J chain represents such a small fraction of the mass of the molecule (approximately 2%) that its presence was overlooked until 1971. (The J chain was discovered by Marian E. Koshland of the University of California.) The J chain appears to be essential for initiating polymerization (through disulfide bonds) of the four-chain units in IgM and IgA.

STRUCTURE OF MEMBRANE-BOUND IgM (IgM$_m$)

The membranes of mature B cells contain immunoglobulins that act as receptors for antigen. Membrane-bound IgM (IgM$_m$) is present as the four-chain monomer rather than as the pentameric form. Our knowledge of the primary structure (amino acid sequence) of IgM$_m$ stems mainly from studies of mouse DNA, discussed in Chapter 6. It has proved difficult to obtain enough IgM$_m$ for detailed amino acid sequence analysis, and the relevant amino acid sequence had to be

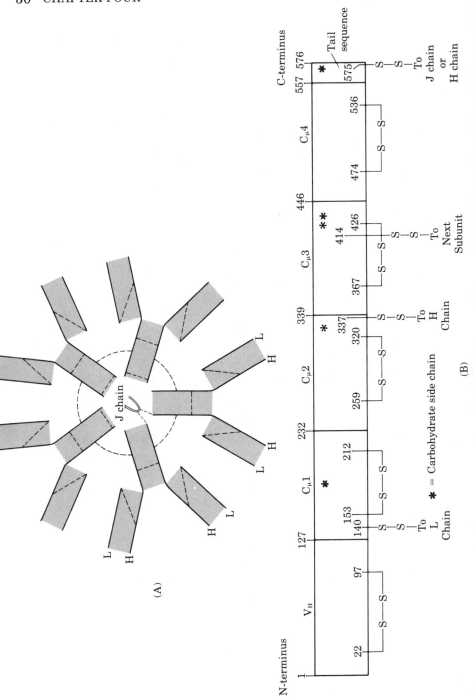

(A)

(B)

◀ **FIGURE 1.** (A) Diagrammatic sketch of a human IgM molecule. The dashed lines represent interchain disulfide bonds. (B) Sketch of a human μ chain, showing locations of domains, disulfide bonds, and carbohydrate. (After Putnam et al., 1973.)

deduced from the DNA sequence. It is now clear that mouse IgM_m differs from the secreted molecule, IgM_s, only near the C-terminal end of the μ chain (Figure 2). The last 20 amino acid residues of the secreted chain ($μ_s$) are missing from $μ_m$ and are replaced by a different sequence of 41 residues, i.e., $μ_m$ is 21 residues longer than $μ_s$. The 41 C-terminal amino acid residues of $μ_m$ include a stretch of about 26 amino acids that is very hydrophobic (Figure 2). It is believed that this portion of the chain is responsible for the insertion of IgM into the cell membrane. The hydrophobic amino acid side chains would be compatible with the lipid of the membrane, and the length of the hydrophobic stretch is sufficient to span the membrane. A hydrophobic C-terminal region is also present in the membrane-bound forms and absent from the secreted forms of mouse $γ_{2a}$, $γ_{2b}$, α, and, probably, δ chains. It seems likely that this structural feature will prove to be common to membrane-bound immunoglobulins of various classes and from various animal species.

IgA

IgA constitutes about 15–20% of the immunoglobulin in normal human serum. IgA in secretory fluids has a special role and structure,

FIGURE 2. Comparison of C-terminal sequences of secreted ($μ_s$) and membrane-bound ($μ_m$) heavy chains of mouse IgM. The sequences are identical up to position 556, but differ thereafter; $μ_s$ has 20 additional residues, whereas $μ_m$ has 41 additional residues. A very hydrophobic stretch of 26 amino acids in $μ_m$ is underlined; it was suggested that this stretch anchors the chain to the hydrophobic lipid portion of the B cell membrane (Rogers et al., 1980). The one-letter code for amino acids is given in Appendix I.

which is discussed in the next section. In serum it occurs principally as the four-chain unit, but small amounts of disulfide-bonded polymers (8 chains or 12 chains) are often present. The four-chain unit has a molecular weight of approximately 160,000.

IgA occurs as two subclasses, IgA1 and IgA2, with the former constituting 80–90% of the total in serum. The C_α regions of the two subclasses are quite similar, exhibiting over 90% homology of amino acid sequence. However, their hinge regions differ considerably. A portion of the sequence of the hinge region present in IgA2 is duplicated in IgA1, making the latter about twice as long (total of 29 amino acids). The H–L disulfide bond is absent in one allotype of IgA2.

Both IgA1 and IgA2 have a relatively high content of carbohydrate (~10%), localized in the $C_\alpha 2$ and $C_\alpha 3$ domains of IgA1 and in all three C_α domains of IgA2. In addition, there are at least two carbohydrate chains attached in the hinge region of IgA1; the latter are absent in IgA2, a finding consistent with the shorter amino acid sequence of its hinge region.

SECRETORY IgA

In 1963, W. B. Chodirker and T. B. Tomasi, at the University of Vermont Medical School, made the important discovery that IgA is the predominant class of immunoglobulin in human saliva, colostrum, and tears. This finding was later extended to other secretory fluids, including nasal, bronchial, and various other fluids bathing mucous membranes in the respiratory and digestive systems.

The secreted molecule was designated secretory IgA or sIgA. Its structure is illustrated in Figure 3. The molecule has a molecular weight of 400,000 and comprises two four-chain units, a polypeptide chain called secretory component (mol. wt., 70,000), and one J chain of molecular weight 15,000. The J chain is identical to that in IgM (Figure 1). Secretory component (SC) is a single polypeptide chain. It is bound to α chains through noncovalent forces as well as disulfide bonds. J chain is linked to the rest of the molecule only through disulfide bonds. Like all immunoglobulins, IgA is synthesized by lymphoblasts and plasma cells (i.e., B cells), which also produce J chains; SC is added when a dimer of IgA, with the J chain attached, subsequently passes through epithelial cells. There is evidence that SC is present on the epithelial membrane, where it acts as a receptor for the newly formed IgA molecule.

Because of its presence near external membranes, sIgA constitutes a first line of defense against microorganisms in the environment. One property of sIgA that is important in this respect is its multivalence,

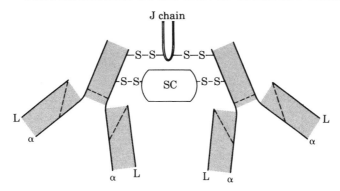

FIGURE 3. Sketch of human IgA1. SC (secretory component) is joined to the α chains by strong noncovalent bonds as well as by disulfide bonds.

which is associated with high avidity of binding to antigens; this may be especially relevant in the neutralization of viruses. sIgA may also combine with certain antigens in food and prevent their absorption into the blood stream, thus reducing the incidence of allergic reactions. The sIgA in colostrum is important in preventing infections in the newborn. sIgA is relatively resistant to degradation by proteolytic enzymes. This property is of physiological importance since proteolytic enzymes are generally present in secretory fluids.

IgE

Of the various isotypes of immunoglobulins, IgE is present at the lowest concentration in serum (Table 1). Its concentration is elevated in some allergic individuals and in patients with parasitic infections such as malaria, schistosomiasis, etc. IgE is biologically important because it mediates reactions of immediate hypersensitivity (allergic reactions). Thus, human allergies are due to the presence of IgE antibodies that have specificity for the allergens in question, such as proteins in animal dander, house dust, ragweed, insect venom, etc. IgE has been identified in many mammalian species. In some species, not including the human, immediate hypersensitivity is also mediated by a subclass of IgG.

In view of the high levels of IgE often observed in patients with parasitic infections, it was proposed that IgE is important in combating such infections. Recent evidence indicates that IgE antibodies can indeed enhance the destruction of parasites by eosinophils and macrophages. Another suggested role involves the increase in vascular permeability associated with release of histamine and other mediators of immediate hypersensitivity; reactions of antigens with IgE antibodies may in this way facilitate the migration of protective leukocytes into infected areas.

The IgE molecule contains two heavy (ε) chains and two κ or λ chains. The ε chain of IgE comprises one V_H domain and four C_ε domains and is thus similar in size to the μ chain. It also has a high content of carbohydrate, which is attached at six positions in the C_ε region and is present in each of the C_ε domains except $C_\varepsilon 4$. The limited sequence homology between the ε chain and heavy chains of other classes (25–33%) indicates that IgE appeared early during the evolution of the immunoglobulins.

IgE was discovered in 1966 by K. Ishizaka and T. Ishizaka, working at the Children's Asthma Research Institute in Denver. This was a remarkable accomplishment in view of its extremely low serum concentration. Since then, a few patients with multiple myeloma have been found whose cells secrete an IgE myeloma protein. The serum of such a patient may contain 10–30 mg/ml of IgE. One milliliter would then contain more IgE than 100 liters of normal serum. The availability of myeloma proteins made possible a variety of studies on the structural and biological properties of IgE. It also permitted development of radioimmunoassays for total serum IgE and for IgE of a particular antigen-binding specificity. Some of these assays are in use in clinical laboratories.

In experimental animals, the presence of IgE antibodies reactive with a given antigen can be demonstrated by the "passive cutaneous anaphylactic" (PCA) reaction (Ovary, 1964). For example, mouse serum containing IgE antibodies specific for antigen X can be inoculated intradermally into a rat. On the next day the rat is inoculated intravenously (not near the skin site) with a solution of antigen X mixed with Evan's blue dye. Where the antigen encounters the IgE antibody, which is fixed to mast cells in the skin at the site of inoculation, SEROTONIN and other mediators are released. This increases the permeability of blood vessels and permits escape of dye into the surrounding tissue. The size of the blue patch that develops on the skin is a measure of the amount of IgE antibody that had been injected. This highly sensitive reaction can detect the presence of nanogram (10^{-9} gram) quantities of IgE antibodies specific for a given antigen.

A similar scheme, referred to as the Prausnitz-Küstner (PK) reaction, is used to identify IgE antibodies in humans. Serum from an allergic individual is inoculated into the skin of a nonallergic volunteer. This is followed 1 or 2 days later by antigen, which in this case is injected into the same skin site. If IgE antibodies are present in the serum initially injected, the skin site becomes swollen and red (wheal and erythema reaction). The IgE antibodies responsible for the PK and PCA reactions are called REAGINS.

Some skin tests for IgE antibodies are now being supplemented by radioimmunoassays for IgE antibodies of a particular specificity.

MECHANISM OF ALLERGIC REACTIONS

IgE antibodies are bound to the membranes of mast cells in skin or to basophilic leukocytes and certain classes of lymphocyte in blood. Each of these cell types has specific membrane receptor molecules that recognize and bind the Fc portion of the IgE molecule. The IgE RE-CEPTOR on rat basophils has been studied by H. Metzger and associates. It comprises two subunits designated α (mol. wt., 50,000) and β (30,000–35,000). The IgE-binding site is in the α subunit. The α subunit has a high content of carbohydrate ($\sim35\%$), whereas the β subunit lacks carbohydrate. The binding affinity of the receptor for IgE is very high.

After binding of IgE to the Fc receptor of the cell, the next stage requires participation of the antigen (e.g., ragweed protein), which crosslinks the IgE antibody that is bound to the cell membrane. This crosslinking reaction causes mast cells or basophils to release numerous granules containing HISTAMINE, which is the most important mediator of immediate hypersensitivity in man. In mice and rats, serotonin is the principal mediator. Other mediators in man include the slow reacting substance of anaphylaxis (SRS-A) and a tetrapeptide that is chemotactic for eosinophils (ECF-A). SRS-A is now known to comprise a mixture of three lipid molecules of low molecular weight called leukotrienes. These molecules, which are related in structure to the prostaglandins, have extremely potent contractile effects on the smaller airways of the respiratory system. At least one component of SRS-A is liberated by macrophages in the presence of complexes containing antigen and IgE, suggesting that macrophages, as well as mast cells and basophils, may be important in human allergic reactions.

The symptoms of allergy are brought on by contractions of smooth muscle, which can cause sneezing and interfere with breathing, and by increased vascular permeability and attraction of leukocytes, which result in inflammation. In extreme cases the reactions of immediate hypersensitivity may cause fatal anaphylactic shock. This can readily be demonstrated in the guinea pig by appropriately spaced inoculations of certain antigens.

One can demonstrate by the following *in vitro* experiment that the

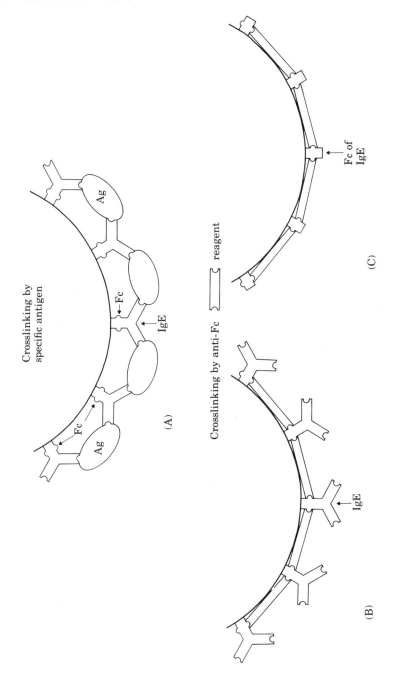

◄ **FIGURE 4.** Illustration of mechanisms leading to degranulation of mast cells or basophilic leukocytes. (A) Antigen crosslinks IgE molecules attached to the cell. The IgE must be specific for the antigen in order for this to occur. (B) and (C) Crosslinking is induced by antibody to the Fc region of IgE. This causes crosslinking and degranulation when whole IgE (B) or the Fc fragment of IgE (C) is bound to the cell.

role of antigen in inducing the allergic response is to crosslink the IgE. Incubate mast cells with Fc fragments of IgE, then wash and add antibody directed against Fc. The antibody, which can crosslink Fc fragments, causes release of histamine (Figure 4). Note that antigen was not used in this experiment. Thus, crosslinking, which of course can be induced by antigen, is a critical step in the induction of the allergic response.

IgD

The IgD content of normal human serum is very low, averaging about 50–100 μg/ml. As in the case of IgE, most of what we know about its physical properties comes from studies of myeloma proteins, which can be obtained in large quantity. Although patients with IgD-secreting myelomas are relatively rare, they are far more numerous than those with IgE. For an unknown reason, a disproportionate percentage (about 80%) of IgD myeloma proteins have λ chains. The IgD that is present as a receptor on lymphocyte membranes has a normal distribution of κ and λ chains (ratio, about 6:4).

Human IgD has a molecular weight of 170,000, which makes it somewhat larger than IgG. The difference is largely due to the relatively high content of carbohydrate (12%) in IgD. The carbohydrate is attached in three locations in the $C_\delta 2$ and $C_\delta 3$ domains in the Fc segment and in four or five positions in the hinge region. The δ chain comprises four domains—one V_H and three $C_\delta 3$.[3] A single disulfide bond joins the heavy chains of IgD; the molecule thus resembles rabbit IgG but differs from the other classes of human immunoglobulin in this respect.

IgD is exquisitely sensitive to proteolysis. A large percentage of an IgD population can be cleaved into Fab fragments by a 1-minute treatment with papain. This sensitivity may be attributable to the fact that IgD has a very large hinge region, consisting of about 60 amino acid residues. In addition to rendering the molecule sensitive to proteolysis, the large hinge region may provide flexibility and

---

[3] Mouse and rat IgD have two rather than three C_δ domains; the domain corresponding to human $C_\delta 2$ is absent.

thereby permit a greater efficiency of crosslinking by antigen—as compared to IgM, which has no identifiable hinge region.

There is no evidence that serum IgD has unique and particularly valuable biological properties. IgD is, however, important as a receptor for antigen on B lymphocytes. As they mature, B cells first acquire IgM receptors, then IgD receptors. The acquisition of IgD is accompanied by an increased resistance to tolerance induction; immature B cells, which have only IgM receptors, are very easily tolerized by exposure to antigen.

The IgM and IgD present on the membrane of an individual B cell share the same specificity and appear to have identical V_H regions and L chains (and, therefore, the same idiotype; Chapter 8). After stimulation by antigen, precursor B cells give rise to progeny, of which some are antibody-producers and others are memory B cells; the memory cells may have receptors of any class. The antibodies produced have the same antigen-binding specificity and idiotype as the IgM and IgD receptors present on the original, precursor B lymphocyte. The flexibility of IgD mentioned earlier may result in greater ease of stimulation by antigen of those cells that have IgD receptors, as compared to ease of stimulation of cells bearing only IgM receptors.

Although IgD is present on the earliest memory cells formed after stimulation by antigen, the membranes of mature memory cells reflect the class of antibody (IgG, etc.) that will be formed after the memory cell undergoes further differentiation into an antibody producer.

It is thus evident that IgD plays an important role in governing the differentiation of the B cell. How this function is mediated by the membrane-bound molecules (i.e., the nature of biochemical events that occur after stimulation by antigen) remains to be elucidated.

BIOCHEMICAL OR BIOLOGICAL FUNCTIONS OF DOMAINS OF γ CHAINS

Shortly after the domain structure of immunoglobulins was elucidated in the 1960s, it was proposed that various domains may have particular biological functions; this would help to account for the evolution of these structurally related, but nonidentical, segments of the molecule. Considerable evidence that supports this view has accumulated. We will summarize here some of the properties associated with the C_γ domains of human IgG. The V_H domain is, of course, associated with the antigen-binding properties of the molecule.

$C_\gamma 1$

The only unique biological function that has been found so far to be associated with this domain is the binding of the fourth component of complement. $C_\gamma1$ is intimately associated with the C_L domain of a κ or γ chain and maintains the structural integrity of the Fab region.

$C_\gamma2$

The binding of the first component of complement, which initiates the classical pathway of complement activation (Chapter 11), takes place through interaction of the C1q component of complement with the $C_\gamma2$ domain of IgG. The complement-binding site in IgM is present in the $C_\mu4$ domain. Of the four subclasses of human IgG, only IgG4 is unable to fix complement through the classical pathway. This reflects the fact that the complement-binding site of IgG4 is not exposed to the external medium; upon treatment with papain, this binding site becomes exposed and the Fc fragment is able to bind the C1q component of complement.

$C_\gamma2$ also appears to control the rate at which IgG is catabolized; the half-life of $C_\gamma2$, but not that of other isolated domains, is very similar to that of intact IgG. The precise mechanisms involved in catabolism are not known.

$C_\gamma2$ and $C_\gamma3$

$C_\gamma2$ and, principally, $C_\gamma3$ are involved in binding of IgG1 and IgG3 to Fc receptors of mononuclear phagocytic cells. Such binding results in enhancement of phagocytosis (opsonization) of cells, such as bacteria, to which the antibodies are bound. Both domains appear to be required for binding of each of the four subclasses of human IgG to phagocytic leukocytes or to receptors in the placental membrane. Some of these properties are summarized in Table 2.

EVOLUTION OF THE IMMUNOGLOBULINS

Immunoglobulins are present in all vertebrate species that have been studied. They have not been identified in invertebrates. Plasma cells are present in higher orders of sharks and all of the more advanced vertebrates (Figure 5). In lower orders of sharks and in the hagfish and lamprey, which are very primitive fish, antibodies are synthesized by cells that resemble lymphocytes. The hagfish and lamprey produce very small amounts of immunoglobulin, even when immunized, and evidence for the presence of the four-chain subunit in these species is inconclusive. All vertebrates studied that are higher on the evolutionary scale do, however, synthesize immunoglobulins that possess the characteristic four-chain subunit. In most, but not all, immunoglobulins, the H and L chains are linked by an interchain

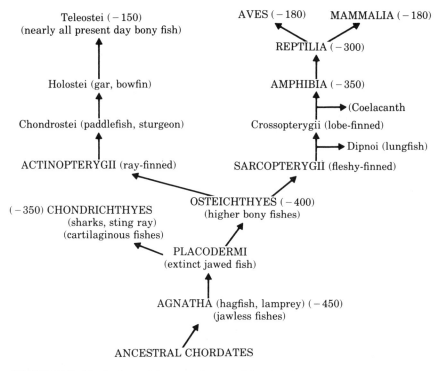

FIGURE 5. Evolution of the vertebrates. The numbers in parentheses show the approximate time of emergence during evolution (years × 10^{-6}). (After Romer, 1970.)

disulfide bond. Among the exceptions are human IgA2 of the A₂m(1) allotype, the IgA of at least one strain of mouse, and all frog immunoglobulins; only a few other species have been investigated carefully for this property. Amino acid sequences of shark L and H chains show a clear resemblance to those of mammals. Also, carbohydrate has been found in all immunoglobulins. Although information on the repertoire of antibody specificities of lower vertebrates is limited, it is known that fish respond to a large variety of antigens.

IgM

With the possible exception of the Agnatha (hagfish and lamprey), IgM evidently exists in vertebrates throughout the evolutionary scale, from fishes to mammals. It is identified by its characteristic polymeric, disulfide-bonded structure and, in most species, by the presence of a J chain. IgM generally occurs as the pentamer of the four-chain unit.

An important exception is the subclass Actinopterygii (Figure 5), which includes nearly all present-day bony fishes. In these fishes IgM exists as a tetramer rather than as a pentamer of the four-chain monomeric subunit. Another exception is the amphibian *Xenopus,* whose IgM comprises six four-chain subunits.

In the Chondrichthyes, which include the sharks, and in some bony fishes, IgM also occurs in serum as a four-chain monomer that is antigenically very similar to the polymeric IgM of the same species. The monomeric form does not constitute a separate class.

IMMUNOGLOBULIN OF LOW MOLECULAR WEIGHT THAT DIFFERS FROM IgM (LMIg)

The most primitive vertebrates expressing a distinct low-molecular-weight immunoglobulin (LMIg) class are the African and Australian lungfish. The existence of LMIg differing in class from IgM is shown by antigenic differences, which undoubtedly reflect differences in the amino acid sequences of C_H regions. The lungfish is the only surviving member of the Sarcopterygii, which are on the line of ascent to mammals, although the lungfish itself is not a direct ancestor. Lungfish require air and have a number of the physiological characteristics of amphibia. It is interesting that this intermediate species is the most primitive to exhibit LMIg. All vertebrates investigated that are higher than fishes on the evolutionary scale—with the possible exception of the most primitive amphibia—also have two or more distinct immunoglobulin classes, including IgM and a class of low molecular weight.

An obvious question is whether the LMIg of lungfish is the direct predecessor of a particular class of mammalian immunoglobulin, such as IgG or IgA. The same question may be asked of the LMIg of amphibia, reptiles, and birds. In most instances, it is not possible to provide an answer. For example, the fact that the LMIg of lungfish is not antigenically related to human IgG would not disprove a direct evolutionary relationship because of the changes in amino acid sequence that occur as a consequence of mutations over a long period of time. The conclusion that IgM is present in lower vertebrates is based on the disulfide-bonded, polymeric structure rather than on antigenic or amino acid sequence analysis. A close resemblance with respect to overall structure has similarly led to the conclusion that secretory IgA is present in birds as well as in mammals. The latter is perhaps the only convincing example of a demonstrated evolutionary relationship between the LMIg of two different classes of vertebrate. In many species belonging to classes of vertebrates more primitive than birds, IgM acts as the secretory immunoglobulin.

TABLE 3. Properties of immunoglobulin classes having a lower
molecular weight than IgM (LMIg).

Species or class	Properties
Lungfish	5.9 S (sedimentation coefficient)[a]
Birds	IgA, IgY (7 S)[b]
Amphibia (anurans)[c]	7 S
Reptiles[d]	7.5 S (180,000); 5.7 S (120,000)

[a] All other fishes studied so far possess an immunoglobulin of low molecular weight that is antigenically identical to IgM; it is not considered to represent a separate class.

[b] The duck has a third class of LMIg with a sedimentation coefficient of 5.7 S.

[c] It is uncertain whether lower amphibia (the urodeles) possess any LMIg.

[d] The data available are limited to a very small number of species.

Table 3 lists some of the classes and properties of the immunoglobulins of several species at different levels on the evolutionary scale.

κ AND λ CHAINS

Light chains with an approximate molecular weight of 23,000 have been conserved throughout the evolution of the vertebrates. As indicated earlier, most or all mammals produce both κ and λ chains; the proportions vary greatly among species. These intraspecies variations may reflect differences in the number of V genes. This is illustrated by the L chains of the mouse, which has far more V_κ than V_λ genes; its normal L chains are about 97% κ.

Although fishes possess L chains that are related to those of mammals in amino acid sequence, the data do not yet permit a conclusion as to whether the L chains of fishes are κ, λ, or both. A similar uncertainty applies to the L chains of the chicken; those chicken L chains that have been studied appear to bear a somewhat closer resemblance to human λ than to human κ chains. One report indicates the presence of two antigenically distinct types of L chain in the alligator; whether these are homologous to human κ and λ is uncertain.

A comparison of the major amino acid sequence of L chains from the antibody of a shark with that of a human κ chain (from a myeloma protein) is shown in Figure 6. The proteins are the same in 15 of 26 positions, including the highly conserved half-cystine at position 23.

```
                        1                                10                     15
Shark Light    Asp Ile Thr Met Thr Glu Ser Pro Pro Val Leu Ser Val Gly Leu
   chain           (Val)

Human V_κI     ————— Gln ————— Gln ————— Ser Ser ————— Ala Ser Val
(Protein OU)
```

```
                        16        20                    26
Shark Light    Gly Gln Thr Ala Thr Ile Thr Cys Thr Ala Ser
   chain

Human V_κI     —— Asp Arg Val ——————————— Arg ———
(Protein OU)
```

FIGURE 6. Comparison of the N-terminal amino acid sequences of light chains prepared from the anti-streptococcal antibody of a nurse shark with that of a human κ chain, obtained from a myeloma protein. A solid line represents identity of the human protein sequence with that of the shark. There are 15 positions of identity out of 26 residues. References are in Appendix III and abbreviations for amino acids in Appendix I.

ANALYSIS OF A REPTILIAN IMMUNOGLOBULIN GENE

A recent report indicates that a V_H gene from a phylogenetically ancient reptile, *Caiman,* is very similar in length to a typical mouse V_H gene (Litman et al., 1983). In addition, a pair of genes from the two species showed about 70% homology in nucleotide sequence and 56% homology in amino acid sequence; an even closer resemblance to certain human V_H genes was noted. *Caiman* was found to possess an extensive family of V_H genes. It is of considerable practical significance that a mouse V_H probe was able to hybridize with the reptilian genes; this suggests the feasibility of examining immunoglobulin genes from many lower species.

MAMMALIAN IMMUNOGLOBULINS

All mammals studied have immunoglobulins resembling human IgM and IgG. For many mammalian species, the relationships can be established clearly through antigenic analysis, i.e., with antibodies prepared against the immunoglobulins. For a few lower mammals, antigenic analysis is inconclusive; the relationships are more tenuous and based on indirect evidence.

Although the data are limited, it seems likely that all mammals will prove to possess immunoglobulins with the characteristics of IgA, including secretory IgA. As noted earlier, IgA has also been identified in birds. Immunoglobulins with the properties of IgE have been detected in nearly all mammalian species investigated so far; however, a marsupial that has been studied appears to lack IgE.

Tables 1 and 2 in Chapter 5 present data on the degree of amino acid sequence homology that exist between mammalian immunoglobulins of various classes and species.

LITERATURE CITED

Chodirker, W. B. and Tomasi, T. B., Jr. (1963). Gamma globulins: quantitative relationships in human serum and nonvascular fluids. *Science 142*, 1080.

Ishizaka, K. and Ishizaka, T. (1966). Physicochemical properties of reaginic antibody. I. Association of reaginic activity with an immunoglobulin other than gamma A or gamma G globulin. *J. Allergy 37*, 169.

Litman, G. W., Berger, L., Murphy, K., Litman, R., Hinds, K., Jahn, C. L., and Erickson, B. W. (1983). Complete nucleotide sequence of an immunoglobulin V_H gene homologue from *Caiman,* a phylogenetically ancient reptile. *Nature 303,* 349.

Metzger, H., Goetze, A., Kanellopoulos, J., Holowka, D. and Fewtrell, C. (1982). Structure of the high-affinity mast cell receptor for IgE. *Federation Proc. 41, 8.*

Ovary, Z. (1964). Passive cutaneous anaphylaxis. In J. F. Ackroyd, Ed., *Immunological Methods.* Oxford, Blackwell Scientific Publications.

Putnam, F. W., Florent, G., Paul, C., Shinoda, T. and Shimuzu, A. (1973). Complete amino acid sequence of the Mu heavy chain of a human IgM immunoglobulin. *Science 182,* 287.

Rogers, J., Early, P., Carter, C., Calame, K., Bond, M., Hood, L. and Wall, R. (1980). Two mRNAs with different 3′ ends encode membrane-bound and secreted forms of immunoglobulin μ chain. *Cell 20,* 303.

Romer, A. S. (1970). *The Vertebrate Body,* 4th ed. Philadelphia, W. B. Saunders.

SUGGESTED ADDITIONAL READING

Bennich, H. and Johansson, S. G. O. (1971). Structure and function of human immunoglobulin E. *Adv. Immunol. 13,* 1.

Koshland, M. E. (1975). Structure and function of the J chain. *Adv. Immunol. 20,* 41.

Marchalonis, J. J. (1977). *Immunity in Evolution*. Cambridge, Harvard University Press.

Metzger, H. (1970). Structure and functions of IgM immunoglobulins. *Adv. Immunol. 12,* 57.

Natvig, J. B. and Kunkel, H. G. (1973). Human immunoglobulins: classes, subclasses, genetic variants and idiotypes. *Adv. Immunol. 16,* 1.

Takahashi, N., Tetaert, D., Debuire, B., Lin, L.-C., and Putnam, F. W. (1982). Complete amino acid sequence of the δ heavy chain of human immunoglobulin D. *Proc. Natl. Acad. Sci. USA 79,* 2850.

Tomasi, T. B., Jr. (1976). *The Immune System in Secretions*. Englewood Cliffs, N.J., Prentice-Hall, Inc.

Immunological Reviews (1978). Volume 41. Several reviews on Immunoglobulin E.

5

PRIMARY AND THREE-DIMENSIONAL STRUCTURE OF ANTIBODIES

OVERVIEW

A large amount of data has been acquired in recent years on amino acid sequences and three-dimensional structures of immunoglobulins. This has led to clear insights as to how antibodies function and how they are genetically controlled. To obtain data on amino acid sequences, homogeneous antibodies are needed: the principal sources are myeloma proteins and, more recently, monoclonal antibodies from hybridomas. Structural features outlined in Chapter 2 are discussed here in relation to amino acid sequence data. These features include the existence of variable and constant domains and of hypervariable, complementarity-determining regions (CDR). Sequence data led to the correct prediction that separate gene segments encode the variable and constant regions of H and L chains. Determination of three-dimensional structures to atomic dimensions became feasible when highly ordered crystals of immunoglobulins or their Fab or Fc fragments were prepared for use in X-ray analysis. Among the important elements of the three-dimensional structure are the existence of identifiable domains, consisting of 110–120 amino acids, and the folding pattern within a domain, which is similar in variable and constant domains. The same studies show that an antigen-binding site is formed by adjacent loops of amino acids derived from CDR of an H chain and an L chain—the contribution of CDR to the combining site had been predicted from amino acid sequence analyses. There are many points of contact between V_L and V_H, between C_L and C_H, and between the two C_H3 domains of an IgG molecule. The two C_H2 domains are separated by carbohydrate.

*   *   *

67

Our understanding of how immunoglobulins function and how they are genetically controlled has been greatly enhanced by information on amino acid sequences and on three-dimensional structures. Some of this information and its implications will be reviewed in this chapter.

IMMUNOGLOBULINS USED FOR AMINO ACID SEQUENCE ANALYSES

Suppose one wishes to determine amino acid sequences of the H and L chains of an antibody that is reactive with a particular antigen. The antibody can be purified from an immune serum by adsorption to and elution from the immobilized antigen (e.g., antigen coupled to Sepharose). In general, however, such a preparation would not be useful for amino acid sequence analysis because of the heterogeneity of antibodies, including those directed against a single antigen or hapten. It is virtually impossible to analyze sequences of a complex mixture. There are three major sources of homogeneous antibodies that account for nearly all of the amino acid sequences that have been reported.

1. *Myeloma proteins.* The disease MULTIPLE MYELOMA is a form of cancer characterized by proliferation of antibody-secreting cells (plasma cells, plasmablasts, lymphoblasts). This generally fatal disease is associated with destruction of bone and repeated infections. In most cases the malignancy arises from a single cell; as a consequence, the proliferating cells secrete a homogeneous immunoglobulin suitable for amino acid sequence analysis. The concentration of the immunoglobulin in serum is usually high, frequently between 10 and 40 mg/ml. In general, the antigen for which the secreted immunoglobulin has specificity is not known, and therefore many of the reported amino acid sequences are those of immunoglobulins of unknown specificity. On the other hand, the antigen-binding specificity of some myeloma proteins has been determined by trial and error. This has made it possible to compare amino acid sequences of different myeloma proteins with the same specificity, e.g., reactive with dextran, the dinitrophenyl group, or phosphorylcholine. Because myeloma tumors vary with respect to the class and subclass of the immunoglobulin secreted, they have been a principal source of material for determination of C-region, as well as V-region sequences. Henry G. Kunkel of The Rockefeller University was one of the first to recognize the applicability of myeloma proteins to our understanding of normal immunoglobulin structure.

Patients (or mice) with multiple myeloma sometimes secrete substantial amounts of homogeneous L chains—called BENCE-JONES PROTEINS—in their urine. This results from the production of an excess of L chains by some or all of the tumor cells. Many individuals produce both a complete myeloma protein and a Bence-Jones protein. When this occurs, the urinary Bence-Jones protein corresponds in structure to the L chain of the myeloma protein. Bence-Jones proteins have been an important source of L chains for use in amino acid sequence analyses.

In humans, a type of lymphoma known as WALDENSTRÖM'S MACROGLOBULINEMIA is associated with the secretion of IgM. Patients with this disease have been the major source of homogeneous human IgM.

Multiple myeloma occurs in humans, mice, rats, dogs, cats, and other species. Most sequence analyses have been carried out, however, with murine and human proteins. Multiple myeloma has been induced in mice by repeated injections of mineral oil or certain plastics into the peritoneal cavity; induction of the disease takes several months (Potter and Lieberman, 1967). Once the tumor is established, it can be maintained indefinitely by successive transfers into mice of the same strain, thus providing a virtually unlimited source of homogeneous immunoglobulin. Very few inbred mouse strains are susceptible to the induction of multiple myeloma by this method; the BALB/c and NZB strains have been the principal sources of myeloma proteins.

2. *Monoclonal antibodies from hybridomas.* Antibodies of this type are the subject of Chapter 10. In brief, MONOCLONAL ANTIBODIES are obtained by fusing an antibody-producing cell, which secretes a single species of antibody molecule, with a myeloma tumor cell. The fused cell secretes the desired antibody but has the characteristic immortality of a tumor cell line. The fused cell line is referred to as a HYBRIDOMA. Hybridomas are now a major source of homogeneous antibodies, which can have almost any desired antigen-binding specificity. Monoclonal antibodies from hybridomas have a great advantage over those from myeloma tumors in that they can be prepared to order against the desired antigen.

3. *Homogeneous antibacterial antibodies.* When immunized with killed bacteria, an animal will sometimes produce a high titer of relatively homogeneous antibodies directed against carbohydrate in the cell wall. A number of amino acid sequence studies of antibodies, particularly rabbit antibodies, to such carbohydrates from streptococci and pneumococci have been reported.

GENETIC INTERPRETATION OF AMINO ACID SEQUENCES

Genetic studies have demonstrated the existence of separate genes coding for V and C regions; the genes recombine (translocate) in such a manner as to put a *V* gene into close proximity with a *C* gene in an antibody-producing cell; this is discussed in detail in Chapter 6. The existence of separate *V* and *C* genes was postulated about 10 years earlier on the basis of the amino acid sequence data discussed in the following section.

AMINO ACID SEQUENCE ANALYSES

The first extensive amino acid sequence analyses on immunoglobulins were reported in 1965 by Norbert Hilschmann and Lyman C. Craig of The Rockefeller University, who determined the sequences of human Bence-Jones proteins. When the first two κ chains were sequenced, it was found that the C-terminal halves differed at only one position out of 106, whereas the N-terminal halves exhibited numerous differences. Subsequent data established the generality of this important finding, i.e., the existence of variable (V) and constant (C) regions. Within a species, the sequences of C regions are invariant for a given type of chain except for minor inherited variations (ALLOTYPES, Chapter 7). The single difference between the two C_κ sequences, mentioned above, proved to be an allotypic difference.

On the basis of the results of Hilschmann and Craig, William Dreyer and J. Claude Bennett of the California Institute of Technology advanced the hypothesis in 1965 that the V and C regions are encoded by separate genes. They correctly reasoned that since there are many *V* genes it would be wasteful for a gene segment controlling the C region to be repeated so many times. Only one *C* gene would be required if some mechanism existed for selecting the *V* gene to be expressed in a given cell and for bringing it into close proximity with the *C* gene. We now know that the existence of separate *V* and *C* genes is a general feature of immunoglobulins and applies to H chains as well as to L chains. As will be seen in Chapter 6, the gene organization is actually somewhat more complex; the V region is actually controlled by two or, in the case of V_H, three gene segments; the C region is under control of a single gene segment.

AMINO ACID SEQUENCES OF V REGIONS OF HUMAN κ *CHAINS*

We have mentioned the presence in H and L chains of variable (V) and constant (C) domains, each containing approximately 110 amino acids, as well as the presence of hypervariable, complementarity-determining regions (CDR) in the V_H and V_L domains. The nature of the variability of sequences is illustrated in Figure 1, which shows partial amino acid sequences (through CDR-2) of the V_κ regions of 15 human myeloma proteins belonging to the $V_\kappa I$ group. (Members of a group have closely related sequences.) Also shown are single representatives of the $V_\kappa II$, $V_\kappa III$, and $V_\kappa IV$ groups. Each κ chain came from a myeloma tumor of a different individual. By convention, amino acids are numbered from left to right, reading from the N-terminal to the C-terminal end. The one-letter code used for the amino acids is described in Appendix I. The symbol FR refers to FRAMEWORK, a term used for those portions of the V region other than the CDR. In a V_κ region there are four framework segments and three CDR. This type of structural pattern is a general feature of immunoglobulin V_L and V_H regions.

The sequences in Figure 1 are aligned to give maximal homology of sequence, i.e., to give a maximum number of positions at which each of the proteins has the same amino acid. This necessitates the arbitrary insertion of gaps at certain positions. It is of interest that gaps frequently occur in CDR. Because these regions determine the specificity of an antibody, variability of length is one source of diversity of specificity. In comparing sequences, the invariant half-cystine residues constituting the intrachain disulfide loop that is characteristic of each domain are always aligned; in human (or mouse) V_κ, they are at positions 23 and 88.

Features to be noted in the V_κ sequences include the hypervariable CDR (positions 24–34 and 50–56); the third CDR, which is not shown, comprises positions 89–97. Outside the CDR are some positions that are invariant and others at which only an occasional substitution is seen.

Members of a group have similar lengths and very similar sequences in their framework regions (>90% homology). In the human there are four V_κ groups ($V_\kappa I$ to $V_\kappa IV$) and at least five V_λ groups. There is uncertainty as to the total number of V_κ groups in the mouse. The available data on sequences suggest that the BALB/c mouse may have 50–100 groups. In contrast there are only two V_λ groups in BALB/c mice. This small number is consistent with the fact that only 2 to 5% of normal mouse serum immunoglobulins are λ; the rest are κ. As already mentioned, the κ to λ ratio varies greatly among mammalian species.

Another example illustrating how the degree of homology is estimated was presented in Figure 5, Chapter 2, which shows the align-

Reference sequence and region boundaries

Region	Positions	Sequence
FR-1	1 … 27	D I Q M T Q S P S S L S A S V G D R V T I T C Q A S Q
CDR-1	27A–30…	D I S I F L N
FR-2	35 … 49	W Y Q Q K P G K A P K L L I Y
CDR-2	50 … 56	D A S K L E A S

Numbering marks: 1, 10, 20, 27, 27A, 28, 30, 40, 48, 50, 56

Vκ sequence comparison (substitutions relative to reference; "_" = conserved)

Protein	FR-1	junction (≈27)	CDR-1	FR-2	CDR-2 (50–56)
Vκ I ROY	D I Q M T Q S P S S L S A S V G D R V T I T C Q A S Q	A (	D Y		
AU	Z … B	R Z (	) T _ S Y B _ Z Z _ (	Z Z … B … A	N … A B H S
OU		R	) T _ (	T … E	E N Q
REI			) _ I K Y _ (	Q V … A … S	A S P S
HAU	R	R	) S _ S Y S _ (	R … R … G	G T T
SCW			) _ R K H _ (	D	
RFZ	N	N	) V _ K S _ (	R … Q	A B
GAL		I R	) G _ R N D _ T (	R _ T … E	A N Q S
LAY	V		) N V N A Y (	L	G T R
EU	T	R	) S _ N T W _ A (	M K … S	S E S
HBJ	T	R	) S V N N W _ A E _ Z (		S K T _ S E R
CAR	T … A	A R	) N _ S W _ A _ V (	V	K S S S
BI	P … S		) _ R N S L I (	F	F E N I
KA	T … V	E	) T V L S Y (		A _ S T
KUE	T Q P	R	) S _ N W _ A _ E (		K T T
Vκ II TEW	V … L … PVTP EPAS _ S _ R S	S L L H S ( ) _ G F D Y		L … Q (48)	N R A S
Vκ III TI	E _ V L … G T … L _ P E _ A _ L S _ R	S (	) V S N S _ A	Q … R … V	S R A T
Vκ IV LEN	V … N _ A V _ L E _ A _ N K S		S V L Y S S N S K N Y _ A	Q P … W	T R S

◀ **FIGURE 1.** Partial amino acid sequences, through the second CDR, of the variable regions of human κ chains, obtained from myeloma or Bence-Jones proteins. Position number 1 is the N-terminus of the chain. The first 15 sequences are of L chains that belong to the $V_κI$ group. The last three sequences are individual representatives of $V_κII$, $V_κIII$, and $V_κIV$, respectively. The solid lines represent identity with the prototype sequence (protein ROY). Parentheses indicate gaps artificially introduced to maximize homologies of sequence. Note the large differences in length after position 27 (in the first CDR) and the concentration of substitutions for the $V_κI$ group in the two CDR regions that are presented. (Sequences in the third CDR are similarly hypervariable). The numbering system and nomenclature for κ groups are from Kabat et al. (1979). References to the original data are in Appendix III.

ment of the three domains of human $C_γ1$, the constant region of the heavy chain of IgG1.

AMINO ACID SEQUENCES OF V_H REGIONS

Figure 2 presents partial sequences of a number of human V_H domains. Seven sequences of the V_HIII group are shown, together with single representatives of V_HI, V_HII, and V_HIV. The V_HIII sequences clearly demonstrate the hypervariability of the two CDR represented. So far only four major groups of human V_H regions have been identified. The same V_H genes, and therefore the same repertoire of V_H sequences, are shared by all the classes and subclasses of human immunoglobulins. There is, of course, a separate C_H gene for each class and subclass. Appendix II includes a few additional amino acid sequences of immunoglobulins.

The best and most complete source of data on immunoglobulin sequences is a monograph by Kabat et al. (1983).

ANALYSIS OF VARIABILITY OF AMINO ACID SEQUENCES

The existence of hypervariable regions was first noted by Wu and Kabat (1970), who analyzed data on sequences available at the time. To obtain a quantitative estimate of variability at each position in the sequence, they used the following index: Variability is equal to the number of different amino acids observed at a given position divided by frequency of occurrence of the most common amino acid at that position. If there are 10 sequences available and amino acid X occurs at position 30 in 6 of the 10 sequences, the frequency of occurrence of the most common amino acid at position 30 (in this case amino acid X) is 0.6. Such a plot of variability for the variable domains of nine

Antibody heavy-chain variable region sequence alignment (Kabat numbering).

Region headers: FR-1 — CDR-1 — FR-2 — CDR-2
Position markers: 1 ... 10 ... 20 ... 30 ... 35A B | 36 ... 40 ... 50 52 A 53 ... 60 ... 65

```
                 FR-1                              CDR-1        FR-2                     CDR-2
                 1        10        20        30   35A  B   36      40        50 52 A 53       60      65
V_HIII  TEI   E V Q L V E S G G G L V Q P G G S L R L S C A A S G F T F S   S T S A V Y ( )( )   W V R Q A P G K G L E W V G   W R Y E G S S L T H Y A V S V Q G
                                                                                                                               S A I G ( ) T A G D Q Y
        BRO                                                                 Y Y N M N   ( )                       V T                                     _ D _ K
        TUR                       L                                         R V L S S   ( )                                    S G _ L N A _ F _ A
        POM                       L                                         S _ M S     ( )                                    A _ K _ N G N D K _ D _ N
        TIL                       L                                         Y V M S     ( )                                    A I Z G L _ V S Z S _ B _ K
        MU                                  K                               T R G G L E ( )                           Z        A _ Z _ L V F S V T _ K F Y T E _ L N
        WAS                       L                             S           S _ D _ M   ( )                                    A _ K _ Q E A _ N S _ F _ D T _ N

                 P*                                   30
V_HI    EU    C  Q _ _ _ _ A E V K K _ S _ V K V _ _ _ K _ _ _ _ G   R S _ I I ( )         Q                 M   G I V P M F G P P N Y A Q K F Q
              A

                 P                             10
V_HII   COR   C  T R _ P A _ K _ T Q T _ T _ T _ T F _ S L S S T G M C V G       I         P       L A R I D ( ) W D D D K Y _ B T _ L E T
              A

                 P
V_HIV   BUS   C  S V _ B G
              A
```

◀ **FIGURE 2.** Partial N-terminal sequences of human heavy chains of four groups. The first seven sequences are of group V_HIII. Single sequences of the V_HI, V_HII, and V_HIV groups are then listed. As indicated, very little data are available for the V_HIV group. For a key to the symbols used, see the legend of Figure 1. Blank spaces without parentheses indicate incomplete data. PCA at position 1 refers to pyrrollidone carboxylic acid (cyclized glutamic acid). Original references are given in Appendix III. The numbering system used is that of Kabat et al. (1983).

human κ chains is shown in Figure 3. The hypervariable regions are clearly evident.

When Wu and Kabat discovered the existence of hypervariable regions, they correctly deduced that these regions contribute in a major way to the structure of the antigen-binding site.

COMPARISONS OF AMINO ACID SEQUENCES OF IMMUNOGLOBULINS

The existence of domains and amino acid sequence homologies among domains led to the hypothesis that a primordial gene encoded a stretch of 110–120 amino acids and that polypeptide chains consisting of more than one domain arose by replication of such a gene, which subsequently underwent mutations during evolutionary time. If all

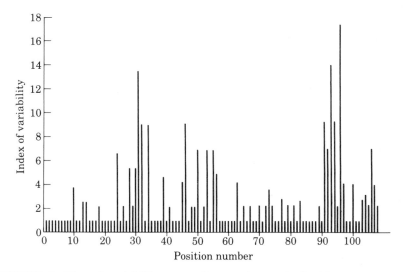

FIGURE 3. Plot of variability, according to the method of Wu and Kabat (1970), for nine human $V_κI$ sequences. The index of variability is defined in the text. Three hypervariable regions are clearly evident.

TABLE 1. Percentage of homology in amino acid sequences of C_H regions.[a]

C_H region	Human γ_1	Human α_1	Human μ	Human ε
Human γ_1	—	31	32	35
γ_3	94	31	34	36
γ_4	92	31	33	35
μ	32	34	—	27
α_1	31	—	34	28
ε	35	28	27	—
Rabbit γ	67	30	31	36
Mouse γ_1	62	29	32	36
Mouse γ_{2a}	61	26	29	35
Guinea Pig γ_2	68	28	30	37

From Dayhoff (1978).

[a] Based on optimal alignment. For IgE (ε) and IgM (μ), the C_H1, C_H3, and C_H4 domains were aligned with C_H1, C_H2, and C_H3, respectively, of the other immunoglobulins.

immunoglobulin domains are indeed descended from a common ancestral gene, one would expect to observe homologies in amino acid sequences among heavy and light chains from various sources; this is, in fact, the case. Data concerning the degree of homology among various immunoglobulins are presented in Tables 1 and 2. The remarkable similarity of the N-terminal sequences of a shark L chain and a human κ chain was shown in Figure 6, Chapter 4.

GENETIC BASIS OF VARIABILITY OF AMINO ACID SEQUENCES

Amino acid sequences of various immunoglobulins were determined over a 10-year period—from 1965 to 1975—before the first direct experiments on immunoglobulin gene organization were carried out. On the basis of amino acid sequence data alone, hypotheses were formulated concerning the genetic basis of the observed diversity of amino acid sequences. Two principal schools of thought emerged from these discussions: One postulated that all diversity is encoded in germline genes; the other, that somatic variation (mutation and/or recombination of genes) during the lifetime of the animal contributes to the diversity of antibodies. It is now evident that both mutation and recombination are indeed important contributory factors. The evidence will be considered in the next chapter, where we will discuss the organization of genes controlling immunoglobulins. The various sources of diversity will also be summarized there.

THREE-DIMENSIONAL STRUCTURE OF IMMUNOGLOBULINS

It is a remarkable fact that the linear arrangement of nucleotides in DNA determines, with great precision, the final three-dimensional structure of the protein encoded by that DNA. The DNA sequence controls the amino acid sequence; how the protein folds to yield the

TABLE 2. Amino acid sequence homologies among various immunoglobulins.[a]

Comparison made	Percentage homology in sequence	Comparison made	Percentage homology in sequence
Intragroup (human)		V_κ(mouse and human)	
$V_{\kappa I}$(Roy) vs $V_{\kappa I}$(Ag)	87	m41 vs m70	57
$V_{\kappa I}$(Ag) vs $V_{\kappa I}$(Eu)	74	m41 vs $hV_{\kappa I}$(Ag)	64
$V_{\kappa II}$(Mil) vs $V_{\kappa II}$(Cum)	82	m41 vs $hV_{\kappa II}$(Cum)	49
$V_{\lambda I}$(New) vs $V_{\lambda I}$(Ha)	75	m70 vs $hV_{\kappa I}$(Ag)	60
$V_{\lambda III}$(Kern) vs $V_{\lambda III}$(X)	73	m70 vs $hV_{\kappa II}$(Cum)	59
Intergroup (human)		Constant regions	
$V_{\kappa I}$(Eu) vs $V_{\kappa III}$(Ti)	68	$hC_{\gamma 1}$(C_H1 domain) vs hC_κ	25
$V_{\kappa I}$(Roy) vs $V_{\kappa II}$(Cum)	51	$hC_{\gamma 1}$(C_H1 domain) vs hC_λ	27
$V_{\lambda I}$(Ha) vs $V_{\lambda III}$(Kern)	55	hC_κ vs hC_λ	36
$V_{\lambda IV}$(Bo) vs $V_{\lambda V}$(Sh)	60	mC_κ vs mC_λ	35
		hC_κ vs mC_κ	60
V_λ and V_κ (human)		hC_κ vs rC_κ	45
		mC_κ vs rC_κ	49
$V_{\lambda I}$(Ha) vs $V_{\kappa II}$(Ag)	47	hC_κ vs mC_λ	36
$V_{\lambda I}$(Ha) vs $V_{\kappa II}$(Cum)	50	hC_λ vs mC_λ	69
$V_{\lambda III}$(Kern) vs $V_{\kappa III}$(Ti)	43	hC_λ vs mC_κ	34
$V_{\lambda III}$(Kern) vs $V_{\kappa II}$(Cum)	45	hC_κ vs $hC_{\alpha I}$(C_H3 domain)	23
		C_H1, C_H2 and C_H3 domains of $hC_{\gamma 1}$	30–33
		Variable and constant regions	
		hC_λ vs $hV_{\lambda I}$(Ha)	12
		hC_λ vs $hV_{\kappa I}$(Ag)	15
		hC_κ vs $hV_{\kappa II}$(Cum)	18

[a] Most of the values presented are from Hood and Talmage (1970) or Dayhoff (1978). The letters h, m, and r refer to human, mouse, and rabbit, respectively.

final structure is, in turn, determined by the sequence of amino acids.

Information as to the overall size and shape of immunoglobulins was first obtained by electron microscopy. This technique provided evidence as to the approximate dimensions of antibody molecules ($\sim$35 Å $\times$ 35 Å $\times$ 140 Å for IgG) and showed that they are flexible. The resolution of the electron microscope is too low, however, for a detailed three-dimensional analysis. Such information has been obtained by single-crystal X-ray diffraction methods, using highly ordered crystalline materials.

When crystallization occurs, a very regular arrangement of identical molecules in three-dimensional space is indicated. This, in turn, implies that the individual molecules in the crystal have a defined three-dimensional structure. Before many proteins had been crystallized, it was not at all self-evident that this would be the case. For a molecule as large as a protein, many different conformations of the same molecule are theoretically possible.

X-rays are suitable for analyzing three-dimensional structures because their wavelengths are of the same order of magnitude as atomic dimensions. If an X-ray beam is allowed to pass through a regular crystal and then impinge on a photographic plate, it produces a dark spot in the center and an array of less dense spots, varying in intensity, around the center. The diffraction pattern thus produced is due to scattering of the X-rays by electrons in the atoms of the protein. Spots on the plate are due to reinforcement of particular rays after they are reflected in the crystal. A typical protein may generate thousands of visible spots. From the location and intensity of these spots, it is in theory possible to deduce the locations of the atoms of the protein in three-dimensional space. It should be noted that the difficulty of interpreting the diffraction pattern increases with the size of the molecule. The process is greatly facilitated if one can introduce a heavy metal atom at one or more defined locations in the protein molecule. The intense scattering of X-rays by the metal atom provides an important frame of reference. The three-dimensional structures of over 100 proteins have now been worked out by these methods. Before summarizing the work on immunoglobulins, we will discuss the general structure of human IgG1.

OUTLINE OF THE STRUCTURE OF HUMAN IgG1

Figures 4 and 5 are schematic diagrams of the structure of human IgG1. There is a total of twelve domains: four in each of the pair of H chains and two in each L chain. Each domain is characterized by the presence of an intrachain disulfide bond. Each H–L pair is linked by

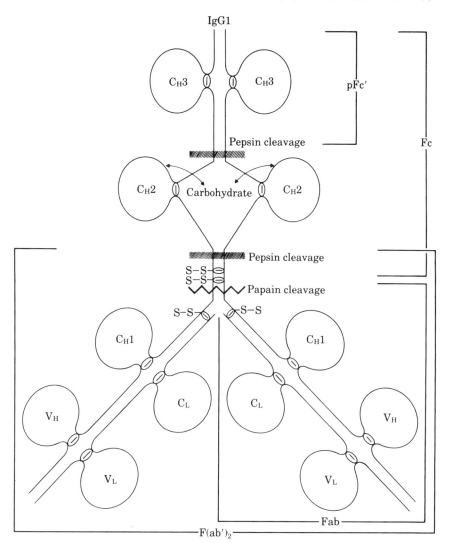

FIGURE 4. Schematic diagram of the human IgG1 molecule, showing the 12 intrachain disulfide loops, interchain disulfide bonds, and location of carbohydrate and of cleavages by papain and pepsin. Papain yields Fab and Fc fragments; pepsin yields $F(ab')_2$ and pFc'. The pFc' fragment contains the two C_H3 domains. The C_H2 domains are degraded by pepsin.

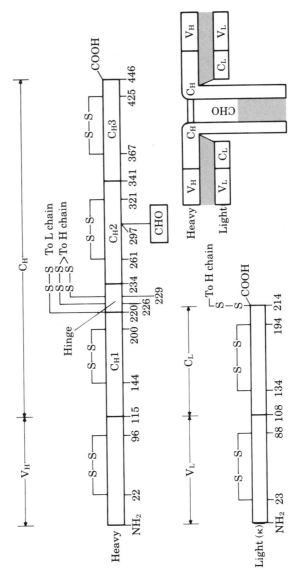

FIGURE 5. Schematic diagram of the H and L (κ) chains of IgG1. The gray areas indicate regions of noncovalent bonding between adjacent chains; CHO, carbohydrate.

a single interchain disulfide bond, and two interchain disulfide bonds join the pair of H chains. The interchain bonds can be reduced under mild, nondenaturing conditions, which leave the intrachain bonds intact. As in rabbit IgG, papain cleaves on the N-terminal side of the interchain disulfide bonds that link the H chains, whereas peptic cleavage occurs on the C-terminal side. The molecular weight of each Fab fragment is approximately 46,000; that of the Fc fragment is approximately 50,000. Strong noncovalent forces act between V_H and V_L, between $C_\gamma 1$ and C_L, and between the two $C_\gamma 3$ domains. The two $C_\gamma 2$ domains are separated by carbohydrate and interact only slightly with one another.

As we have indicated, X-ray crystallography has localized the atoms of several immunoglobulins in three-dimensional space. Reviews by Amzel and Poljak (1979) and by Davies et al. (1975) can be consulted for detailed models and for descriptions of structures. We will discuss here some of the main features of the three-dimensional structures common to immunoglobulins. Figures 6 and 7 are space-filling models of a molecule of human IgG1, which illustrate some important structural aspects of the molecule. One can see that there is a tight fit and many points of contact between the V_H and V_L regions. In contrast, the juncture between V_H and $C_\gamma 1$ (heavy solid arrow) or between V_L and C_L (light solid arrow) is much less pronounced, i.e., there are relatively few contact points between the successive domains of the same polypeptide chain. By careful choice of conditions, it is possible to cleave some immunoglobulins (with a proteolytic enzyme) at or very near the positions identified by the two arrows. These are referred to as "switch positions" because they represent the points at which the $C_\gamma 1$ and C_L amino acid sequences begin. The concept of "domain," derived from amino acid sequence data, was greatly strengthened by the finding that each domain is a distinguishable unit in the three-dimensional structure.

The very dark regions in Figures 6 and 7 represent carbohydrate. The carbohydrate is localized between the $C_\gamma 2$ domains of the two heavy chains and prevents them from making contact with one another. (The carbohydrate in the molecule shown here also prevents strong interactions between the $C_\gamma 1$ and $C_\gamma 2$ domains of an *individual* heavy chain.) Thus, the pair of $C_\gamma 2$ domains are not in close contact with one another, but there are many points of contact between the two $C_\gamma 3$ domains, between $C_\gamma 1$ and C_L, and between V_L and V_H.

X-ray diffraction data have also shown that all antibodies of a given class have the same basic structure, determined by framework (non-CDR) amino acids. The CDR form loops protruding from the backbone. The loops vary in size and amino acid sequence from one

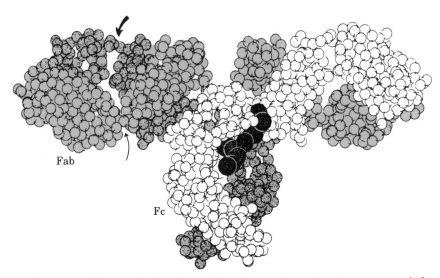

FIGURE 6. Schematic drawing of the three-dimensional structure of the human IgG molecule, based on X-ray crystallographic analysis. One of the heavy chains is represented by the white circles; the other heavy chain is dark gray. The two light chains are a lighter shade of gray. Hexose units constituting the carbohydrate of the molecule are represented as large black spheres. The carbohydrate lies between the C_H2 domains of the two heavy chains. This particular IgG molecule has a deletion of the hinge region. (From Silverton et al., 1977.)

antibody to the next, thus accounting for the huge repertoire of antibody specificities. The CDR loops are in contact with solvent and have little, if any, influence on the backbone structure of the molecule. As is true of many globular proteins, the interior of the molecule is rich in amino acids with hydrophobic side chains (valine, phenylalanine, etc.), whereas the exterior consists of both hydrophobic and polar residues.

Figure 8 is a diagram of a model that shows a hapten in contact with the combining region of an antibody. The data were obtained by X-ray crystallography of a human IgG1 myeloma protein that selectively binds a hydroxyl derivative of vitamin K_1. The vitamin K_1 derivative was allowed to diffuse into the crystal structure of Fab′ fragments, and its effect on the diffraction pattern was used to localize the hapten in three-dimensional space. The contacts with the hapten involve amino acid side chains of the CDR of both the H and L chain. Many of the contacts involve hydrophobic portions of the hapten molecule and hydrophobic side chains of the antibody; this type of bond

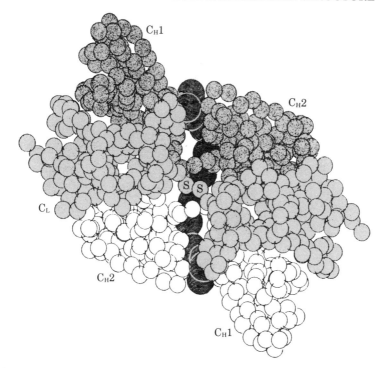

FIGURE 7. A space-filling view of C_L, C_H1 and C_H2 of the same molecule that is shown in Figure 6. As in Figure 6, the heavy chains are represented by white and dark gray circles, the C_L segments by a lighter shade of gray. The very dark large circles represent hexose units in the carbohydrate. This figure shows more clearly how the carbohydrate serves to separate the two C_H2 domains. It also minimizes direct contact, in this molecule, between C_H1 and C_H2. (From Silverton et al., 1977.)

evidently accounts for most of the binding energy of this antibody–hapten pair.

Another X-ray diffraction study was carried out with a myeloma protein that binds a hapten (phosphorylcholine) that has one positive and one negative charge. In this case, the binding was shown to be due in large part to the presence of oppositely charged groups in the hapten and the contacting amino acid side chains of the myeloma protein; the opposite charges are in close proximity when the hapten is present in the crystal. Hydrogen bonds also play an important role in the interaction (Davies et al., 1975).

The findings of the two studies mentioned above confirmed earlier conclusions, based on investigations of antibody–hapten binding, that

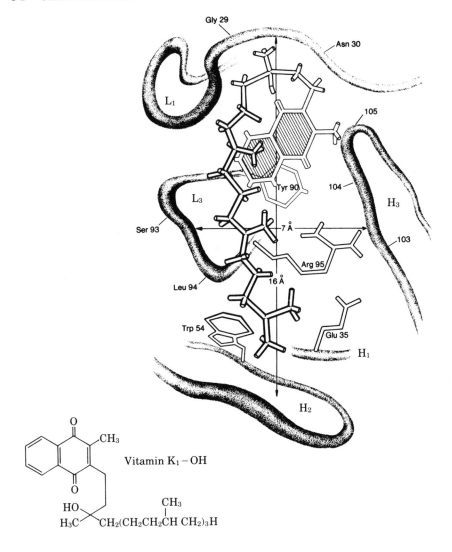

Vitamin K₁ – OH

FIGURE 8. Schematic diagram of a hydroxyl derivative of vitamin K_1 (structure at bottom left) present in the antigen-binding site of a human myeloma protein that specifically binds vitamin K_1-OH. L_1 and L_3 refer to the first and third hypervariable regions (CDR) of the L chain. H_1, H_2, and H_3 designate the first, second, and third CDR of the H chain. Tyrosine-90 and arginine-95 of the light chain are located at the bottom of a shallow crevice located between the H and L chain. Tryptophan is in close contact with the end of the hydrocarbon chain of the vitamin K_1-OH. Close contacts are also made with residues 104 and 105, present in the third CDR of the heavy chain, and with residues 29 and 30 in the first CDR of the L chain. (From Amzel et al., 1974.)

the chemical nature of the antibody combining site can vary markedly, depending on the nature of the hapten, and that various types of noncovalent bonds may play a role in binding. These bonds include hydrophobic and hydrogen bonds, as well as charge–charge interactions and van der Waal's forces. The latter are nonspecific, very short range forces that act between two atoms separated by a precisely appropriate distance.

The size of the cavity in the phosphorylcholine-binding myeloma protein (15 Å × 20 Å × 12 Å deep) is larger than that in the protein that binds vitamin K_1; the latter is a rather shallow groove with dimensions 15 Å × 6 Å × 6 Å deep. The cavity that accommodates the phosphorylcholine is considerably larger than the hapten itself.

THE IMMUNOGLOBULIN FOLD

Immunoglobulins contain very little α-helix. The structural feature that predominates is a β-pleated sheet, illustrated in Figure 9. This structure is stabilized by multiple hydrogen bonds acting between carbonyl and amide groups of amino acids that are present in the backbone of the chain. This pleated sheet is formed by the appropriate

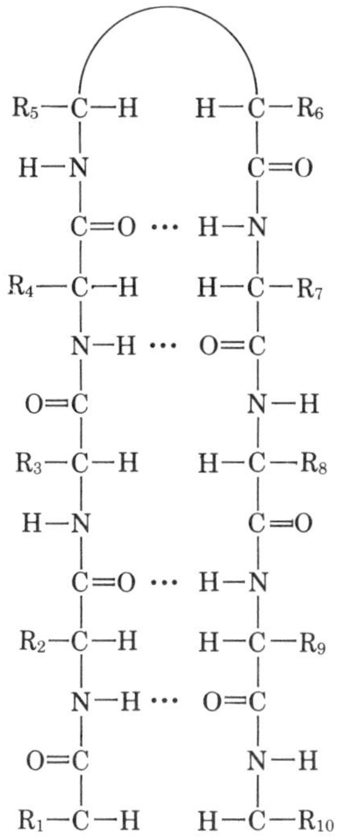

FIGURE 9. Sketch of a segment of antiparallel β-pleated sheet. The dotted lines represent hydrogen bonds, which are repeated at regular intervals and stabilize the structure. The loop at the top represents a continuing segment of the polypeptide chain.

folding of a single polypeptide chain. The strands making up the sheet in the illustration are referred to as antiparallel because the chain turns back on itself so that the adjacent strands run in opposite directions.

Each domain in H and L chains exhibits the basic immunoglobulin fold. This consists of two β-pleated sheets, one comprising four strands and the other three (sometimes five) strands, as illustrated in Figures 10 and 11. The four-stranded set is indicated by the white arrows and the three-stranded set by striated arrows in Figure 11. It is apparent that the chain does not consist entirely of β-pleated sheet structure. About half of the amino acids are involved in that structure; the remainder of the amino acids make up the terminal segments and the

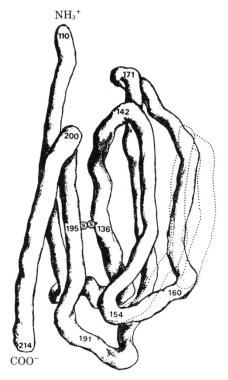

FIGURE 10. Diagram of the basic immunoglobulin fold, showing the folding of the polypeptide chain in the C_L or C_H1 domains of a human IgG1λ myeloma protein. The numbers are positions in the amino acid sequence of the λ chain. The C_L region begins at position 110; the C-terminus is position 214. The dotted lines indicate the position of an additional loop present in V_L and V_H regions. (From Poljak et al., 1973.)

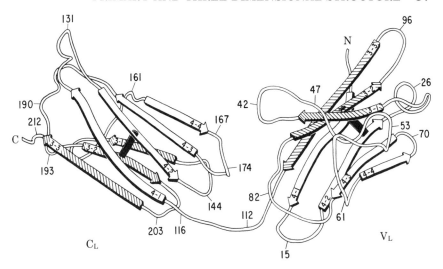

FIGURE 11. Schematic diagram of the V_L and C_L regions of one λ chain present in a crystallized dimer of λ chains (Bence-Jones protein, obtained from the urine of a patient with multiple myeloma). The directional arrows are superimposed on chain segments forming antiparallel β-pleated sheets. Three-chain layers are indicated by striated arrows and four-chain layers by white arrows. The numbers represent positions in the amino acid sequence. The arrows all point in a C-terminal direction, i.e., toward higher numbers. The black rectangles represent intrachain disulfide bonds. This protein differs from that described in Figure 10 in that the V domain has a three-stranded rather than a five-stranded β-pleated sheet. (From Edmundson et al., 1975.)

loops connecting the antiparallel chains. The hypervariable amino acids of both the H and the L chain are present in such connecting loops, which are adjacent to one another in three-dimensional space.

The interior of the molecule, between the four-stranded and the three-stranded sheets, is rich in hydrophobic amino acid side chains; thus, the interaction of the two sheets with one another is stabilized by hydrophobic bonds. The two sheets are also held together by the intrachain disulfide bond characteristic of each domain.

The structure of a V domain differs from that of a C domain in human IgG1 (Figure 10) in that it contains an additional loop. The three-stranded structure is therefore replaced by a five-stranded β-pleated sheet. The structures of V and C domains are otherwise quite similar.

It is of great interest that the three-dimensional structures of domains in H and L chains are very similar to one another despite the facts that they diverged so early during evolution and that their amino acid sequences show only a moderate degree of homology. As evolution proceeded, mutations were permitted that greatly altered the amino acid sequence but had very little effect on the three-dimensional structure. This is a general principle of the evolution of globular (nonfibrous) proteins; the three-dimensional structure is often highly conserved despite marked changes in amino acid sequence.

LITERATURE CITED

Amzel, L. M., Poljak, R. J., Saul, F., Varga, J. M. and Richards, F. F. (1974). The three-dimensional structure of a combining region-ligand complex of immunoglobulin NEW at 3.5 Å resolution. Proc. Natl. Acad. Sci. USA 71, 1427.

Amzel, L. M. and Poljak, R. J. (1979). Three-dimensional structure of immunoglobulins. Annu. Rev. Biochem. 48, 961.

Davies, D. R., Padlan, E. A. and Segal, D. M. (1975). Three-dimensional structure of immunoglobulins. Annu. Rev. Biochem. 44, 639.

Dayhoff, M. O. (1978). Atlas of Protein Sequence and Structure. Washington, National Biomedical Research Foundation, 205.

Dreyer, W. J. and Bennett, J. C. (1965). The molecular basis of antibody formation: a paradox. Proc. Natl. Acad. Sci. USA 54, 864.

Edmundson, A. B., Ely, K. R., Abola, E. E., Schiffer, M. and Panagiotopoulos, N. (1975). Rotational allomerism and divergent evolution of domains in immunoglobulin light chains. Biochemistry 14, 3953.

Hilschmann, N. and Craig, L. C. (1965). Amino acid sequence studies with Bence-Jones proteins. Proc. Natl. Acad. Sci. USA 53, 1403.

Hood, L. and Talmage, D. W. (1970). Mechanism of antibody diversity: germ line basis for variability. Science 168, 325.

Kabat, E. A., Wu, T. T., Bilofsky, H., Reid-Miller, M. and Perry, H. (1983). Sequences of Proteins of Immunological Interest. Bethesda, MD, National Institutes of Health Publication.

Poljak, R. J., Amzel, L. M., Avey, H. P., Chen, B. L., Phizackerley, R. P. and Saul, F. (1973). Three-dimensional structure of the Fab′ fragment of a human immunoglobulin at 2.8 Å resolution. Proc. Natl. Acad. Sci. USA 70, 3305.

Potter, M. and Lieberman, R. (1967). Genetics of immunoglobulins in the mouse. Adv. Immunol. 7, 92.

Silverton, E. W., Navia, M. A. and Davies, D. R. (1977). Three-dimensional structure of an intact human immunoglobulin. Proc. Natl. Acad. Sci. USA 74, 5140.

Wu, T. T. and Kabat, E. (1970). An analysis of the sequences of the variable regions of Bence-Jones proteins and myeloma light chains and their implications for antibody complementarity. *J. Exp. Med.* *132,* 211.

SUGGESTED ADDITIONAL READING

Cold Spring Harbor Symp. Quant. Biol. 1976. Volume 41. *The Origins of Lymphocyte Diversity.* Numerous articles relating to antibody structure.

Colman, P. M., Deisenhofer, J., Huber, R., and Palm, W. (1976). Structure of the human antibody molecule "Kol"; an electron density map at 5 Å resolution. *J. Mol. Biol.* *100,* 257.

Poljak, R. J. (1975). X-ray diffraction studies of immunoglobulins. *Adv. Immunol.* *21,* 1.

Potter, M. (1972). Immunoglobulin-producing tumors and myeloma proteins of mice. *Physiol. Rev.* *52,* 631.

Smith, G. (1973). *The Variation and Adaptive Expression of Antibodies.* Cambridge, Harvard University Press.

6

THE ORGANIZATION OF GENES CONTROLLING IMMUNOGLOBULINS

OVERVIEW

Genes controlling immunoglobulins have a unique and very functional pattern of organization. Genes controlling the biosynthesis of κ or λ chains are made up of four gene segments: a leader sequence, and the *V, J,* and *C* segments. There are two V_λ genes in the mouse, but a large number (probably hundreds) of V_κ and V_H genes. A single V_L and a single V_H gene are expressed in the secreted product of an antibody-producing cell (allelic exclusion). The *V* gene to be expressed undergoes recombination (translocation), bringing it into proximity with a *J* and a *C* gene; in the case of H chains, a fourth segment, called *D,* also participates. The *D* segment encodes most of the third CDR of the H chain. After translocation, introns (segments that are transcribed into RNA but not translated into protein) still remain in the DNA. Their RNA transcripts are removed from the mRNA by a splicing mechanism. The number of C_H genes is small; for example, there is one C_H gene for each isotype (IgG$_1$, IgG$_{2a}$, IgM, etc.) of mouse immunoglobulin. Translocation events are controlled by sequences, that are recognized by enzymes, in the DNA adjacent to the gene segments involved. Among factors contributing to antibody diversity are the ability of *V* genes to recombine with several different *J* segments (and *D* segments in the case of V_H genes). Another source of diversity is the slight variation with respect to the position in the sequence at which the recombination events take place. Mutations occurring during the lifetime of the animal are another major factor contributing

91

to the diversity of antibodies. Although only one productive set of translocations occurs in an antibody-producing cell, abortive translocations are a common occurrence.

*　　*　　*

Before 1976 there was little direct information concerning the number of genes that control the immunoglobulins or their arrangement in chromosomes. The work of Susumo Tonegawa and his collaborators at the Basel Institute of Immunology in Switzerland opened up this area of research and led to rapid advances in a number of laboratories. Most of our current information pertains to mouse and human immunoglobulins. The organization of genes in the two species is similar in many respects. The chromosomal locations of the gene families controlling κ, λ, and H chains in the human and mouse are shown in Table 1.

We have discussed evidence based on amino acid sequence analysis that suggests that there are many V genes and only one C gene for an L or an H chain of a given type (κ or λ) or class, respectively. It was proposed that the V gene to be expressed was somehow brought into proximity with the correct C gene. Such a process would make it unnecessary for the C gene to be repeated for each V gene. This concept—"two genes–one polypeptide"—was supported by the discovery of patients with multiple myeloma whose cells secreted two myeloma proteins (e.g., IgG and IgM) that shared the same V_H regions. This could be explained by a translocation of the V_H gene (e.g., first to a position adjacent to a C_μ gene, then to a position adjacent to a C_γ gene) in one or more cells. Some of the descendant cells would make

TABLE 1. Chromosomal locations of the genes controlling H and L chains in the human and mouse.[a]

Polypeptide chain	Chromosome	
	Human	_Mouse_
H	14	12
κ	2	6
λ	22	16

[a] Genes of the major histocompatibility complex of the human and mouse are on chromosomes 6 and 17, respectively. Genes for β_2-microglobulin of the human and mouse are on chromosomes 15 and 2, respectively.

a complete μ chain and some a complete γ chain, both with the same V_H region.

A translocation of this type—to yield a single polypeptide chain—was virtually unprecedented. The direct demonstration of its occurrence by Hozumi and Tonegawa in 1976 was therefore of great interest. They used the following procedure.

1. Purify messenger RNA (mRNA) for κ chains from a mouse myeloma tumor (called MOPC 321). (A myeloma tumor was used because it contains a large quantity of a homogeneous mRNA. The RNA was biosynthetically labeled *in vivo* with a radioisotope or labeled with ^{125}I *in vitro*.)

2. Digest the DNA from the MOPC 321 tumor with a restriction enzyme, which cleaves the DNA into a limited number of fragments of various sizes. As a control, digest DNA from a normal embryo, with the same restriction enzyme under the same conditions.

3. Subject each of the two digested DNA preparations to electrophoresis under conditions that separate the fragments of DNA according to size.

4. Determine which of these electrophoretic fractions hybridizes with radioactive MOPC 321 mRNA. The ability to hybridize demonstrates the presence of DNA sequences that are complementary to the mRNA.

Strikingly different results were obtained with the digests of embryonic and myeloma DNA. The mRNA hybridized with two fragments of embryonic DNA: one with a molecular weight of 6.0×10^6 (fraction A) and one with a molecular weight of 3.9×10^6 (fraction B). In contrast, the mRNA hybridized with only one tumor DNA fragment: molecular weight 2.4×10^6 (fraction C). Subsequent experiments indicated that embryonic fractions A and B contained genes for C_κ and V_κ, respectively, whereas fraction C, from the myeloma, contained both. These results were consistent with translocation of the V_κ gene in the myeloma, but not in the embryo, bringing it into proximity with C_κ, so that the V_κ gene and C_κ gene appeared in the same fraction in the myeloma DNA digest.[1] As will be seen, the V and

---

[1] The fact that no unrearranged genes were observed in the myeloma DNA preparation seems at first to contradict the principle of allelic exclusion. Because only one molecular species of immunoglobulin is secreted, one might expect that the genes of one chromosome would remain in the embryonic or germ-line configuration. It appears that in this tumor the homologous chromosome was deleted. (In many other cases, one finds that both chromosomes are rearranged but only one is expressed. This occurrence is discussed later in the chapter.)

C genes are brought into close proximity but not into direct contact.

As a control for the above experiments, mRNA from a tumor unrelated to MOPC 321 was used. With this mRNA as probe, no differences in the hybridization patterns of the two preparations (embryo and MOPC 321 tumor) were seen. These results are consistent with the possibility that the V_κ gene corresponding to the MOPC 321 protein had selectively undergone translocation in the MOPC 321 tumor but not in the unrelated tumor or in embryonic tissue.

Evidence for a similar rearrangement of a V gene was subsequently obtained by Tonegawa and collaborators with a mouse myeloma that secretes λ rather than κ chains. DNA from the myeloma cells was digested with a restriction enzyme, and fragments were identified that hybridized with the myeloma messenger RNA for λ chains. These DNA fragments were cloned in bacteria in order to obtain large quantities. The presence and arrangement of the V_λ and C_λ genes in each fragment were studied by hybridization with the messenger RNA, followed by electron microscopy. It was found that in the myeloma, but not in embryonic cells, the V_λ and C_λ genes are in close proximity, although not in contact with one another. They are separated by a nontranslated stretch of DNA called an INTRON. (Introns are transcribed into RNA but are not translated into protein; the translated portions of the genome are referred to as EXONS.) The presence of introns can be demonstrated by electron microscopy of DNA hybridized with mRNA or cDNA.[2]

A description of the various procedures used to elucidate the arrangement and structure of genes is beyond the scope of this text. Papers by Susumo Tonegawa, Philip Leder, or Leroy Hood and collaborators (references listed at the end of this chapter) describe the methods in detail.

A COMPLETE VARIABLE REGION IS ENCODED BY TWO GENE SEGMENTS, V_κ AND J_κ

By electron microscopy and DNA sequencing, it was shown that the DNA coding for the variable region of the κ chain is actually present as two separate segments in cells that are not producing antibody. One segment (V_κ) codes for the first 95 amino acids and the second (J_κ; "J" for "joining"), encodes the last 13 amino acids of the variable region, residues 96–108. There are several hundred V_κ genes and five J_κ, of which $J_{\kappa 3}$ is defective and inactive. When translocation

---

[2] cDNA is DNA complementary to mRNA; it is synthesized *in vitro* by using the RNA as a template.

takes place, one V_κ segment is moved into direct contact with a J_κ segment; a 2.5 to 4-kilobase intron still separates $V_\kappa J_\kappa$ from C_κ. The distance between J_κ and C_κ is fixed and does not change during the translocation. This process is illustrated in Figure 1.[3]

LEADER SEQUENCE IN V_κ REGIONS

When a κ chain is first synthesized, it contains an additional stretch of 22 amino acids (most of which are hydrophobic) at the N-terminal end. These 22 amino acids, referred to as the LEADER SEQUENCE, are removed enzymatically before the antibody is secreted from the cell, or are inserted into the B cell membrane to act as a receptor. It is of interest that the leader sequence itself is not encoded by a continuous stretch of DNA but is split by an intron of 175 bases (Figure 1B). It has been proposed that the leader sequence, which is very hydrophobic, is important for transport of L chains within the cell.

EXCISION AND SPLICING OF mRNA

We have seen that after translocation of V_κ the DNA contains two introns that are not translated into polypeptide. When the DNA is transcribed, the RNA copy produced includes the entire region from the leader sequence through C_κ, including the two nontranslated introns (and any intervening J segments and their introns). Enzymes, called splicing enzymes, cleave the RNA and repair it in such a way as to remove RNA corresponding to the introns, leaving an mRNA molecule coding for the leader sequence, V, J, and C as one continuous stretch. (The mRNA contains additional, nontranslated sequences, characteristic of eukaryotic mRNA, 5′ and 3′ to the coding sequences; the sequences include a stretch of poly(A) at the 3′ end.) The presence of noncoding introns, which are removed from mRNA by this cut-and-splice mechanism, is a common feature of eukaryotic, but not of prokaryotic genes. A splicing enzyme recognizes specific nucleotide sequences in the RNA, which identify points of attack for the enzyme.

---

[3] In diagrams of the genome, the 5′ end of the DNA is placed at the left and the 3′ end at the right. To express the idea that gene X is closer to the 5′ end than gene Y, the phrases "gene X is 5′ to gene Y" or "gene X is 8 kilobases (kb) 5′ to gene Y" are often used.

DNA sequences present in nonlymphoid tissues are considered to represent sequences that are inherited, i.e., are present in the germ line. Frequently embryonic tissue is used to establish such sequences. DNA sequences for the immunoglobulins appear to be identical in all nonlymphoid tissues.

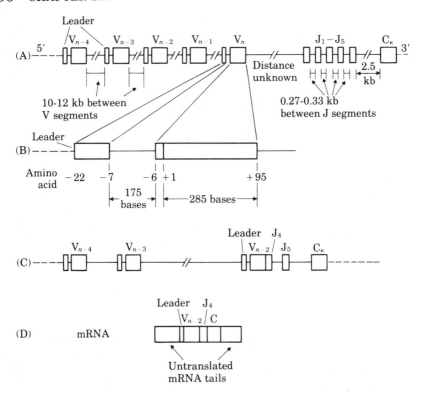

FIGURE 1. (A) Arrangement of κ genes on chromosome 6 of the mouse. (B) A separate stretch of DNA codes for the first 16 amino acids of the leader amino acid sequence (designated -22 to -7). An intron of 175 bases separates this from the next exon, which codes for the rest of the leader amino acid sequence (-6 to -1) and for the V_κ sequence (1–95). A V_κ gene (in this case V_{n-2}) is selected, and a translocation occurs (C), bringing the V next to one of the J_κ segments, in this case J_4. (J_3 is inactive.) Introns remain between the DNA segments coding for the leader sequence and V_κ, between J_4 and J_5, and between J_5 and C_κ. The entire stretch is transcribed into RNA, but the introns and J_5 are subsequently removed during the splicing process that produces mRNA (D). The leader sequence is translated into protein but is cleaved from the κ chain by a proteolytic enzyme before secretion from the cell.

ORGANIZATION OF GENES CODING FOR MOUSE λ CHAINS

Genes controlling mouse λ chains are arranged as shown in Figure 2. There is a total of two V_λ, four J_λ, and four C_λ genes; however, $J_{\lambda 4}$ and $C_{\lambda 4}$ are probably not expressed. (The possible presence of additional C_λ genes has not been ruled out, but it is very unlikely that there are more than five.) Note that there are two clusters of genes—

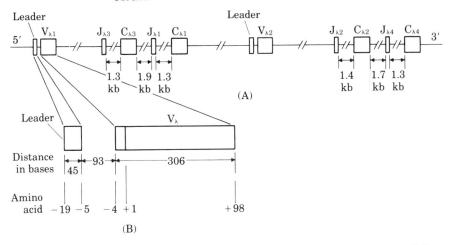

FIGURE 2. (A) Arrangement of the λ gene family on chromosome 16 of the mouse. (B) shows details of the arrangement of a V_λ gene and its leader DNA. Each of the two leader sequences is in two parts, separated by a 93-base intron. The first part codes for amino acids designated -19 to -5; the second part, which is connected to the V gene, codes for amino acids -4 to -1. The V_λ gene encodes amino acid residues 1 to 98. $V_{\lambda 1}$ generally combines (translocates) so as to interact with $J_{\lambda 3}$ or $J_{\lambda 1}$; $V_{\lambda 2}$ usually interacts with $J_{\lambda 2}$. ($J_{\lambda 4}$ and $C_{\lambda 4}$ are inactive.) In one cell line, however, $V_{\lambda 2}$ was found in association with $J_{\lambda 3}$ and $C_{\lambda 3}$; this suggests that $V_{\lambda 2}$ is actually located 5′ to $V_{\lambda 1}$, since translocation of V genes takes place in the 3′ direction. An inactive J segment (pseudogene) has been identified between $J_{\lambda 3}$ and $C_{\lambda 3}$. The distances between V_λ genes and JC clusters are unknown. (From Blomberg et al., 1981.)

J_3C_3, J_1C_1 and J_2C_2, J_4C_4—and that each J_λ segment appears to function only in conjunction with its corresponding C_λ gene. It has been proposed that $V_{\lambda 1}$ can be translocated to $J_{\lambda 3}C_{\lambda 3}$ or to $J_{\lambda 1}C_{\lambda 1}$; and $V_{\lambda 2}$ to $J_{\lambda 2}C_{\lambda 2}$. (In at least one instance, however, the $V_{\lambda 2}$ has been found in association with $J_{\lambda 3}C_{\lambda 3}$.) Each J segment is located on the 5′ side of its C_λ gene, at a distance of approximately 1.3 kilobases; this distance does not change during the translocation event. The distance between V_λ and J_λ segments prior to translocation is not known; after translocation, V_λ is in immediate contact with a J_λ segment. That the gene clusters are not in numerical order in the genome is due to the fact that nomenclature was assigned to the protein products before the gene structure was determined.

Immunoglobulins corresponding in amino acid sequence to the $C_{\lambda 1}$, $C_{\lambda 2}$, and $C_{\lambda 3}$ genes have been identified. The three C_λ protein products differ in 5 to ~35% of their amino acid residues. A common ancestral gene for the C_λ genes is indicated by this similarity in sequence. The ancestral gene is presumed to have undergone replication during evolution.

There are a number of points of similarity in the organization of mouse κ and λ genes.

1. A complete variable region is encoded by two gene segments: V and J. The corresponding κ and λ gene segments are very similar in size.

2. The V genes are widely separated (distance unknown) from J and C in tissues that are not producing antibody, but a V gene is brought into contact with a J segment in an antibody-producing cell.

3. Introns are present between the J segments and between the last (3′) J segment and the C gene.

4. A hydrophobic leader sequence and an intron, which splits the leader DNA, precede each V gene. The leader sequences in κ and λ chains are similar in size (22 and 19 amino acid residues, respectively).

There are also important differences between the arrangements of the κ and λ genes.

1. The five $J_κ$ gene segments are arranged sequentially, whereas each $J_λ$ gene segment is adjacent to a $C_λ$ gene. One of the $J_κ$ segments (J_3) is defective (because of a mutation) and is not expressed in proteins; it is sometimes referred to as a pseudogene. So far, the protein product of $J_{λ4}$, $C_{λ4}$ has not been observed.

2. There is one $C_κ$ gene, but four $C_λ$ genes.

3. Each of the $J_κ$ segments can interact with the same $C_κ$ gene, whereas only one $J_λ$ interacts with each $C_λ$.

4. There appears to be no restriction on V–J joining in the κ system. Any $V_κ$ gene can apparently link up with any $J_κ$ segment. The restrictions on $V_λ$ translocations were indicated above.

5. Only two $V_λ$ genes have been identified, whereas it is estimated that there are several hundred $V_κ$ genes. This is reflected in the high κ/λ ratio in the immunoglobulins of normal mouse serum (~25 to 1).

The estimate of the number of $V_κ$ genes is made as follows: A given radiolabeled $V_κ$ probe (mRNA or cDNA) generally hybridizes with 5 to 10 genes. This is shown by the "Southern blot" technique[4] carried

---

[4] This procedure was developed by Edward M. Southern (1975). Large segments of DNA (sometimes the entire genome) are cleaved with one or more restriction enzymes,

out on total mouse DNA digested with restriction enzymes. The genes that hybridize with a given probe have closely related nucleotide sequences and are thought to correspond to a V_κ group, as defined by amino acid sequence analysis. From amino acid sequence data, it is estimated that the total number of V_κ groups is 50–100. The total number of V_κ genes is estimated by multiplying the number of groups (50–100) by the number of V_κ genes per group (5–10).

RECOMBINATION OF V GENES IS ACCOMPANIED BY REMOVAL OF GENETIC MATERIAL

For the purpose of illustration, we will assume that there are n V_κ genes in the mouse; by convention, these are numbered from the 5' to the 3' end of the genome. In addition, there are known to be five J_κ gene segments, of which $J_{\kappa3}$ is inactive. Suppose that a V_κ gene recombines with an acceptor site on the 5' side of $J_{\kappa4}$. This is illustrated in Figure 2, in which the V gene undergoing translocation is designated V_{n-2}. All the intervening genetic material will be removed in the process. The material removed includes V_κ genes V_{n-1} and V_n, $J_{\kappa1}$, $J_{\kappa2}$, and $J_{\kappa3}$, and all the noncoding genetic material between the V-gene cluster and the J cluster. The fate of the DNA is unknown. There is evidence that it is still present in the genome. Rearrangements, involving deletions of this type and associated with differentiation of the cell, have so far been described only for the immunoglobulins and not for any other biological system.

ORGANIZATION OF GENES CONTROLLING HEAVY CHAINS

Most available data on genes controlling heavy chains pertain to the mouse. How these genes are organized in the mouse is illustrated in Figure 3. Reading from 5' to 3', there are multiple V_H genes (probably between 100 and 200), four J_H segments, and eight C_H genes, one for each of the eight isotypes of mouse immunoglobulin. In addition to V_H and J_H, the variable region is controlled by a third segment, designated D, which codes for a sequence between V_H and J_H. The number of D segments in the genome is unknown; there are at least

---

the fragments are separated by electrophoresis and transferred by a blotting procedure to nitrocellulose filter paper. Those fragments on the filter paper that hybridize with radiolabeled mRNA or DNA complementary to the mRNA (cDNA) are then identified by autoradiography. From this type of analysis, one can ascertain how many restriction fragments of the entire DNA digest will hybridize with a given mRNA or cDNA probe, as well as the sizes of such fragments. After isolating and cloning the DNA that hybridizes, its nucleotide sequence can be determined.

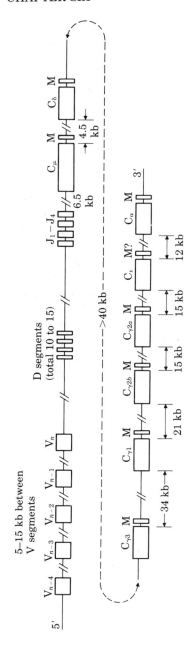

FIGURE 3. Arrangement of structural genes controlling mouse H chains on chromosome XII of the mouse. The numbers shown represent distances in kilobases between segments. A V gene is selected for translocation to a D segment; VD is then translocated to one of the J segments. Uncertainties in the diagram: (1) The number of V genes is unknown but probably exceeds 100. (2) The precise number of D segments is uncertain, but the number is probably 10–15. (3) It is not certain that all the D segments are localized, as shown, between the V and J clusters. (4) More than one D segment may possibly be used in the construction of the complete gene. It also is not certain that V to D joining occurs before D to J joining. Segments labeled M are used in the biosynthesis of membrane-bound immunoglobulins. Translocations take place in the 5′ to 3′ direction.

eleven.[5] The V_H gene segment encodes amino acids 1–97, and J_H encodes the last 16 to 20 residues of the V sequence. The D segments, or combinations of D segments, enclode most or all of the third hypervariable region of the H chain, which lies between V and J. The number of amino acid residues in the D region can range from 3 to as many as 14. During maturation of an antibody-producing cell, a translocation occurs that brings a D segment into direct contact with a J_H segment. This is followed by a second translocation, yielding a continuous $V–D–J$ sequence. After each translocation, the intervening DNA is deleted; whether it is simply excised or recombines with another stretch of DNA is uncertain. There is no evidence so far for restrictions with respect to the ability of a given V_H gene to combine with a particular D or J_H segment. When the $V–D–J$ complex is formed, J does not move with respect to C_μ, i.e., the intron separating J and C_μ remains intact. After transcription, the intron and any intervening J segments are removed from the mRNA by an enzyme-splicing mechanism.

Each $V–D–J$ complex can be translocated by successive recombinations to the eight different C_H genes shown in Figure 3. The first translocation is to C_μ and, as a consequence, IgM is normally the first class to be expressed after immunization. The rules that govern subsequent translocations are not yet clear. However, we do know that a cell producing IgM can convert to IgG synthesis, but that the reverse normally does not occur. There is evidence that the switch from the synthesis of IgM to another class may be antigen-driven and require input from thymus-derived helper cells. The very low concentration of IgE produced upon immunization may possibly reflect a low frequency for the required recombination. The binding specificity and idiotype of the product are not affected by a switch in class because V regions are not involved.

The mechanism of class switching (say, from μ to γ_3) involves removal of most of the DNA that lies between J and the C gene that is to be expressed. The mechanism is illustrated in Figure 4. Note that part, but not all, of the intron between J and C_μ is excised during the first class switch and that an intron remains between J and the new C_H gene that is to be expressed. A consequence of this mechanism is that a portion of the intron that originally was located 5′ to the C_μ gene is 5′ to another C gene (e.g., $C_{\gamma3}$) after the recombination event takes place.

---

[5] It has been suggested that $D–D$ joining may also occur, thus adding to the diversity of DNA sequences. There is still uncertainty as to the precise location of all the D segments in relation to V and J segments; one D segment has been located close to and on the 5′ side of a J_H segment.

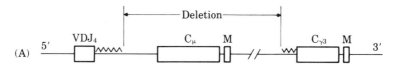

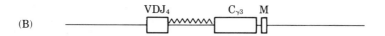

FIGURE 4. Mechanism for switching the class of immunoglobulin produced by a B cell and its descendants. (A) The cell is producing IgM after a *VD* recombination (translocation) to the J_4 segment. (B) The cell produces IgG$_3$ after an additional recombinational event. The segment that is deleted is indicated in the diagram. Note that the intervening sequence between *VDJ* and $C_{\gamma 3}$, after the switch, contains DNA originally present on both sides of the C_μ gene. Translocations of this type normally proceed only in the 5' to 3' direction.

MECHANISM OF V–J OR V–D–J JOINING

How does the *V* gene undergo precise translocation to a site next to a *D* or *J* segment? The process is mediated through defined sequences of nucleotides that are present in introns, immediately adjacent to *V, D,* and *J*. With slight variations, the same sequences are found next to *V* genes and *J* segments of genes encoding mouse κ, λ, and H chains, and they are present in introns adjacent to *D* segments as well. In the case of the *D* segment these defined sequences are present in introns on both sides of *D*; this is consistent with the fact that *D* undergoes recombination both on its 5' side (with *V*) and on its 3' side (with *J*) to form *V–D–J*. Such nucleotide sequences are referred to as RECOGNITION SEQUENCES. Thus, the sequence immediately 3' to a V_κ gene is

$$
\begin{array}{cc}
\text{(a)} \quad 12 \pm 1 \text{ nucleotides} & \text{(c)} \\
\end{array}
$$

$$
\begin{array}{l}
5' \quad V_\kappa \;\; \text{CACAGTG} \underline{\hspace{2cm}} \text{GACACAAACC} \\
\qquad\qquad \text{GTGTCAC} \underline{\hspace{2cm}} \text{CTGTGTTTGG} \underline{\hspace{0.5cm}} \\
\qquad\quad \text{(b)} \qquad\qquad\qquad\qquad\quad \text{(d)}
\end{array}
$$

The sequence of the intron immediately 5' to a J_κ segment is

$$
\begin{array}{ccc}
\text{(e)} & 23 \pm 1 \text{ nucleotides} & \text{(g)} \\
\end{array}
$$

$$
\begin{array}{l}
5' \;\underline{\hspace{0.5cm}}\text{GGTTTTTGTA}\underline{\hspace{2.5cm}}\text{CACTGTG} \;\; J_\kappa \\
\quad\; \underline{\hspace{0.5cm}}\text{CCAAAAACAT}\underline{\hspace{2.5cm}}\text{GTGACAC} \\
\qquad\qquad \text{(f)} \qquad\qquad\qquad\qquad\qquad \text{(h)}
\end{array}
$$

Note that the segment labeled (g) is an inverse copy of segment (b) and that (e) closely resembles an inverse copy of (d), etc.

Based on the presence of these inverted nucleotide sequences it has been proposed that recognition sequences adjacent to V hybridize with sequences adjacent to J (or D) by taking advantage of the ability to form a large sequence of correct G·C or A·T base pairs. The hybridization would require the formation of a very large loop containing all of the DNA between V and J or V and D. The intervening DNA, contained in the loop, would then be spliced out or rearranged in some other manner so as to leave the V and J (or V and D) sequences contiguous to one another. D and J would join in a similar fashion. The idea that one or more enzymes are involved in this process is supported by the fact that 12 ± 1 or 23 ± 1 nucleotides separate the adjacent recognition sequences (see preceding sketch). These numbers correspond closely to one or two turns of the DNA helix. These fixed distances may correspond to distances between two combining sites on each of two putative joining enzymes.

In an alternative proposed mechanism, the recombination would take place during meiosis and involve two sister chromatids rather than a single chromatid. For example, by recombination the V segment of one chromatid could be brought next to a J segment on the sister chromatid. Support for this mechanism comes from the observation that, in some myelomas, DNA on the 5' side of the J segment is still present somewhere in the genome even after V–J recombination. For a detailed discussion of these mechanisms see Early et al. (1980a) and Honjo (1983).

The recombination that leads to a switch in H chain isotype involves a mechanism different from that involved in V and D translocations; there is no evidence for a requirement for "inverted-repeat" sequences. Instead, recombination that leads to a switch in class is facilitated by the presence of closely related segments of DNA in the spacers that separate the various C_H genes. Within each spacer region, certain short sequences of DNA are repeated many times. It seems probable that the recombinations are mediated by enzymes recognizing portions of these sequences. Whether the recombination occurs within one chromosome or involves two sister chromatids has not been proved; current evidence favors the latter hypothesis.

PRESENCE OF INTRONS IN C_H REGIONS

Figure 5 is a diagram of the structure of the mouse $C_{\gamma 1}$ gene. Note that this gene exists as four segments. There are small introns (each less than 0.5 kilobase in length) between each of the four gene seg-

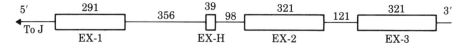

FIGURE 5. Organization of gene segments in the region coding for the γ_1 chain of mouse IgG1. Exons labeled EX-1, EX-H, EX-3, and EX-4 code for the C_H1, hinge, C_H2, and C_H3 regions, respectively. The exons are separated by introns, as indicated by a solid line. The numbers indicate the approximate lengths of segments, expressed as numbers of bases in the DNA. The entire segment shown, together with $V_H D_H J_H$, is transcribed to produce one length of RNA; the introns are removed by splicing when mRNA is produced. (The mRNA has additional material, characteristic of all eukaryotic mRNA, on its 5' and 3' ends.) In all heavy chains studied so far, gene segments coding for individual domains and for the hinge region are separated by small introns.

ments coding for C_H1, the hinge region, C_H2, and C_H3. The presence of a separate exon for each domain provides strong support for the conjecture, originally based on amino acid sequence homologies among domains, that a primordial gene encoded a single domain of 110–120 amino acids and that this gene subsequently underwent replication and mutation. The presence of a separate gene segment coding for the hinge is consistent with the unrelatedness of the amino acid sequence of this region to sequences in other parts of the immunoglobulin molecule. Introns have been identified between the gene segments controlling C_H domains and hinge regions of all immunoglobulins investigated so far.

STRUCTURE OF THE C_μ GENE

Mouse IgM occurs in two forms: secreted (IgM_s) and membrane-bound (IgM_m). The secreted form has 10 μ and 10 L chains; the membrane-bound form is an IgM monomer with two μ and two L chains (Chapter 4). The membrane-bound molecule acts as an antigen receptor on all primary and on some secondary B cells.[6] Amino acid sequence analyses have been carried out on IgM_s, which can be obtained in large quantity as a myeloma protein, but the membrane-bound protein has been available in small amounts, so that sequence data are very limited. Interestingly, the information that we do have on the partial amino acid sequence of IgM_m has come from determinations of sequences of DNA, which is obtained in useful quantities by cloning

---

[6] Primary B cells are those that have not been stimulated by antigen. Secondary B cells (memory cells) are generated from primary cells after antigenic stimulation.

procedures. The C-terminal structures of $C_{\mu s}$ and $C_{\mu m}$ were shown in Figure 2, Chapter 4. IgM$_s$ has an additional 20 residues beyond position 556, whereas IgM$_m$ has 41 residues. These 41 residues include a highly hydrophobic stretch of 26 amino acids.

The $C_{\mu s}$ region consists of four domains (as compared to three for C_γ). As in C_γ, the gene segments coding for the C_μ domains are separated by introns (Figure 6). No hinge region has been identified in IgM.[7] As indicated above, $C_{\mu s}$ and $C_{\mu m}$ differ only in the C-terminal region. The B cell has solved the problem of manufacturing two such closely related molecules in the following manner:

1. All four of the exons used by $C_{\mu s}$ are also used in the synthesis of $C_{\mu m}$.

2. The $C_{\mu m}$ gene has two additional exons at the 3' end (Figure 6). The first codes for amino acid residues 557–595; the second for only two residues, 596 and 597. The first additional exon is separated from the last $C_{\mu s}$ exon by an 1850-base pair intron. The final $C_{\mu m}$ exon, coding only for the last two amino acids, is separated by an additional 118 base pairs.

How are the mRNAs produced that code for $C_{\mu s}$ and $C_{\mu m}$? For $C_{\mu s}$, there is no apparent difficulty because $C_{\mu s}$ DNA is a continuous stretch, except for the introns between its domains. To produce the two required mRNA molecules, the entire C_μ DNA region up to and including the last exon of $C_{\mu m}$ is transcribed into RNA. This RNA is then cleaved and spliced in two different ways to produce mRNAs for $C_{\mu s}$ and $C_{\mu m}$. This is made possible by the presence of an appropriate recognition sequence for the splicing enzyme at a position correspond-

[7] It has been suggested that the hinge region in IgG, IgA, and IgD may be a vestige of the C_H2 domain in IgM.

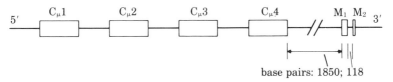

base pairs: 1850; 118

FIGURE 6. Organization of the $C\mu$ gene. M_1 and M_2 code for 39 and 2 amino acids, respectively, at the C-terminus of membrane-bound IgM (see text). When mRNA for the membrane-bound molecule is produced, RNA corresponding to the last 20 amino acids of the $C_\mu 4$ domain is removed by splicing enzymes and replaced by the RNA corresponding to M_1 and M_2 gene segments (41 amino acids). (From Rogers et al., 1980; Early et al., 1980b.)

ing to position 556 in the amino acid sequence. (As noted earlier, position 556 is the position beyond which $C_{\mu s}$ and $C_{\mu m}$ differ.) Enzyme recognition sequences for mRNA splicing are, of course, also present at the beginning and end of each intron. As a consequence, a cell producing both IgM$_s$ and IgM$_m$ contains, simultaneously, two different mRNA molecules, each specific for one of the two C_μ chains. Each RNA molecule also contains the usual sequences found in mRNA, including the poly(A) tail at the 3′ end.

As indicated in Chapter 4, the presence of a hydrophobic C-terminus appears to be a general characteristic of heavy chains of membrane-bound immunoglobulins. One would expect to find two species of mRNA in any cell producing both the membrane-bound and secreted forms. Evidence for an M exon, similar to that of IgM, has also been obtained for the other isotypes of mouse immunoglobulin.

EXPRESSION OF IgD

During the development of a B cell it initially expresses only surface IgM; at this stage it is called a pre-B cell. Primary B cells have IgM and IgD as receptors on their surface membranes. One possible explanation for their coexistence is that the two isotypes can be synthesized at the same time. Also, it has been shown that the IgM and IgD present on a given cell have identical V regions. These observations can be interpreted on the basis of the gene organization shown in Figure 7. The C_δ gene is close to the C_μ gene, starting only 2 kilobases "downstream" (on the 3′ side). The simultaneous production of IgM and IgD is brought about by the synthesis of a lengthy RNA transcript, which includes the V_H, D, J, C_μ, and C_δ regions. This RNA is processed in two different ways by splicing enzymes, yielding separate mRNAs for the μ and for the δ chain, which then coexist in the cell. This accounts for the sharing of the V_H region by μ and δ, as well as for the simultaneous production of the two isotypes.

Next consider a mature plasma cell that secretes IgD. In such a cell the C_μ gene has been deleted from that sequence which includes V, D, J, and C_δ (Figure 7). Thus, there are two alternative mechanisms that operate in the synthesis of IgD. The C_μ gene is still present in nonsecreting cells; the RNA splicing mechanism is used for the synthesis of membrane-bound IgD. In contrast, DNA rearrangement, with the deletion of C_μ, takes place in mature, IgD-secreting plasma cells. (Note, however, that very little IgD is present in the serum of normal or immunized mice or humans.)

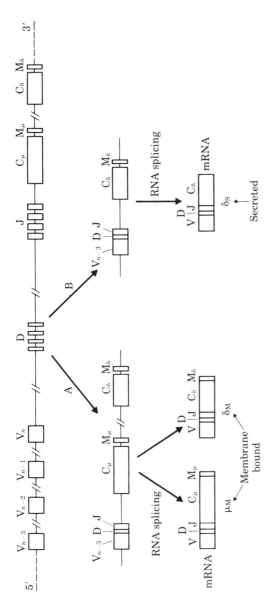

FIGURE 7. Alternative mechanisms for the production of IgD. (A) Membrane-bound IgD. Translocations bring V, D, and J together, separated by an intron, and by any remaining J segments, from C_μ. The RNA transcript that is made includes V, D, J, C_μ, M_μ, C_δ, and M_δ. This transcript is spliced in two alternative ways to yield mRNAs for the μ_m and δ_m chains. (B) Secreted IgD. VDJ is translocated to a position near C_δ, deleting C_μ and M_μ. After transcription and splicing, the mRNA produced codes for the secreted form of the chain, δ_s (lacking the M_δ segment). (After Moore et al., 1981.)

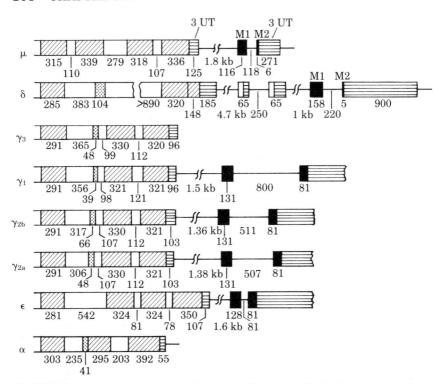

FIGURE 8. Structures of mouse C_H genes. The numerical values are numbers of nucleotide base pairs. Oblique-lined, solid, dotted and lined rectangles indicate domain exons, membrane exons, hinge exons, and 3' untranslated regions, respectively. White spaces between exons represent introns. The 3' untranslated regions are transcribed into messenger RNA but are not translated into polypeptide. (From Honjo, 1983.)

DETAILS OF GENE ORGANIZATION OF MOUSE C_H GENES

Figure 8 shows details of the structure of C_H genes in the mouse. The descending order of the genes is the same as their order (5' to 3') in the mouse genome.

GENE ORGANIZATION AND ALLELIC EXCLUSION

Normally, only one H chain and one L chain are expressed in an antibody-producing cell, despite the fact that allelic genes are present on two chromosomes. When translocation of V genes was first established, it was tempting to assume that allelic exclusion was attributable to the occurrence of a translocation on only one chromosome. The data now indicate, however, that rearrangements of genes frequently occur on the second, homologous chromosome as well. Nevertheless, in a given antibody-producing cell, only one set of rearrangements is productive, i.e., yields an antibody that is secreted. Nonsecreted, defective polypeptide chains or fragments of antibodies are sometimes produced as a result of a translocation in the nonproductive chromosome, but more often the rearrangement is abortive and yields no protein product. Results of this type suggest that some, perhaps many, B cells may undergo abortive rearrangements on both chromosomes and fail to produce any immunoglobulin at all.

In both mouse and human cells, there is strong evidence that κ genes are rearranged prior to λ genes. These experiments suggest that if the κ rearrangement yields a useful product, λ is not rearranged. If the κ rearrangements are nonproductive, λ rearrangements may then occur. Whether this reflects a precise regulatory mechanism, or simply a much higher rate of recombination for the κ locus, is not yet established.

HEAVY CHAIN DISEASE

Some individuals have a lymphatic disease called "heavy chain disease," which is characterized by secretion of free heavy chains from which part of the chain is deleted. L chains are absent from the secreted molecules. The structures of a few such incomplete H chains, each from a different individual, are shown in Figure 9. Note that the deletion in each case ends precisely at the beginning of a defined segment of the molecule, such as the hinge region or the C_H2 domain.

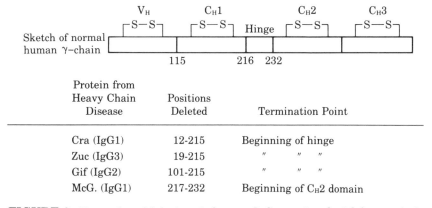

Protein from Heavy Chain Disease	Positions Deleted	Termination Point
Cra (IgG1)	12-215	Beginning of hinge
Zuc (IgG3)	19-215	″ ″ ″
Gif (IgG2)	101-215	″ ″ ″
McG. (IgG1)	217-232	Beginning of C_H2 domain

FIGURE 9. Examples of deletions in human IgG associated with heavy chain disease. (After Frangione and Franklin, 1973.)

This is consistent with the fact that the hinge region and each C_H domain are encoded by separate exons. Deletions thus terminate at the end of an exon.

GENETIC BASIS FOR THE DIVERSITY OF ANTIBODIES

We will consider here only V-region diversity, as it determines the repertoire of antigen-binding specificities. The following sources of variability exist:

1. *Multiple germ-line genes controlling* V *segments.* The best estimates are that there are 200–1000 inherited V_κ, two V_λ, and at least 100 V_H genes in the mouse.

2. *Multiple, perhaps random, combinations of V and J or, for* H *chains, of V, D, and J gene segments.* Many of these recombinants, especially those involving V and D, may give rise to different antigen-binding specificities. There is no evidence at present for restrictions on the ability of a given V_κ or V_H gene to combine with any J or, in the case of V_H, any D segment. (V_λ recombination is restricted, as discussed earlier.)

3. *Variability in the precise locus of joining of* V *and* J, *of* V *and* D, *or of* D *and* J. This is illustrated in Table 2. This mechanism has been shown to give rise to considerable variation at one or two positions in the third hypervariable region of L chains. The variability is even more pronounced in the case of *V–D* and *D–J* joining where *insertions* as well as deletions have been observed. The insertions may be caused by the action of an enzyme, called terminal nucleotide transferase, that can add nucleotides to the existing germline sequences during recombination. This mechanism, as well as the spectrum of sizes of D segments, may contribute to the considerable variability of length of the third hypervariable region of H chains.

4. *Multiple combinations of* L *and* H *chains:* Because both the L and H chain contribute to the formation of the antigen-binding site of an antibody, pairing of a given L chain with different H chains, or vice versa, may give rise to different specificities. For example, at a maximum, 2000 L chains and 2000 H chains could yield 4×10^6 different antibodies by random combination. It is probable, however, that some L chains and H chains cannot interact with one another to form a useful combining site and that not all combinations yield antibodies with different specificities.

TABLE 2. Potential diversity in amino acid sequences brought about by displacement of the site of recombination of V_κ *and* J_κ gene segments.

Germ-line genes	Junction sequence	Codons potentially generated	Amino acid corresponding to codon
$V_\kappa 41^a$	⌐C⌐ C⌐ C	C C C	Pro^c
$J_\kappa 1^b$	⌊T ⌊G ⌊G	T G G	Trp^c
		C G G	Arg^c
		C C G	Pro^c
$V_\kappa 41$	C C C	C C C	Pro^c
$J_\kappa 2$	T A C	T A C	Tyr^c
		C A C	His
$V_\kappa 41$	C C C	C C C	Pro
$J_\kappa 4$	T T C	T T C	Phe^c
		C T C	Leu
$V_\kappa 41$	C C C	C C C	Pro
$J_\kappa 5$	C T C	C T C	Leu^c

From Max et al. (1979).

^{a} Corresponds to the germ-line V_κ gene expressed in the mouse myeloma tumor M41.

^{b} The authors number the J_κ segments from the 3' toward the 5' end (right to left). The numbering system used here is from left to right.

^{c} Accounts for a κ chain with a known J-region sequence.

5. *Somatic point mutations.* This refers to mutations in immunoglobulin genes occurring in B cells (not germ cells) during the lifetime of the embryo or animal. The following evidence indicates that such mutations occur. As already mentioned, one can approximate the number of V genes in a group by hybridization techniques. Typically, it is found by the Southern blot technique that a given V_κ or V_H radioactive probe (mRNA or cDNA) will hybridize under stringent conditions with 4 to 10 DNA fragments, most of which contain only one copy of the V gene in question. In the mouse, a V_λ probe hybridizes with only two fragments. It is believed that this defines the number of V genes in a group. However, amino acid sequences carried out on immunoglobulins belonging to the same group have shown that the number of different known sequences greatly exceeds the number of V genes in

a group. In most cases the amino acid substitutions, which occur in framework and, more frequently, hypervariable regions, reflect single base changes in DNA and are consistent with point mutations. The excess of V-region amino acid sequences over the number of V genes in a group, most clearly shown in the mouse, is strong evidence for somatic variation. Somatic variation, attributed to mutations, also takes place at moderate frequency in J segments, as shown by differences between the amino acid sequences of J regions and the corresponding germ-line DNA sequences. Whether somatic mutations occur in D segments is still uncertain.

6. *Somatic recombination*. It has been proposed that recombinational events during cell division, in addition to those specified above under (2) and (3) may cause further diversity in V regions. How much this mechanism actually contributes to diversity is not certain.

SOMATIC MUTATIONS MAY AFFECT IgG AND IgA SEQUENCES MORE FREQUENTLY THAN IgM

Amino acid sequence analyses have been carried out on closely related members of a family of mouse antibodies, all of which react with the same hapten (phosphorylcholine) and have very similar V regions (idiotypes, Chapter 8). The heavy chains of all the antibodies are evidently controlled by the same germ-line V_H gene. The interesting observation was made that all the independently isolated IgM proteins in this family had the same V_H amino acid sequences, but a variety of substitutions were observed in individual IgG or IgA antibodies. These experiments suggest that somatic mutation may be associated with a switch in class, from μ to γ or α. Alternatively, mutations may be associated with cell divisions, which occur at higher frequency during and after class switching. It should be noted that in other experimental systems somatic variants have occasionally been observed in IgM, and germ-line (nonmutated) configurations in IgG and IgA.

ORGANIZATION OF HUMAN IMMUNOGLOBULIN GENES

Although human immunoglobulin genes have not been studied as extensively as those of the mouse, a substantial body of information is available. It appears that the principles governing the behavior of the genes, and many of their structural features, are very similar in the two species. In the human, as in the mouse, there is a single active gene for the constant region of each class or subclass of heavy or light chains. As in the mouse, there are three gene complexes for κ, λ and H chains; in man they are on chromosomes 2, 22, and 14, respectively. The order of C_H genes in man is μ, δ, γ3, γ1, α1, γ2, γ4, ε, α2. Little is known, however, about the distances between the C_H genes. In each species one finds similar recognition sequences and spacers responsible for recombination on the 3' side of each V segment, the 5' side of each J segment, and on both sides of D_H. Leader sequences similar in size precede human and mouse V segments. The organization of genes differs somewhat in the two species, and some of these differences will be summarized next.

The human $J_κ$ cluster contains 5 rather than 4 active $J_κ$ segments. For human heavy chains there are 6 active and 3 inactive J_H segments; in the mouse the corresponding numbers are 4 and 1. The number of $V_κ$ genes appears to be considerably smaller in man than in the mouse (~20–30 vs. several hundred). There are several allelic forms of $C_κ$ (allotypes, Chapter 7) in the human but so far such alleles have not been identified in the mouse. The number of $C_λ$ genes in man varies among individuals from 6 to 9; in the mouse there is a fixed number, namely 3, of functional $C_λ$ genes. On the basis of amino acid sequence analysis of immunoglobulins, the number of $V_λ$ genes is expected to be much greater in humans than in the mouse. This would correspond with the fact that about 40% of normal human immunoglobulins are λ, as compared to about 5% in the mouse. In both species each $C_λ$ gene appears to have its own $J_λ$, as contrasted with the κ locus, where the $J_κ$ segments are in a single cluster.

Several D segments have been identified in the human genome but have not yet been associated with known amino acid sequences. One D segment has been localized quite close to J_{H1}, on its 5' side.

The number of human V_H genes is not yet known; however, they seem to belong to four major families, a number that corresponds with the number of groups predicted from earlier studies of amino acid sequences of V_H regions.

IMMUNOGLOBULIN GENES AND CANCER

It has recently become apparent that the immunoglobulin-encoding region of the genome is involved in an unexpected way in the induction of certain types of cancer. In this section we will review some of the data, after first providing background information.

During the past few years genes have been discovered in tumor cells that are responsible, completely or in part, for the uncontrolled growth of these cells. Such genes, called oncogenes, are activated when a normal cell undergoes transformation to the malignant state. The presence of oncogenes can be demonstrated, for example, by extracting DNA from cancer cells and using it to transform normal cells into cancer cells *in vitro*. Also, certain viruses contain genes that, when incorporated into the DNA of normal cells, induce malignancy. Other viruses (retroviruses) carry the information for tumor induction in their RNA, which is converted into DNA by an enzyme, reverse transcriptase, after the virus enters a cell.

Oncogenes that are extracted from cancer cells are very closely related structurally to genes that are present in all normal cells; these closely related, but nontransforming, genes of normal cells are referred to as proto-oncogenes. There are at least 4 different proto-oncogenes in normal human cells. It is of considerable interest that the oncogenes of retroviruses are actually proto-oncogenes that are picked up by the virus from the mammalian cells that they infect and then somehow are converted by the viruses into active oncogenes. Mutations may cause the conversion of a proto-oncogene into an active oncogene. Current evidence suggests that the same proto-oncogene, when activated, can give rise to several different forms of cancer, including leukemias, carcinomas, and sarcomas.

Limited information is available as to the nature of the mutations that cause the conversion of a proto-oncogene into an oncogene. In one instance, the striking observation was made that a single base change was sufficient for conversion. It should be stressed that, although conversion of a proto-oncogene to an oncogene is a necessary step in the induction of many forms of cancer, it may not be sufficient; there is considerable evidence that more than one biochemical event is required.

Proto-oncogenes can be activated by recombinational events as well as by mutations. Such a mechanism has been observed in a human malignancy called Burkitt's lymphoma and in multiple myeloma of the mouse. In Burkitt's lymphoma recombination of chromosome 8 with another chromosome is frequently observed. The second chromosome can be either number 14, 2, or 22. These three chromosomes contain genes encoding H, κ, or λ chains, respectively. It was further discovered that these recombinations bring a proto-oncogene on chromosome 8 into very close proximity with an immunoglobulin gene on the other chromosome. The translocation causes activation of the proto-oncogene. It has been hypothesized that the same genetic mechanism that activates an immunoglobulin gene (i.e., causes it to be transcribed) serves to activate the proto-oncogene after translocation of chromosome 8. A stretch of DNA that activates immunoglobulin gene transcription is known to be present between the J_H and μ genes. It seems possible that this same "enhancer sequence" serves to activate the proto-oncogene.

LITERATURE CITED

Blomberg, B., Traunecker, A., Eisen, H. and Tonegawa, S. (1981). Organization of four mouse λ light chain immunoglobulin genes. *Proc. Natl. Acad. Sci. USA 78*, 3765.

Early, P., Huang, H., Davis, M., Calame, K. and Hood, L. (1980a). An immunoglobulin heavy chain variable region gene is generated from three segments of DNA: V_H, D and J. *Cell 19*, 981.

Early, P., Rogers, J., Davis, M., Calame, K., Bond, M., Wall, R. and Hood, L. (1980b). Two mRNAs can be produced from a single immunoglobulin μ gene by alternative RNA processing pathways. *Cell 20*, 313.

Frangione, B. and Franklin, E. C. (1973). Heavy chain diseases: clinical features and molecular significance of the disordered immunoglobulin structure. *Semin. Hematol. 10*, 53.

Honjo, T. (1983). Immunoglobulin genes. *Annu. Rev. Immunol. 1*, 499.

Hozumi, N. and Tonegawa, S. (1976). Evidence for somatic rearrangement of immunoglobulin genes coding for variable and constant regions. *Proc. Natl. Acad. Sci. USA 73*, 3628.

Max, E. E., Seidman, J. G. and Leder, P. (1979). Sequences of five potential recombination sites encoded close to an immunoglobulin κ constant region. *Proc. Natl. Acad. Sci. USA 76*, 3450.

Moore, K. W., Rogers, J., Hunkapiller, T., Early, P., Nottenburg, C., Weissman, I., Bazin, H., Wall, R. and Hood, L. E. (1981). Expression of IgD may use both DNA rearrangement and RNA splicing mechanisms. *Proc. Natl. Acad. Sci. USA 78*, 1800.

Rogers, J., Early, P., Carter, C., Calame, K., Bond, M., Hood, L. and Wall, R. (1980). Two mRNAs with different 3' ends encode membrane-bound and secreted forms of immunoglobulin μ chain. *Cell 20*, 303.

Southern, E. M. (1975). Detection of specific sequences among DNA fragments separated by gel electrophoresis. *J. Mol. Biol. 98*, 503.

SUGGESTED ADDITIONAL READING

Cohn M., Blomberg, B., Geckeler, W., Raschke, W., Riblet, R. and Weigert, M. (1974). First-order considerations in analyzing the generation of diversity. In E. Sercarz, A. Williamson and C. F. Fox, Eds., *The Immune System: Genes, Receptors, Signals*. New York, Academic Press.

Flanagan, J. G. and Rabbitts, T. H. (1982). Arrangement of human immunoglobulin heavy chain constant region genes implies evolutionary duplication of a segment containing γ, ϵ and α genes. *Nature 300,* 709.

Korsmeyer, S. J., Bakhshi, A., Arnold, A., Siminovitch, K. A. and Waldemann, T. A. (1984). Genetic arrangements of human immunoglobulin genes. In M. I. Greene and A. Nisonoff, Eds., *Biology of Idiotypes.* New York, Plenum Press.

Leder, P. and Seidman, J. G. (1978). The arrangement and rearrangement of antibody genes. *Nature 276,* 790.

Tonegawa, S., Brack, C., Hozumi, N., Matthyssens, G. and Schuller, R. (1977). Dynamics of immunoglobulin genes. *Immunol. Revs. 36,* 73.

Weinberg, R. A. (1983). A molecular basis of cancer. *Sci. Amer. 249,* 126.

Yaoita, Y. and Honjo, T. (1980). Deletion of immunoglobulin heavy chain genes from the expressed allelic chromosome. *Nature 286,* 850.

Immunological Reviews. (1981). Volume 59. Three review articles on immunoglobulin gene organization.

7

ALLOTYPES OF IMMUNOGLOBULINS

OVERVIEW

Allotypes, or genetic variants, exist for the L or H chains of various immunoglobulin classes in many species. Most if not all allotypes reflect the presence of allelic genes, i.e., closely related genes that can occupy the same locus. Allotypic differences in amino acid sequence can usually be identified by the use of antisera. The epitopes recognized by such antisera are called allotypic determinants. Investigations of allotypes have aided our understanding of immunoglobulin structure and have proved useful in a variety of genetic studies. This chapter discusses the allotypes of rabbit, mouse, and human immunoglobulins and their patterns of inheritance.

*   *   *

ALLOTYPES are genetic variants of immunoglobulins and are inherited according to simple Mendelian laws. In this chapter we will emphasize general principles of allotypy. The allotypes of rabbit IgG will be discussed in some detail; those of the mouse and human will be considered briefly.

The concept of allotypy can be introduced by considering the constant region of human κ chains (C_κ). The available evidence suggests that there is a single structural gene for C_κ on human chromosome 2. It might seem possible then that the amino acid sequence of the C_κ region would be identical in all individuals. This is not, however, the case; there are three different molecules, designated Km(1,2), Km(1), and Km(3).[1] A Km(1,2) κ chain expresses antigenic (allotypic) determinants Km(1) and Km(2). The Km(1) and Km(3) κ chains express

---

[1] Formerly, the notation Inv was used rather than Km, i.e., Inv(1,2), etc.

117

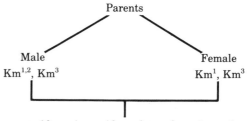

FIGURE 1. Mode of inheritance of genes controlling allotypes of the constant regions of human κ chains. As indicated, four different genotypes are possible in the offspring of the mating shown. A child that inherits two different genes will express the corresponding allotypes in his immunoglobulin molecules. A single molecule will, however, express only one gene product, because only one gene for $C_κ$ is expressed in an antibody-producing cell. In the case of the Km(1,2) allotype, two allotypic determinants, Km(1) and Km(2), are present on a single light chain; i.e., these two determinants are encoded by a single gene ($Km^{1,2}$).

determinants Km(1) and Km(3), respectively. The three polypeptide chains are under the control of allelic $C_κ$ genes, $Km^{1,2}$, Km^1 and Km^3. (ALLELES are genetic variants at a single locus.[2]) An individual may be homozygous for any one of the genes $Km^{1,2}$, Km^1, or Km^3 (i.e., each chromosome of the pair may carry the same gene) or heterozygous, possessing two of the three alleles. The Km^1 gene is, however, rare.[3]

Thus, there are three known $C_κ$ alleles in the human population. These alleles are inherited according to simple Mendelian laws of independent assortment (Figure 1). The three $C_κ$ amino acid sequences controlled by these genes differ only slightly from one another, being identical except for two positions in the sequence, as shown in Table 1. Despite these very slight differences, immunoglobulins bearing the three different markers can be distinguished by antisera and, in fact, were discovered by serological rather than amino acid sequence analysis. The antigenic determinants that distinguish the three chains are referred to as ALLOTYPIC DETERMINANTS, ALLOTYPIC MARKERS, or ALLO- TOPES. The genes that an individual possesses, which determine the collection of allotypic determinants expressed, are referred to as the ALLOTYPE of the individual.

The genes controlling Km(1,2), Km(1), and Km(3) behave as al-

[2] Italics are used to denote genes.

[3] An individual who possesses a $Km^{1,2}$ gene produces L chains with allotypic determinants 1 and 2 on the same chain.

TABLE 1. Differences in amino acid sequences of human κ chains associated with the Km allotypes.

	Position in sequence	
Allotype	153	191
Km(1,2)	Alanine	Leucine
Km(3)	Alanine	Valine
Km(1)	Valine	Leucine

leles. These genes, and all allelic genes controlling allotypes that have been studied so far, are codominant, i.e., the immunoglobulin product of each of the two genes that an individual possesses is found in serum, although not necessarily in a 1:1 ratio. It is believed that allelic genes arose from a single gene that underwent mutation and became fixed in part of the human population.

Allotypic determinants may be present on L chains, H chains, or both. Their presence is quite unpredictable; it varies with the class of immunoglobulin, the type of L chain (κ or λ), and the species. Table 2 gives the locations of allotypic determinants identified in humans, rabbits, and mice.

Family studies show that genes controlling allotypic markers on the same H chain (e.g., on the V_H or the C_H region) or on different classes or subclasses of H chains, are linked to one another. However, genes controlling allotypic markers on H, κ, and λ chains are unlinked. This reflects the fact that genes controlling V and C regions of the various H chains are on the same chromosome, whereas genes con-

TABLE 2. Localization of allotypes in L or H chains.

Species	Present on light chain	Present on V_H	Present on C_H
Rabbit	$C_κ$, $C_λ$	All classes[a]	γ, μ, α
Mouse	$V_κ$	None identified	γ1, γ2a, γ2b, α, δ, ε
Human	$C_κ$	None identified	γ1, γ2, γ3, γ4, α2[b]

[a] The same V_H regions are shared by each class of immunoglobulin.

[b] Heavy chain of IgA2.

trolling heavy, κ, and λ chains are on separate chromosomes. Table 1, Chapter 6, lists these chromosomal locations for humans and mice.

Most of the known allotypic markers are localized in C_H or C_L regions. An important exception occurs in rabbit immunoglobulins, which have allotypic markers in V_H as well as C_H regions. This property has proved useful for studies of the linkage of V_H and C_H genes. It also provided early evidence that the same set of V_H genes contributes to the biosynthesis of the various classes (IgG, IgM, etc.), each of which is represented by a different C_H gene.

Allotypes were discovered by using antisera that recognize allotypic determinants. Jacques Oudin identified the first allotypic markers in the rabbit in 1956, at about the same time that human allotypes were discovered (Grubb and Laurel, 1956). Nearly all of the early studies that defined the genetic properties of allotypes were carried out with antisera. However, some of the amino acid sequences that are associated with allotypic determinants have now been worked out.

PREPARATION OF ANTI-ALLOTYPE ANTISERA

The methods used for obtaining anti-allotype sera vary considerably. In the rabbit, most allotypic determinants are identified with HOMOLOGOUS ANTISERA, i.e., with antisera prepared in other rabbits. The antigen used for immunization can be purified immunoglobulin or an antigen–antibody complex (e.g., bacteria coated with anti-bacterial antibody). The recipient rabbit will produce antibodies directed against determinants that the recipient lacks. For example, there are four alleles for the allotypic determinants of the C_κ region of L chains in most rabbit populations; these are designated b^4, b^5, b^6, and b^9. An individual rabbit can be homozygous for one of the four genes (e.g., b^4,b^4) or heterozygous (e.g., b^5,b^9). If immunoglobulin from a b^5,b^9 rabbit is injected into a b^4,b^5 recipient, the recipient will eventually make anti-b9 antibodies; it will not make anti-b5 because the rabbit is tolerant to its own determinants.

Antisera against rabbit allotypes can also be prepared in a heterologous species, such as the goat. In contrast to the rabbit, the goat will make antibodies to many antigenic determinants in addition to allotypic markers. (The rabbit is tolerant to those determinants that are common to rabbit immunoglobulins.) The goat antiserum can be rendered specific for the allotype in question by adsorption with appropriate insolubilized immunoglobulin. Suppose the rabbit whose immunoglobulin was used for immunizing the goat has the hypothetical allotypic markers X, Y, and Z. The goat antiserum can be made specific for Z by adsorption with globulin from another rabbit that has markers X and Y but lacks Z. This will remove anti-X, anti-Y, and antibodies directed to various other regions of the rabbit immunoglobulin molecule, leaving anti-Z.

Antibodies against mouse allotypes can similarly be prepared by immunization of another mouse differing in allotype from the donor. An important distinction from the rabbit is that many inbred strains of mice are available. All mice of a given strain have the same allotype, but some strains differ from others. Thus, there are more than 50 inbred strains of mice, which express 10 major allotypes. Anti-allotype antibodies are therefore prepared by immunizing an inbred mouse of one strain with immunoglobulin of another strain that differs in allotype. Some, but comparatively little, work has been done with outbred or wild mice.

In the human, direct immunization is generally not feasible. Nevertheless, human serum is an important source of antibodies against human allotypes. Anti-allotype antibodies are found in some patients with rheumatoid arthritis, which is associated with autoimmune (anti-self) reactions; in certain individuals who have received transfusions of blood; in some women who have had multiple pregnancies; and, occasionally, in a normal individual. In several instances, antibodies to human allotypes have been prepared in a heterologous species, in particular in the monkey or rabbit. Mouse monoclonal antibodies (Chapter 10) are becoming a major source of anti-human allotype antibodies. Anti-allotype antibodies made in nonhuman species must in general be adsorbed with human globulins lacking the allotype in question. This is not true of monoclonal antibodies because they recognize a single determinant.

ASSAYS FOR ANTI-ALLOTYPE ANTIBODIES

Anti-allotype antibodies are demonstrated by a variety of methods (Chapter 9), such as precipitation in agar gel (including immunoelectrophoresis) and radioimmunoassays. Note that in these assays the antigen as well as the antibody is an immunoglobulin. Another method that was employed by Grubb in his discovery of human allotypes is still in widespread use. The latter technique is illustrated in Figure 2. The allotypic determinant being detected is called G1m(1); it is present on human IgG1. For the test, Grubb made use of red blood cells bearing antigenic determinants, called Rh, and human anti-Rh antibodies that coat the red blood cells but do not agglutinate them ("incomplete" anti-Rh antibodies). The anti-Rh antibodies used carry the G1m(1) allotype. Upon subsequent addition of anti-G1m(1), agglutination of the coated cells occurs and they rapidly settle out of

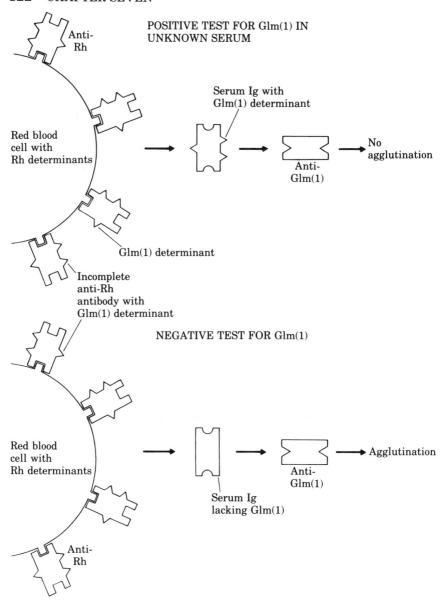

POSITIVE TEST FOR Glm(1) IN
UNKNOWN SERUM

Serum Ig with
Glm(1) determinant

Anti-
Rh

Red blood
cell with
Rh determinants

Anti-
Glm(1)

No
agglutination

Glm(1) determinant

Incomplete
anti-Rh
antibody with
Glm(1) determinant

NEGATIVE TEST FOR Glm(1)

Red blood
cell with
Rh determinants

Anti-
Glm(1)

Agglutination

Serum Ig
lacking Glm(1)

Anti-
Rh

FIGURE 2. Diagram illustrating the method initially used (and still widely employed) to screen human sera for the presence of certain allotypic determinants. In the example shown, only those sera containing IgG1 that expresses the G1m(1) determinant will inhibit the agglutination (see text). (After Grubb and Laurel, 1956.)

suspension. If, however, serum containing G1m(1) is simultaneously added to the mixture, it blocks the agglutination by occupying the combining sites of the anti-G1m(1); if the serum added lacks G1m(1), it will fail to inhibit agglutination. With this system one can rapidly screen many sera for the presence or absence of G1m(1). To screen for another marker, such as G1m(2), one uses nonagglutinating anti-Rh bearing G1m(2), together with anti-G1m(2), and again tests for inhibition of agglutination by various sera.

ALLOTYPES ON INDUCED ANTIBODIES

Consider a rabbit that is heterozygous at the κ chain locus, possessing b^4 and b^9. Suppose one immunizes with an antigen—say, bovine serum albumin (BSA)—isolates the anti-BSA from the immune serum, and determines which allotypic markers are present. Almost invariably, the anti-BSA will express both b^4 and b^9, although not necessarily in a 1:1 ratio. Certain allotypes are frequently dominant over others; for example, there is likely to be more b4 than b9 in the anti-BSA, as well as in normal immunoglobulin. The reason for this "pecking order" is not known. If there are single genes encoding $C_{\kappa b4}$ or $C_{\kappa b9}$, the dominance of b4 would not be attributable to gene dosage. One possibility is that it is due to the arrangement of the genes in the chromosome, making a translocation of a V_κ gene to $C_{\kappa b4}$ more probable.

ARE GENES CONTROLLING ALLOTYPES STRUCTURAL OR REGULATORY?

Some animals (in particular, rabbits) sometimes express low concentrations of allotypes that are controlled by genes that the animal should not have possessed, according to expected inheritance patterns. These are referred to as LATENT ALLOTYPES. On this basis it has been proposed that individual animals may possess genes for a variety of allotypes, but inherit *regulatory* genes that behave as alleles and determine the allotypes that are to be expressed. If this were correct, genes such as b^4 and b^5 would not occupy homologous positions in the chromosome and would be "pseudoalleles." This is an unsettled question and, for simplicity, we will discuss such genes as if they were allelic and structural. Definitive answers should shortly be forthcoming from studies of DNA. At present it appears very likely that the C_κ allotypes of the human and the C_H allotypes of the mouse are true alleles.

RABBIT ALLOTYPES

Although allotypic markers are present on rabbit IgA and IgM, we will consider in some detail only those associated with IgG; this will serve to illustrate principles that control the inheritance of allotypes. Table 3 lists allotypic determinants present on rabbit IgG, IgA, and IgM. For purposes of illustration, we will first consider the allotypes of κ chains and V_H regions.

As already indicated, the genes b^4, b^5, b^6, and b^9 behave as alleles controlling C_κ regions; a^1, a^2, and a^3 act as alleles controlling V_H regions. The a and b genetic loci are unlinked, i.e., genes of the two loci assort independently. To illustrate this, the cross

$$\text{Dam} \quad \times \quad \text{Sire}$$

$$a^1,a^2,b^4,b^4 \qquad a^3,a^3,b^5,b^6$$

would yield the following offspring: a^1,a^3,b^4,b^5; a^1,a^3,b^4,b^6; a^2,a^3,b^4,b^5; and a^2,a^3,b^4,b^6.

A rabbit that is, for example, a^1,a^3,b^4,b^5 will produce IgG molecules that are a1,b4; a1,b5; a3,b4; and a3,b5. Note that an individual molecule does not possess both a1 and a3 or b4 and b5, despite the fact that the molecule has two H chains and two L chains. This is a consequence of the fact that an individual antibody-producing cell secretes only one molecular species of H chain and one of L chain (allelic exclusion). It should be noted also that the V and C genes that contribute to the synthesis of a single chain are, in all or nearly all molecules, derived from the same chromosome.

RABBIT λ CHAINS

Seventy to ninety percent of the light chains of most rabbits are of the κ type; the remainder are λ. Two antigenic markers, designated c7 and c21, have been identified on λ chains; they are present on separate molecules. The inheritance pattern is rather complex. Some chromosomes carry only c^7 genes. (About half of the rabbit population fails to express c21 and presumably lacks the corresponding gene.) When a c^{21} gene is present, it is almost always on the same chromosome as c^7, and the two markers are inherited as a unit. If one breeds a c^7,c^7 rabbit with one that is $c^{7,21},c^{7,21}$, all of the offspring will express both markers in their immunoglobulins. However, in the offspring the two homologous chromosomes will differ, with one bearing c^7 and the other c^7 and c^{21}. Because the c7 and c21 specificities are not present on the same molecule, occurrence of the two genes on one chromosome indicates that there are at least two genes in the rabbit coding for λ chains. Whether c^{21} encodes markers on the V_λ or C_λ region, or both, has not been ascertained.

TABLE 3. Allotypic determinants on rabbit immunoglobulins.

Polypeptide chain	Genetic locus	Location on chain	Allotypic determinants[a]
κ	b	$C_κ$	b4, b5, b6, b9, b variant
λ	c	Uncertain	c7, c21
V_H	a	V_H	a1, a2, a3[b]
V_H	x	V_H	x32
V_H	y	V_H	y33
γ(IgG)	de	C_H[c]	d11, d12, e14, e15
μ(IgM)	n	$C_μ$	n80 to n87[d]
α(IgA)	f	$C_α$[e]	f69 to f73
α(IgA)	g	$C_α$[e]	g74 to g77

[a] We have listed here only those determinants commonly found in domestic rabbits. A number of other determinants have been identified in wild rabbits.

[b] These determinants exhibit microheterogeneity, probably reflecting sequence variations in V_H regions.

[c] The "d" determinants are present in the hinge region; "e" determinants are in the C_H2 domain (see text for further details). The locus is specified as de because both sets of determinants are in the C_H region and the genetic linkage between them is very tight.

[d] Some of these determinants appear on the same IgM molecule, e.g., a single molecule may express n81 and n87, etc. Also, some n locus antigenic determinants are not expressed unless an appropriate V_H or C_L segment is also present. Other investigators have studied the IgM allotypes independently and use a different nomenclature, with the prefix Ms instead of n. (For details, see Gilman-Sachs et al., 1982; Naessens et al., 1979.)

[e] Separate determinants controlled by this locus have been identified in the C_H1 domain and the Fc segment (C_H2 + C_H3).

An interesting rabbit was discovered, at the Basel Institute of Immunology in Switzerland, whose L chains were almost entirely of the λ type. Through breeding, a partially inbred strain of rabbits has been developed that has this unusual distribution of L chain types. It has proved useful for a variety of genetic studies.

ALLOTYPIC MARKERS ON THE C_H REGION OF RABBIT IgG

The d and e allotypic markers are present in the C_H region of rabbit IgG; the markers are d11, d12, e14, and e15. DNA sequences controlling the d and e allotypic markers are present on the same $C_γ$ gene. Thus, d and e are inherited as a unit. If a chromosome possesses $d^{12}e^{15}$, the two markers will be transmitted together to offspring. Furthermore, the d12 and e15 allotypic determinants will be present on the same IgG molecules. Crossovers are very infrequent. The d11 and d12 determinants are associated with the presence of a methionine or threonine, respectively, at position 225 in the hinge region; e14 and e15 are associated with threonine or alanine, respectively, at position 309, which is in the C_H2 domain. As in the case of the human Km markers, single amino acid substitutions alter the antigenic properties of the molecule sufficiently to permit serological typing, i.e., typing by the use of antisera.

INHERITANCE OF V_H (a LOCUS) AND C_H (de LOCUS) ALLOTYPES

One can best understand this inheritance pattern in terms of the genes present on each of the pair of chromosomes that control H chains. Consider the following mating:

	Dam	×	Sire
First chromosome	$a^1de^{11,15}$		$a^1de^{12,14}$
Second chromosome	$a^3de^{12,15}$		$a^2de^{12,15}$

In the offspring, the four possible genotypes at the H chain locus are $a^1de^{11,15}$, $a^1de^{12,14}$; $a^1de^{11,15}$, $a^2de^{12,15}$; $a^3de^{12,15}$, $a^1de^{12,14}$; and $a^3de^{12,15}$, $a^2de^{12,15}$.

Consider next a rabbit with the second genotype of the four listed above, i.e., $a^1de^{11,15}$, $a^2de^{12,15}$. The immunoglobulin of the rabbit will contain molecules that are a1,d11,e15 or a2,d12,e15. Other combinations, such as a1,d12,e15 will not be present in individual molecules or will be present at very low frequency.[4] Thus, the structure of an individual H chain is controlled by the genes of one chromosome.

We note again that the inheritance of L chain allotypes is independent of the inheritance of H chain allotypes because the genes are on different chromosomes. When a rabbit is heterozygous at loci controlling both H and L chains, L chains of each allotype assort, apparently at random, with H chains of the two allotypes in the immunoglobulin produced by that rabbit (Table 4).

ALLOTYPES ON RABBIT IgA AND IgM

Allotypic determinants associated with the C_H regions of these classes are shown in Table 3. The various isotypes of immunoglobulin

---

[4] A very small percentage of molecules controlled by elements of two chromosomes is usually observed; this may reflect a crossover occurring in an occasional antibody-producing cell, probably during cell division.

TABLE 4. Illustration of random assortment of allotypes on L chains and H chains of individual rabbit IgG molecules.

Genotype of the rabbit (doubly heterozygous)	a^1a^2 (H chain); b^4b^5 (L chain)
Allotypic determinants present on individual IgG molecules[a]	a1,b4; a1,b5; a2,b4; a2,b5

[a] Note that an individual molecule expresses only one H chain allotype and one L chain allotype despite the presence of two chromosomes, controlling two different allotypes, in the antibody-producing cell.

(IgG, IgA, IgM, etc.) share the same V_H regions and L chains and, therefore, the same V_H, κ, and λ allotypes.

LINKED SETS OF V_H AND C_H GENES IN THE RABBIT POPULATION

In theory, all combinations of genes controlling V_H regions, or the C_H regions of IgG, IgA or IgM, might be found among rabbits. In fact, a limited number of combinations are present in the populations investigated so far. These are shown in Table 5. Each combination listed in the table represents the genes present on a single chromosome, because the chromosome is the unit of inheritance and the V_H and C_H genes are present on the same chromosome. A group of allotypes that is inherited as a unit is called a HAPLOTYPE or HAPLOGROUP.

CROSSOVER FREQUENCIES

The fact that stable groups of linked genes controlling heavy chains are present in the rabbit population suggests that the frequency of effective crossovers, yielding new and stable combinations of genes in the germ line, must be low. In laboratory breeding studies with rabbits, an occasional crossover is observed between V_H and C_H genes. The crossover frequency is, however, well under 1%. The frequency of crossovers among the various C_H genes, controlling C_γ, C_μ, and C_α, is extremely low, reflecting close proximity in the chromosome.

Crossover frequencies between V_H and C_H genes have been studied rather extensively in the mouse by making use of inherited antigenic markers that are present in V_H regions (idiotypes, Chapter 8). The frequencies range from a few tenths of 1% to as high as 7%. It is

TABLE 5. Haplogroups of rabbit heavy chains.[a]

Designation	Variable region			Constant region			
	a	x	y	μ	α	α	γ
A	a^1	x^-	y^-	n^{81}	f^{73}	g^{74}	$de^{12,15}$
B	a^1	x^-	$y^{30,33}$	$n^{80,83}$	f^{71}	g^{75}	$de^{12,15}$
C	a^1	x^-	$y^{30,33}$	$n^{80,83}$	f^{72}	g^{74}	$de^{11,15}$
I	a^1	x^-	$y^{30,33}$	$n^{80,83}$	f^{69}	g^{77}	$de^{12,14}$
J	a^1	x^-	y^-	n^{81}	f^{70}	g^{76}	$de^{12,15}$
E	a^2	x^{32}	$y^{33,-}$	$n^{80,82,87}$	f^{71}	g^{75}	$de^{12,15}$
F	a^2	x^{32}	$y^{33,-}$	$n^{80,82,87}$	f^{69}	g^{77}	$de^{12,15}$
M	a^2	x^{32}	$y^{33,-}$	$n^{81,87}$	f^{73}	g^{74}	$de^{12,15}$
G	a^3	x^{32}	y^-	$n^{80,84,86,87}$	f^{71}	g^{75}	$de^{12,15}$
H	a^3	x^{32}	y^-	$n^{81,84,85}$	f^{72}	g^{74}	$de^{11,15}$

From Gilman-Sachs et al. (1982).

[a] The order of the a, x, y, n, f, g, and de genes is an arbitrarily chosen one and does not imply a known gene order. These haplogroups are found in closed laboratory colonies of rabbits. Other haplogroups would undoubtedly be found in wild rabbits. Nevertheless, the number of known haplogroups is a very small fraction of the 3840 possible combinations. A haplogroup comprises the genes present on one chromosome.

possible that the crossover frequency depends on the proximity of a particular V_H gene to the C_H gene cluster in the chromosome.

MOUSE IMMUNOGLOBULINS

Heavy chains

Allotypic variation occurs in the heavy chains of the mouse; nearly all markers discovered so far are in C_H regions. Variations in L chains occur in V_κ segments; so far no allotypes of λ or C_κ have been reported.

If a donor mouse has immunoglobulins with allotypic determinants that are absent from the recipient, anti-allotype antibodies can be produced upon immunization. The principal methods used for studying mouse allotypes are precipitation in agar gel and radioimmunoassay. Allotypic determinants have been demonstrated in the C_H regions of mouse γ_{2a}, γ_{2b}, γ_1, α, δ, and ε chains. Some of these are listed in Table 6. Each class and subclass has its own set of allotypic determinants, which can be identified with antisera prepared in a mouse that lacks such determinants.

The approach that has been used in studying mouse allotypes differs somewhat from that applied to human or rabbit immunoglobulins because of the existence of a large number of inbred strains of mice; inbred mice have been used in most investigations of allotypy. In such studies, all mice of an individual strain are interchangeable because, with the exception of certain sex-linked genes, they are genetically identical.

Recent data on DNA sequences indicate that the differences among strains of mice, differing in allotype for a given class of immunoglobulin, can range from minor (less than 1%) to substantial (5–10%) (Ollo and Rougeon, 1983).

Although certain strains differ from one another allotypically, there are groups of strains that have identical allotypes. Nearly all inbred strains fall into 10 groups that differ from one another with respect to allotypic determinants present on their γ_{2a} chains; i.e., strains within a single group are identical with respect to allotypic

TABLE 6. Distribution of allotypes present on C_H regions of mouse immunoglobulins of various classes.

		Locus and chain						
Haplotype	Prototype strain	Igh-1 γ_{2a}	Igh-2 α	Igh-3 γ_{2b}	Igh-4 γ_1	Igh-5 δ	Igh-6 μ	Igh-7 ε
a	BALB/c	a	a	a	a	a	a	a
b	C57BL	b	b	b	b	b	b	b
c	DBA/2	c	c	a	a	a	—[b]	—
d	AKR	d	d	d	a	a	—	a
e	A	e	d	e	a	e	e	a
f	CE	f	f	f	a	a	—	—
g	RIII	g	c	g	a	a	—	—
h	SEA	h	a	a	a	a	—	—
j	CBA	j	a	a	a	a	a	a[c]
k	KH-1[a]	k	c	a	a	—	—	—
l	KH-2[a]	l	c	a	a	—	—	—
m	Ky[a]	m	b	b	b	—	—	—
n	NZB	e	d	e	a	a	e	—

After Lieberman (1978), Green (1979), and Sánchez Borges et al. (1981).

[a] Wild mice.

[b] Not determined.

[c] One member of this group of strains, C3H, expresses the a allele in its IgE. The prototype, CBA, has not been tested.

determinants of γ_{2a}. These 10 groups of strains are designated $Igh\text{-}1^a$, $Igh\text{-}1^b, \ldots, Igh\text{-}1^h, Igh\text{-}1^j$, and $Igh\text{-}1^n$.

If two strains are identical with respect to γ_{2a} allotype, they will, with an occasional exception, be identical with respect to allotypic markers present on all other H chain classes and subclasses, such as γ_{2b} or α. However, the converse is not necessarily true. Strains that differ with respect to γ_{2a} allotype may nevertheless be identical with respect to allotypic determinants on another H chain class. For example, 9 of 10 different groups of strains, defined by differences in their γ_{2a} markers, are identical with respect to γ_1 allotype.

The nomenclature used for defining the genetic loci that control allotypes is as follows: $Igh\text{-}1$ (γ_{2a}), $Igh\text{-}2$ (α), $Igh\text{-}3$ (γ_{2b}), $Igh\text{-}4$ (γ_1), $Igh\text{-}5$ (δ), $Igh\text{-}6$ (μ), and $Igh\text{-}7$ (ε).

Light chains

Strain-specific variants of mouse κ, but not λ, chains have been described. Variants identified so far in κ chains are confined to the V_κ region. The situation here is unique in that the proof of variation comes from studies of peptide maps and isoelectric focusing, rather than serology or amino acid sequence analysis of κ chains. Antisera that can distinguish the mouse V_κ allotypes have not been developed. Distinctions are based on the presence of a particular cysteine-containing peptide in a map of a tryptic digest of the V_κ region or on isoelectric focusing patterns of κ chains. Four inbred strains (PL, AKR, C58, RF) exhibit an extra peptide that is not found in the V_κ peptides of all other strains tested. When mating studies are carried out, this property (i.e., the extra spot) is inherited according to simple Mendelian laws, with the appearance of the spot being dominant. There is evidence that the overall V_κ repertoires of the four strains that express the unique peptide may differ markedly from those of other mouse strains. (As in other species, genes controlling the κ, λ, and H chains segregate independently.)

It was found that the V_κ genes are closely linked to genes controlling certain surface antigens—the Lyt 2 and Lyt 3 antigens—on thymus-derived lymphocytes. The same four strains that show the unique V_κ peptide also possess unique Lyt antigenic determinants on their T cells, and genes controlling the two phenotypes—the V_κ peptide and Lyt antigens—are very tightly linked on chromosome 6.

ALLOTYPES IN WILD MICE

Wild mice exhibit most of the same C_H allotypes that are found in inbred strains. However, unusual combinations are sometimes observed; these are indicative of crossovers that have occurred in wild populations. Crossovers involving the genes for C_H regions are very rare in inbred mice. Three examples of allotypes in wild mice are shown in Table 6.

ALLOTYPES OF HUMAN IMMUNOGLOBULINS

Light chains

Allotypes of human κ chains (the so-called Km or Inv markers) were mentioned earlier in introducing the concept of allotypy. So far, allotypes have not been described for human λ chains.

Heavy chains

Human as well as mouse immunoglobulins differ from those of the rabbit in that there are multiple subclasses of IgG, rather than one; in the human these are designated IgG1–IgG4. Each subclass has its own associated allotypes, all of which are present in C_H regions. Allotypes associated with IgG1 are designated with the prefix G1m; for IgG2, the prefix is G2m, etc. Allotypes of human IgA, of which there are two subclasses, have also been identified. A summary of allotypic markers on human IgG and IgA is given in Table 7.

An interesting area of human genetics concerns the geographical and racial distribution of allotypes and the nature of the linked sets of allotype genes (haplotypes) found in various populations. The reader is referred to reviews by Grubb (1970) and by Natvig and Kunkel (1973) for detailed information.

SUPPRESSION OF ALLOTYPIC SPECIFICITIES

Most of the work to be discussed here has been carried out with rabbits. It was first shown by Sheldon Dray in 1962 that exposure of a fetal or newborn rabbit to anti-allotype antibody can induce suppression of that allotype. For example, if a neonatal b^4,b^5 rabbit is inoculated with anti-b4, profound and prolonged suppression of the b4 allotype occurs. There is a compensatory synthesis of the allotype controlled by the allelic b^5 gene. An alternative way of inducing suppression is to immunize a pregnant mother with immunoglobulin of the b4 allotype,[5] thus inducing the synthesis of anti-b4, which is transferred through the fetal yolk sac to the fetus.

---

[5] This can only be done if the maternal parent lacks b^4 because a b^4 rabbit is tolerant of b4. However, b4 immunoglobulin can be injected into a b^5,b^5 female that has been mated to a b^4,b^4 male. The b^4,b^5 offspring will be suppressed with respect to production of the b4 allotype.

TABLE 7. Allotypes of C_H regions of human IgG and IgA.

Class and subclass	Allotype		Location of determinant
	Alphabetical designation	Numerical designation[a]	
IgG1	G1m(a)	G1m(1)	C_H3
	(x)	(2)	C_H3
	(f)	(3)	C_H1
	(z)	(17)	C_H1
IgG2	G2m(n)	G2m(23)	C_H2
IgG3	G3m(b0)	G3m(11)	C_H3
	(b1)	(5)	C_H2
	(b3)	(13)	C_H3
	(b4)	(14)	C_H2
	(b5)	(10)	C_H3
	(c3)	(6)	
	(c5)	(24)	
	(g)	(21)	
	(s)	(15)	
	(t)	(16)	
	(u)	(26)	
	(v)	(27)	
IgA2		A2m(1)	
		A2m(2)	

After WHO Committee Report (1976).

[a] The alphabetical designations were introduced first and are still used by some authors.

By using special techniques, it is possible to suppress the expression of both alleles at the b locus, which controls the synthesis of κ chains. When this is done, there is a compensatory synthesis of λ chains in the newborn rabbit.

Suppression of allotypes on heavy chains can be achieved by similar methods. The rules that govern such suppression can be illustrated as follows. Suppose a rabbit has the a^1 (V_H) and n^{81} (μ chain) genes on one chromosome, with a^2 and n^{82} on the other. If allotype a1 is suppressed, there will be concomitant suppression of IgM bearing n81. This can be explained on the basis that suppression takes place at the level of the antibody-producing cell, and cells producing n81 in this rabbit also produce a1.

LITERATURE CITED

Dray, S. (1962). Effect of maternal isoantibodies on the quantitative expression of two allelic genes controlling γ-globulin allotypic specificities. *Nature 195,* 677.

Gilman-Sachs, A., Roux, K. H., Horng, W. J. and Dray, S. (1982). Characterization of additional rabbit IgM allotypes and the effect of suppression of a V_H locus allotypes on the expression of n C_μ locus allotypes. *J. Immunol. 128,* 451.

Green, M. C. (1979). Genetic nomenclature for the immunoglobulin loci of the mouse. *Immunogenetics 8,* 89.

Grubb, R. (1970). *The Genetic Markers of Human Immunoglobulins,* New York, Springer-Verlag.

Grubb, R. and Laurel, A. B. (1956). Hereditary serological human serum groups. *Acta Path. Microbiol. Scand. 39,* 390.

Lieberman, R. (1978). Genetics of the IgCH (allotype) locus in the mouse. *Springer Seminars in Immunopathol. 1,* 7.

Naessens, J., Hamers-Casterman, C., Hamers, R. and Kelus, A. S. (1979). Allotypes of rabbit IgM linked to the b locus of the kappa polypeptide chain. *Immunogenetics 8,* 571.

Natvig, J. G. and Kunkel, H. G. (1973). Human immunoglobulins: classes, subclasses, genetic variants and idiotypes. *Adv. Immunol. 16,* 1.

Ollo, R. and Rougeon, R. (1983). Gene conversion and polymorphism: generation of mouse immunoglobulin γ2a chain alleles by differential gene conversion by γ2b chain gene. *Cell 32,* 515.

Oudin, J. (1956). Réaction de précipitation specifique entre des sérums d'animaux de meme espèce. *Compt. Rend. Acad. Sci. (Paris) 242,* 2489.

Sanchez Borges, M., Kumagai, Y., Okumura, K., Hirayama, N., Ovary, Z. and Tada, T. (1981). Allelic polymorphism of murine IgE controlled by the seventh immunoglobulin heavy chain allotype locus. *Immunogenetics 13,* 499.

WHO Committee Report (1976). "Review of the Notation for the Allotypic and Related Markers of Human Immunoglobulins." *J. Immunogenetics 3,* 357.

SUGGESTED ADDITIONAL READING

Kindt, T. (1975). Rabbit immunoglobulin allotypes: Structure, immunology and genetics. *Adv. Immunol. 21,* 35.

Mage, R., Lieberman, R., Potter, M. and Terry, W. D. (1973). Immunoglobulin allotypes, In M. Sela, Ed., *The Antigens,* Vol. 1. New York, Academic Press.

8

IDIOTYPES OF IMMUNOGLOBULINS

OVERVIEW

The hypervariable region of an antibody molecule (antibody A) can act as an antigenic determinant. Anti-antibodies (antibody B) directed to this region of the molecule may be highly specific, i.e., unreactive with other antibodies. Antigenic determinants associated with hypervariable regions of antibody A are called idiotypic determinants or idiotopes. The collection of idiotypic determinants on a molecule constitutes its idiotype. The anti-antibody (antibody B) is called anti-idiotypic antibody. Early studies, with rabbits, indicated that each animal makes antibodies of a given specificity with an idiotype unique to that animal. Sharing of idiotype by antibodies from different animals is more frequent when inbred mice are used as the source of antibody A. In some cases, antibodies of a given specificity from all immunized mice of a particular inbred strain share the same idiotype; this idiotype may be absent from antibodies of the same specificity from mice of another strain. When this occurs, idiotype can be used as a genetic marker. Inheritance of an idiotype is determined by genes linked to those controlling the synthesis of C_H regions and, in some instances, is also determined by genes controlling L chain biosynthesis. Regulation of the immune response occurs in part through the actions of regulatory T cells having specificity for idiotypic determinants. There is also evidence to suggest that spontaneously arising anti-idiotype antibodies may have a role in regulation. The molecular basis of idiotypy has been elucidated by amino acid sequence analyses of antibodies that share idiotype.

*   *   *

135

The discovery of IDIOTYPY (Slater et al., 1955; Oudin and Michel, 1963) has led to new insights into the genetics of immunoglobulins and the regulation of their biosynthesis. It is the topic of a large and increasing number of investigations. The concept and definition of idiotypes can best be introduced by a description of relevant experiments.

One early demonstration of idiotypy in antibodies was that of Oudin and Michel at the Pasteur Institute in Paris. They injected rabbit anti-salmonella antibody into another rabbit of the same allotype and showed that the recipient eventually made antibodies that reacted with the immunogen, i.e., that anti-antibodies reactive with the anti-salmonella were produced. One might ask why the recipient rabbit was not tolerant of the rabbit antibodies that were inoculated. The result can be understood if one considers the enormous diversity of sequences in hypervariable regions. Any given sequence may be absent from the recipient rabbit, or present at such a low concentration that it cannot induce tolerance. It is principally the hypervariable regions of the injected antibodies that are immunogenic.

Oudin and Michel further noted that the anti-anti-salmonella reacted with the anti-salmonella that was injected but not with anti-salmonella from other rabbits. Again, this can be interpreted on the basis of the great diversity of antibodies. Each rabbit can make anti-salmonella antibodies that differ somewhat from the anti-salmonella antibodies of other rabbits. The antigenic determinants that induce antibody formation in this type of immunization are referred to as IDIOTYPIC DETERMINANTS or IDIOTOPES; the collection of idiotypic determinants on the inducing antibody determine its IDIOTYPE; the anti-antibodies are ANTI-IDIOTYPIC or ANTI-IDIOTYPE (anti-Id) antibodies. Anti-Id antibodies reactive with a single determinant are referred to as ANTI-IDIOTOPE antibodies.

Several lines of evidence indicate that idiotypic determinants are indeed associated with hypervariable regions. First, they have been localized to V regions—by testing fragments of the molecule consisting only of such regions. Second, a specific antigen or hapten will often interfere with an idiotype–anti-idiotype reaction. For example, if one prepares anti-Id against anti-benzoate antibodies, free benzoate derivatives will inhibit, at least in part, the reactions of the anti-Id with the anti-benzoate antibodies (Figure 1).[1] This type of observation localizes the idiotypic determinants to the region of the benzoate-binding site and therefore to hypervariable regions. A third type of evidence

[1] That subpopulation of anti-Id antibodies that is not inhibitable by hapten probably reacts with hypervariable regions that are located very close to, but are not part of, the hapten-binding site.

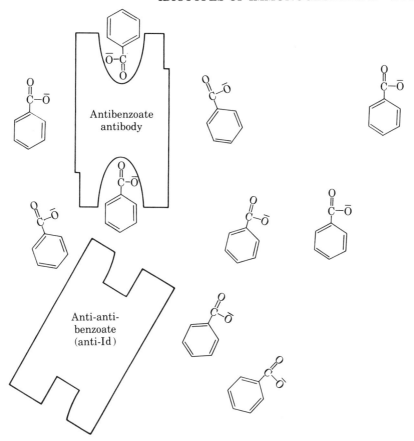

FIGURE 1. Test to ascertain whether anti-Id (anti-anti-benzoate) directed against anti-benzoate antibody reacts with the hapten-binding region of the anti-benzoate. If free hapten (benzoate) interferes with the idiotype–anti-idiotype reaction, the anti-Id is presumed to interact with the hapten-binding site of the anti-benzoate. (A less likely possibility is that the hapten, when combined with anti-benzoate, changes the conformation of the anti-benzoate so that idiotypic determinants *outside* the combining site are altered and become unreactive with anti-Id.)

comes from correlations of amino acid sequences with idiotypy. Differences in idiotype have been shown to be associated directly with differences in amino acid sequences of hypervariable regions. Although nonhypervariable (framework) amino acids may contribute to the formation of some idiotypic determinants, it is likely that virtually all idiotypic determinants contain one or more hypervariable amino acids.

Idiotypic determinants are sometimes localized in isolated H chains or L chains. More frequently, idiotypic determinants require the participation of both the H and L chains. Such idiotypic determinants may include amino acids from both the H and L chain; alternatively, the two chains may interact with one another in such a manner as to stabilize an idiotypic determinant that could be entirely on one or the other chain. It is very difficult to distinguish between the two possibilities experimentally.

In an immunized animal, idiotypic determinants are in general associated with antibodies of a particular specificity. This was demonstrated in Oudin's experiments by removing the anti-salmonella antibody from the serum of the donor rabbit by adsorption onto salmonella; this eliminated its capacity to react with the anti-Id antiserum. However, shared idiotypic determinants have occasionally been demonstrated among antibodies that differ in specificity. In fact, by appropriate immunization with anti-Id, one can induce antibodies that differ in antigen-binding specificity but share idiotype. Whether idiotype is induced or suppressed (see below) by immunization with anti-Id depends upon the procedure used for immunization (Takemori et al., 1982).

Anti-Id antibodies need not be prepared within the same species. For example, anti-Id antibodies directed against mouse antibodies are often prepared in the rabbit. The rabbit will, of course, make antibodies specific for many other parts of the mouse immunoglobulin molecule. The anti-Id antiserum must therefore be thoroughly adsorbed with mouse immunoglobulins that lack the antibody used for immunization. After such adsorption, the antiserum becomes specific for idiotypic determinants on the antibody. It will be recalled that anti-allotype antibodies can also be prepared by immunizing an animal of a different species with an immunoglobulin. It is essential therefore that the protein used to adsorb the anti-Id antiserum contain all of the allotypic determinants present on the antibodies used to immunize the rabbit. This presents no great difficulty. For example, if the antibodies used to induce anti-Id are from a strain A mouse, the rabbit antiserum can be adsorbed with normal immunoglobulin from the same strain; this normal fraction will contain all of the allotypic determinants present on the antibody used for immunization, and only anti-idiotype antibodies will remain after the adsorption.

RELATIONSHIP OF IDIOTYPES TO ISOTYPES AND ALLOTYPES

As previously mentioned, isotypes are immunoglobulins or polypeptide chains characteristic of a species. In mice, for example, there is one isotype of κ chains, three of λ chains, and eight isotypes of C_H regions (C_μ, $C_{\gamma 1}$, etc.). Allotypes are polymorphic forms of a given isotype found within a species. Thus, in the rabbit there are four major allotypes of κ chains (b4, b5, b6, and b9). The genes controlling allotypes behave as codominant alleles. Idiotypes are associated with hypervariable regions and, generally, with antibodies of a given specificity. The number of different idiotypes vastly exceeds the number of allotypes or isotypes. The number of idiotypes within a species may be extremely large, perhaps greater than 1×10^8. A given idiotype may be associated with various isotypes or allotypes.

IDIOTYPE AS A MARKER FOR CLONES OF ANTIBODY-PRODUCING CELLS

Idiotypy has been used to study the persistence of clones of antibody-forming cells during immunization of an animal. By quantitatively assaying for a given idiotype in serum over a long period of time, it has been possible to draw conclusions concerning the persistence of the clone of cells producing that idiotype. The assumption is made that the descendants of a given cell will continue to produce the same idiotype. In such studies, idiotypes have been found to be gradually replaced by new sets of idiotypes over a period of time; in some cases, they persist for months or even years within an immunized animal. This necessarily reflects the persistence of antibody-forming cells and their descendants, since the antibodies themselves have relatively short half-lives—typically 6 to 20 days.

Within a clone, switches in the class of antibody produced may occur (e.g., from IgM to IgG). The switch does not result in a change of idiotype because idiotypy is associated with V regions and the switch involves C_H segments; thus, different C_H segments can be associated with the same V_H segment. An interesting example of this occurs in an occasional patient with multiple myeloma who produces immunoglobulins of two different classes at the same time. These immunoglobulins have in some instances been shown to share idiotype. Different hybridomas (Chapter 10), made by fusing the spleen cells of a single mouse with a myeloma cell line, often produce monoclonal antibodies of different classes with the same idiotype.

Monoclonal antibodies, such as myeloma proteins or the antibodies produced by hybridomas, possess a single set of idiotypic determinants or idiotype. In contrast, serum antibodies directed against a single antigen or hapten are heterogeneous and contain multiple idiotypes.[2]

---

[2] Because antibodies of a given specificity express multiple idiotypes, idiotypy has a much finer discriminatory power than antibody specificity.

IDIOTYPY AS AN INHERITED CHARACTERISTIC

As noted earlier, antibodies prepared against the same antigen in different rabbits generally differ with respect to idiotype. The rabbits used in such studies are outbred. (Inbred rabbits, developed recently, are very expensive.) When studies of idiotypy were carried out with inbred mice, examples were discovered of idiotypes that are shared by most or all mice of a given inbred strain. This is not a predictable phenomenon; the sharing of idiotype depends on the antigen used and on the strain of mice. An antigen that induces a shared idiotype in one strain may not do so in another strain. Even when the idiotype of a given antibody—say anti-X—is shared within a strain, the idiotype is not present on all molecules of anti-X. Part of the anti-X population within a mouse may share idiotype with anti-X of other mice of the same strain, whereas the remainder of the anti-X may comprise multiple idiotypes that are not shared with the anti-X antibodies of most other mice of the same strain. Sharing of idiotypes can also cross strain barriers; shared idiotypes are frequently observed among different strains of mice that have the same C_H allotypes.

Some shared idiotypes are encoded by genes that are present in the germ line of every mouse of that strain. (If the polypeptide chains of an immunoglobulin are encoded by genes that have undergone a number of random somatic mutations in hypervariable regions, it is less probable that the same idiotype will occur at high frequency in other mice of the same strain.) Some moderate alterations in amino acid sequence can be tolerated without changing the idiotype of the molecule, i.e., its ability to react with anti-Id antibodies. Whether a particular amino acid substitution or substitutions affects the idiotype depends on the location in the sequence and the nature of the amino acids. Because the idiotype is a collection of idiotopes, particular substitutions may affect none, part, or all of these idiotopes.

There is a school of thought that maintains that some mutations are not random but are programmed within the mouse. This is hard to reconcile with the presence of certain idiotypes that are found in an individual mouse but are present at extremely low frequency in other mice of the same strain. In addition, although the evidence is not conclusive, data on amino acid sequences of monoclonal antibodies are suggestive of random mutations. It is conceivable that some mutational events are programmed, whereas others occur at random.

LINKAGE OF INHERITANCE OF IDIOTYPE TO GENES CONTROLLING C_H AND V_κ REGIONS

For those idiotypes that are inherited, the inheritance pattern almost invariably shows linkage to the C_H gene cluster, i.e., to C_H

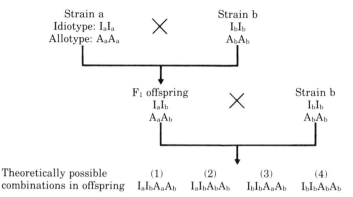

Theoretically possible   (1)   (2)   (3)   (4)
combinations in offspring $I_aI_bA_aA_b$ $I_aI_bA_bA_b$ $I_bI_bA_aA_b$ $I_bI_bA_bA_b$

FIGURE 2. Demonstration of genetic linkage of idiotype to heavy chain (C_H) allotype of mice. All the F_1 offspring of the first mating shown are heterozygous for both idiotype (I_aI_b) and allotype (A_aA_b). The F_1 mice are next "backcrossed" to Strain b. Conceivably, four different combinations of idiotype and allotype are possible in their offspring (numbered 1 through 4 in the figure). In fact, combinations 2 and 3 are not observed, or occur at low frequency. Offspring that inherit allotype a will normally inherit idiotype a and vice versa. The reason for this is that the V_H genes, which contribute to idiotype, are on the same chromosome as the C_H genes, which determine allotype. Except when a crossover occurs, the V_H and C_H genes (and therefore idiotype and allotype) are inherited as a unit. The frequency of crossovers is determined by breeding large numbers of mice and determining the frequency of occurrence of combinations 2 or 3.

allotype. A diagram illustrating such an inheritance pattern is shown in Figure 2. The linkage of genes controlling idiotype and C_H sequences reflects the facts that the V_H region contributes to idiotypic determinants and that V_H and C_H genes are on the same chromosome. In breeding studies, occasional crossovers are observed among genes controlling the expression of idiotype and C_H allotype.

The frequent observation of linkage of genes controlling idiotype expression and C_H allotype, without linkage to the genetic locus controlling L chains, was somewhat puzzling because many idiotypes require the contribution of the L chain, and genes controlling L and H chains are unlinked. The explanation appears to be that most inbred strains of mice have closely related repertoires of L chains; when a breeding study is carried out, using mice of two different inbred strains, either strain is generally capable of supplying the necessary L chains.

Linkage of inheritance of idiotype to the locus controlling κ chains (as well as to the H chain locus) has in fact been demonstrated in a few instances by using mice that exhibit the $V_κ$ polymorphism (the extra peptide spot, Chapter 7) as one mating partner in a breeding study. This suggests that the repertoires of L chains in the four strains that show this polymorphism may differ considerably from those of other strains.

Table 1 lists a few of the idiotypes that are cross-reactive within mouse strains and that have been studied extensively. It also shows the frequency of crossovers, observed in breeding studies, between V_H genes controlling several idiotypes and the C_H gene cluster.

STRUCTURAL CORRELATES OF IDIOTYPE

We have mentioned that idiotypic determinants are associated with hypervariable regions of an antibody molecule. The evidence cited was the inhibition of idiotype–anti-idiotype reactions by hapten reactive with the idiotypic antibody. Additional evidence is based on amino acid sequence analyses. One excellent example is the paper by Schilling et al. (1980). These investigators prepared a series of monoclonal mouse antibodies (Chapter 10) that are reactive with α-1,3-dextran. They also had available two mouse myeloma proteins that bind α-1,3-dextran; one of these, called M104E, was selected as the prototype for comparisons. All but 1 of 11 proteins shared some idiotypic determinants with M104E and 2 were idiotypically identical. A comparison of the amino sequences of the. V_H regions of these proteins with that of M104E is shown in Figure 3. The figure only shows differences and not the total sequences. A solid line represents identity with M104E.

TABLE 1. Recombination frequencies between V_H (idiotype) and C_H (allotype) markers in inbred mice.

Strain of mouse	C_H allotype	Idiotype on antibody against:	Recombinants found	Frequency (%) and 95% confidence interval[a]
BALB/c	$Igh\text{-}1^a$	Dextran	8/1949	0.41 (0.2–0.8)
BALB/c	$Igh\text{-}1^a$	Inulin	2/82	2.44 (0.3–8.5)
A/J	$Igh\text{-}1^e$	Streptococcus Group A	2/82	2.44 (0.3–8.5)
BALB/c	$Igh\text{-}1^a$	Streptococcus Group A	3/78	3.84 (0.8–10.8)
C57BL	$Igh\text{-}1^b$	Sheep red cells	8/148	5.40 (2.4–10.8)

After Weigert and Potter (1977).

[a] The recombination frequency for V_H (a allotype) and C_H (de allotype) in the rabbit is about 0.3%.

The figure also specifies the degree to which each protein shares idiotypic determinants with M104E.

Note that all of the proteins have very similar V_H sequences. In many instances, substitutions are seen only in the third complementarity-determining region (CDR-3). The close similarities would account for the sharing of most idiotypic determinants. This might suggest that the differences in idiotype, as compared to M104E, might be due to substitutions in the third CDR.[3] Indeed, there is quite direct evidence that this is the case. The two antibodies that share all idiotypic determinants with M104E (namely, Hdex7 and Hdex8) are very similar or identical to M104E in the third CDR. These data suggest that only small differences can be tolerated in the third CDR without changing the idiotype. Thus, the third CDR contributes strongly to the idiotype of this molecule. It does not necessarily mean that the other CDR are unimportant. In fact, the data also show that CDR-2 in the V_H region contributes to the shared idiotypic determinants; hybridoma Hdex10, the last one listed in the table, has substitutions in CDR-2, lacks the carbohydrate attached to CDR-2 of M104E, and shares no idiotypic determinants with M104E even though its V_H sequence is otherwise quite similar to that of M104E. In addition, all of the proteins that have the same sequence in CDR-2 share at least one idiotypic determinant with one another.

Another informative study compared the amino acid sequences of the V_H regions of 19 BALB/c myeloma proteins or monoclonal antibodies from hybridomas (Chapter 10), all of which had specificity for the same hapten, phosphorylcholine (Gearhart et al., 1981). Many of these proteins also shared a common idiotype. The V_H sequences, up to position 95 where the D segment begins, were very similar for all the proteins, Id-positive or Id-negative, and were subsequently shown to be derived from a single germ-line gene. The differences in sequences therefore reflect somatic mutations. Sequences of the variable region are shown in Figure 4. A majority of the mutations occur in the hypervariable or complementarity-determining regions but a significant number are also present in framework regions.

No mutations were found in any of the five IgM proteins through the V_H segment, whereas the IgG and IgA proteins showed a significant number (a total of 22 in the 14 molecules examined). Although subsequent research has demonstrated that somatic mutations can occur in V_H regions of IgM, it appears that mutations may be more likely to take place during or after the switch from IgM to IgG or IgA

---

[3] The possibility must also be considered that differences in light chain sequences contributed to the differences in idiotype. However, evidence so far indicates that the light chains, all of which are λ, are very similar to one another in the proteins investigated.

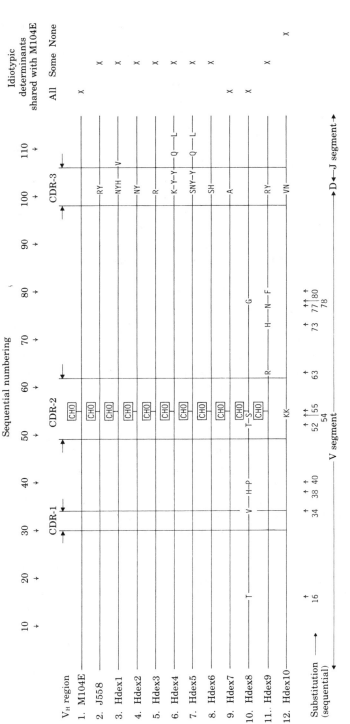

FIGURE 3. A comparison of amino acid sequences of V_H regions and of idiotypes for 12 mouse monoclonal proteins that bind α-1,3-dextran. The prototype for the sequences is the first listed, M104E; only differences in sequence with respect to this protein are shown. The symbol CHO represents a carbohydrate side chain. The one-letter code is given on the first page of the Appendix. (From Schilling et al, 1980.)

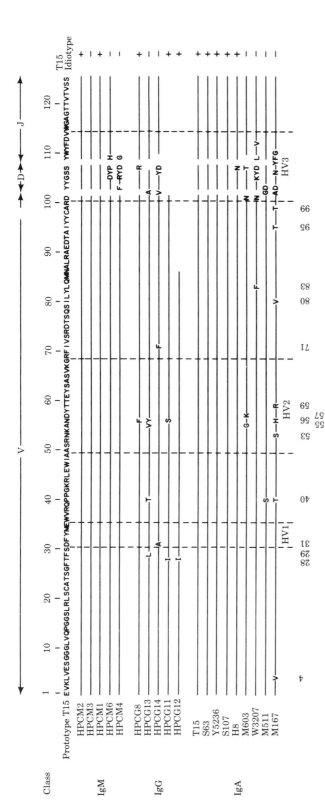

FIGURE 4. Amino acid sequence of the V_H regions of 19 mouse monoclonal antibodies with specificity for phosphorylcholine. The designation HP indicates that the protein is the product of a hybridoma (Chapter 10). The remainder are myeloma proteins. (From Gearhart et al., 1981.)

production (Chapter 6). There is evidence suggesting that one mechanism for the production of somatic variants involves the enzymatic excision of a segment of DNA, followed by repair with an occasional error.

REGULATION OF THE IMMUNE RESPONSE VIA IDIOTYPIC DETERMINANTS

Suppose all mice of an inbred strain express a shared idiotype in their antibodies directed against antigen X. If one injects anti-Id antibodies, specific for anti-X, prior to immunizing with X, the anti-X antibodies that subsequently appear will often fail to exhibit the shared idiotype. In other words, one can selectively suppress the production of an idiotype by inoculating anti-Id antibodies. Anti-Id antibodies can, in this way, regulate the nature of the immune response.

Recent experiments have, in addition, indicated that an animal can make anti-Id antibodies against its own antibodies. This has led Niels Jerne (1974) to propose that there is a network of idiotypes and anti-idiotypes within an animal and that the immune response is regulated in part through this network. The expression of a given idiotype may be under control of the corresponding anti-idiotype. Jerne proposed that when antigen is introduced it perturbs this network and allows expression of the idiotype. As an idiotype builds up in the circulation, this buildup leads to the production of anti-idiotype, which acts as a feedback inhibitor to prevent excessive production of the idiotype.

Certain indirect evidence supports the validity of such a control mechanism. It has been shown that in some animals anti-Id antibodies arise spontaneously after the production of a given idiotype. Furthermore, some suppressor cells of thymic origin (T cells), which are important in regulating the immune response, exercise this regulation by interacting with idiotypic determinants, either on other T cells or on B cells (antibody-producing cells). Such T cells can be stimulated by inoculating anti-Id antibodies or by inoculating the idiotype-bearing antibodies themselves. Idiotype-specific suppressor T cells have been identified that have receptors bearing the idiotype; other suppressor T cells have anti-idiotypic receptors. Some observers believe that idiotypic regulation through T cells may prove to be of greater physiological significance than regulation through spontaneously produced anti-Id antibodies.

Other kinds of suppressor T cells have receptors for antigen or for isotypic or allotypic determinants on immunoglobulins. Quantitative information is needed as to the extent to which each of these suppressive mechanisms contributes to the regulation of immune responses.

LITERATURE CITED

Gearhart, P. J., Johnson, N. D., Douglas, R. and Hood, L. (1981). IgG antibodies to phosphorylcholine exhibit more diversity than their IgM counterparts. *Nature 291*, 29.

Jerne, N. K. (1974). Towards a network theory of the immune system. *Annal. Immunol. (Paris) 125C*, 373.

Oudin, J. and Michel, M. (1963). Une nouvelle form d'allotypie des globulins γ du sérum de lapin, apparrement lieé a la fonction et a la specificité anticorps. *Compt. Rend. Acad. Sci. (Paris) 257*, 805.

Schilling, J., Clevinger, B., Davie, J. M. and Hood, L. (1980). Amino acid sequence of homogeneous antibodies to dextran and DNA rearrangements in heavy chain V-region gene segments. *Nature 285*, 35.

Slater, R. J., Ward, S. M. and Kunkel, H. G. (1955). Immunologic relation among the myeloma proteins. *J. Exp. Med. 101*, 85.

Takemori, T., Tesch, H., Reth, M. and Rajewsky, K. (1982). The immune response against anti-idiotype antibodies. Induction of the idiotype-bearing antibodies and analysis of the idiotype repertoire. *Eur. J. Immunol. 12*, 1040.

Weigert, M. and Potter, M. (1977). Antibody variable-region genetics: summary and abstracts of the homogeneous immunoglobulin workshop VII. *Immunogenetics 4*, 401.

SUGGESTED ADDITIONAL READING

Bona, C. A. (1981). *Idiotypes and Lymphocytes.* New York, Academic Press.

Capra, J. D. and Kehoe, J. M. (1975). Hypervariable regions, idiotypy and antibody combining sites. *Adv. Immunol. 20*, 1.

Eichmann, K. (1978). Expression and function of idiotypes on lymphocytes. *Adv. Immunol. 26*, 195.

Hopper, J. E. and Nisonoff, A. (1971). Individual antigenic specificity of immunoglobulins. *Adv. Immunol. 13*, 58.

Immunological Reviews. (1977). Volume 34. Several articles on the topic "Idiotypes on T and B cells."

Rajewsky, K. and Takemori, T. (1983). Genetics, expression and function of idiotypes. *Adv. Immunol. 1*, 569.

9

IMMUNOLOGICAL ASSAYS AND THE PURIFICATION OF ANTIBODIES

OVERVIEW

A variety of qualitative and quantitative procedures are used to assay for the presence of antibody in an immune serum. Many of these tests for antibody can be modified to enable identification and quantitation of specific antigens present in a complex mixture. Among the most sensitive assays for antigens and antibodies are the radioimmunoassays. Such assays generally require that a small amount of the radiolabeled ligand (antigen or antibody) be available in pure form. In a recently developed method, an enzyme instead of a radiolabel is attached to the antigen or antibody; the enzyme must have the property of liberating a colored product from a colorless substrate. Methods for the purification of antibodies are also described. Two levels of purification are considered. One yields an immunoglobulin fraction, which contains antibodies of all specificities relatively free of other serum proteins. The second level, called specific purification or affinity purification, isolates that fraction of the antibody population that is reactive with a particular antigen or hapten.

* * *

This chapter will first describe serological assays for antigens and antibodies. This will be followed by a discussion of methods for isolation of a serum fraction that contains the immunoglobulins and for SPECIFIC PURIFICATION of antibodies, i.e., purification that makes use of antigen and yields an antibody population, nearly all of which is reactive with the antigen. The antibody is generally purified by adsorption to an insolubilized antigen, followed by elution with a reagent that breaks the noncovalent bonds that link the two molecules; such

149

a method of specific purification is called AFFINITY CHROMATOGRAPHY or AFFINITY PURIFICATION. This chapter is not intended to be a comprehensive survey of methodology. Its major purpose is to illustrate the principles that underlie the more commonly used immunological methods.

PRECIPITATION REACTIONS

When a soluble antigen is injected repeatedly into an experimental animal (usually by a subcutaneous, intramuscular, or intravenous route), the serum of the animal will eventually contain antibodies that can form a precipitate with the antigen injected. The mechanism of precipitation, involving crosslinking of antigen with antibody, was illustrated in Figure 1, Chapter 1. The PRECIPITIN TEST is carried out by mixing the protein antigen (a few micrograms to as much as a milligram) with a few tenths of a milliliter of immune serum. The mixture turns cloudy and a small pellet eventually settles out. The pellet can be shown to contain both antigen and antibody. The rate at which the precipitate forms depends on the amount of antigen–antibody complex. If only 25 μg are present, it may require 24 hours or more. If the amount of complex is, say, 500 μg, the precipitate may settle out within an hour. To quantitate the total protein in a precipitate, a variety of assays can be used, including the micro-Kjeldahl assay for nitrogen, colorimetric tests for protein, or optical density measurements in the ultraviolet wavelength region on the dissolved precipitate. In all cases, the precipitate is centrifuged and washed repeatedly with dilute salt solution before quantitation.

The precipitin reaction has been extensively investigated with carbohydrate antigens and protein–hapten conjugates, as well as with protein antigens. Free carbohydrates are often poor antigens; however, antibodies to carbohydrates can readily be generated by injecting certain heat-killed bacteria, such as pneumococci or streptococci, whose cell walls contain carbohydrate. The antibodies formed will react with free carbohydrate as well as with the bacterial immunogen.

Suppose one sets up a series of test tubes, each containing, say, 0.3 ml of anti-egg albumin antiserum. Increasing amounts of egg albumin in solution are then added to the series of tubes. As one would expect, the amount of precipitate increases with increasing antigen concentration; however, the amount of precipitate falls off after reaching a peak. The mechanism that causes a decrease in the amount of precipitate when a large excess of antigen is used is illustrated in Figure 1. A typical precipitation curve is shown in Figure 2. With certain antigens, the amount of precipitate reaches a plateau and does not fall off, or falls very gradually with increasing amounts of antigen. This

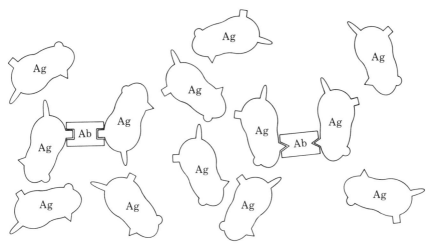

FIGURE 1. Solubility of immune complexes in excess antigen. With a very large excess of free antigen, the probability becomes high that both combining sites of an individual antibody molecule will be occupied by a free antigen molecule, i.e., an antigen molecule that is not attached to another antibody. Under such conditions, extensive crosslinking cannot occur and soluble complexes are the result. If, in a series of experiments, this large antigen concentration is gradually reduced, the average size of complexes gradually increases and, with an appropriate antigen concentration, a precipitate is formed.

is due to nonspecific, weak-binding interactions of the antigen–antibody complexes. (By "nonspecific" we mean interactions that do not involve the specific combining sites of the antigen or antibody.)

With certain antibodies (the classic example is horse anti-protein), the solubility observed with a large excess of antigen is also seen when a large excess of antibody over antigen is present. This region of antibody excess, where precipitation falls off, is known as a PROZONE. A prozone often occurs in agglutination reactions.

AGGLUTINATION REACTIONS

The term "agglutination" is used when the antigen undergoing the reaction with antibody is a particulate substance, such as a bacterium, red cell, or lymphocyte. Antigen–antibody complexes will sediment out of the suspension, as in the case of a protein antigen, but most of the weight of the pellet will be contributed by the antigen. For example, agglutination of bacteria may be brought about with as few as 50 molecules of antibody per bacterial cell. Because a bacterium may be a million times as heavy as an antibody molecule, it is obvious that the weight-ratio of bacteria-to-antibody in the pellet will be very large. As

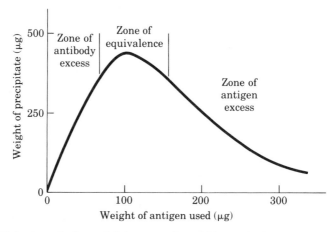

FIGURE 2. A typical precipitin curve for rabbit antibody interacting with a protein antigen. In a series of test tubes, the amount of antiserum is held constant and the concentration of antigen is varied. In the zone of antibody excess, the supernatant fluid, after removal of the precipitate by centrifugation, contains antibody but very little antigen. In the zone of antigen excess, free antigen and antigen–antibody complexes are found in the supernatant fluid. At equivalence, the amounts of either antigen or antibody in the supernatant fluid are at a minimum. However, precipitates do have a finite solubility and, even at equivalence, the amount of precipitate decreases with increasing total volume of the reaction mixture.

a result of this weight-magnification effect, the agglutination reaction is much more sensitive than the precipitin reaction in terms of weight of antibody required to form a visible pellet, and therefore in its capacity to detect small amounts of antibody. Relative sensitivities of various assays are indicated in Table 1.

AGGLUTINATION OF COATED RED BLOOD CELLS

The fact that the agglutination reaction, involving particulate antigens, is much more sensitive than the precipitin reaction has been exploited to increase the sensitivity of detection of anti-protein and anti-hapten antibodies. A protein or hapten can be chemically linked to erythrocytes; anti-protein or anti-hapten antibodies will then cause agglutination of the cells. The process is termed PASSIVE HEMAGGLU-TINATION. The extent to which an antiserum can be diluted and still cause agglutination is a measure of the concentration of antibody in the antiserum.

Passive hemagglutination can be adapted to quantify antigen

rather than antibody. One sets up a series of tubes containing a constant amount of red blood cells coated with antigen X and a constant amount of anti-X (just enough to agglutinate the cells). Now, if free antigen X is added to a mixture, it will occupy combining sites of the antibody and prevent agglutination. This can be used as a quantitative assay for antigen if a sample of known antigen content (or pure antigen) is available. Using this "known" sample, one determines the degree of inhibition of agglutination as a function of the amount of free antigen present. The concentration of antigen in an unknown sample can then be ascertained by determining the volume of unknown that is needed to cause the same degree of inhibition as a sample of known concentration.

VIRAL NEUTRALIZATION

Many viruses are inactivated (neutralized) by antibodies that bind to critical sites on the viral surface. Such a site may, for example, be involved in penetration of the virus into its host cell. One very sensitive assay involves antibody to viruses that infect bacteria (bacteriophages). A single viral particle may infect a bacterial cell, multiply,

TABLE 1. Approximate sensitivities of a variety of assays for antibody.

Assay	Approximate sensitivity (µg antibody in 0.1 ml)
Precipitin test (liquid medium)	10
Precipitin test (agar gel)	5–10
Immunoelectrophoresis	100
Agglutination of erythrocytes	0.01
Passive agglutination of erythrocytes[a]	0.002
Agglutination of bacteria	0.01
Passive cutaneous anaphylaxis	0.005
Complement fixation	0.1
Neutralization of bacteriophage	0.0001
Radioimmunoassays	0.0001–0.1[b]
ELISA	0.001–0.1[b]

[a] Analysis for antibodies directed against an antigen artificially conjugated to the erythrocyte surface.

[b] Highly variable, depending on the nature of the assay.

cause the cell to burst, and then infect neighboring cells. The effect of a single viral particle can in this way become visible as a PLAQUE in a lawn of bacteria contained in an agar gel. A very small number of antibodies may be sufficient to neutralize (inactivate) a virus and thereby reduce the number of plaques (Table 1). This assay has also been modified to enable quantitation of anti-hapten antibodies. The hapten is covalently attached to bacteriophages; antibodies to the hapten will then neutralize the virus. The sensitivity for detection of anti-hapten antibodies is, by this technique, brought into the same range as the extremely high sensitivity of detection of anti-phage antibodies.

Because free antigen or free hapten will inhibit neutralization of the virus (by occupying combining sites of the antibody), inhibition of viral neutralization can be used as an assay for antigen (or hapten). A graph relating degree of inhibition to antigen concentration is first constructed by using an antigen solution of known concentration; comparison with this standard curve then permits quantitation of antigen in unknown samples.

OUCHTERLONY ASSAYS (DOUBLE DIFFUSION IN AGAR GEL)

This assay, devised by Örjan Ouchterlony in the 1950s, is widely used as a qualitative test for either antigen or antibody. It can also provide information as to whether two substances are antigenically related.

Typically, a Petri dish containing a 2 to 4-mm layer of agar or agarose is used. Small circular wells are made by pouring the agar around a suitable template and then allowing it to solidify. Antigen solution is introduced into one well and antibody into an adjacent well (Figure 3). Molecules of antigen and antibody will diffuse through the agar until they meet, and a visible band of precipitate will form where they intersect. Obviously this can serve as a test for the antigen, if antibody is available, or as a test for the presence of antibody in serum.

1. *Reaction of identity.* Figure 3A illustrates what happens if the same antigen is placed in two adjacent wells, with the antiserum in a central well. The two precipitin bands merge to form a continuous band called a LINE OF IDENTITY. Because the concentration of antibody increases logarithmically in the direction of the well containing antibody, one can think of the precipitin line as representing a barrier

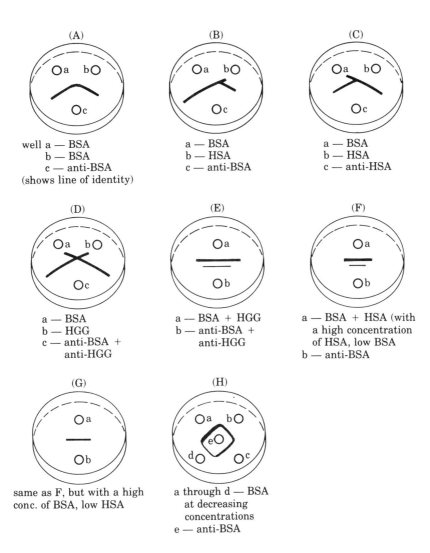

(A)

well a — BSA
b — BSA
c — anti-BSA
(shows line of identity)

(B)

a — BSA
b — HSA
c — anti-BSA

(C)

a — BSA
b — HSA
c — anti-HSA

(D)

a — BSA
b — HGG
c — anti-BSA +
anti-HGG

(E)

a — BSA + HGG
b — anti-BSA +
anti-HGG

(F)

a — BSA + HSA (with
a high concentration
of HSA, low BSA
b — anti-BSA

(G)

same as F, but with a high
conc. of BSA, low HSA

(H)

a through d — BSA
at decreasing
concentrations
e — anti-BSA

FIGURE 3. Ouchterlony patterns. The experiments are carried out in small Petri dishes coated with a thin layer of agar or agarose. Solutions of antigens or antibodies are introduced into the circular wells. BSA, bovine serum albumin; HSA, human serum albumin; HGG, human IgG. Note that in pattern H lines become fainter with diminishing concentrations of BSA and, because of lower diffusion rates, move closer to the antigen well. The other patterns are discussed in the text.

through which the antigen does not penetrate. This accounts for the sharpness of the band formed as well as for the merging of the two bands. The line of identity can help to establish the presence of a given antigen in an unknown sample.

2. *Reaction of partial identity.* Suppose, next, that two closely re-lated, but nonidentical, antigens [e.g., human serum albumin (HSA) and bovine serum albumin (BSA)] are placed in adjacent wells. Anti-serum to BSA is placed in the center well (Figure 3B). Both antigens will form precipitin bands; however, some, but not all, of the anti-BSA molecules react with HSA. Those antibody molecules that are non-reactive with HSA will penetrate the "HSA barrier" and continue diffusing until they reach the "BSA barrier," giving rise to the pattern shown in Figure 3B; this is referred to as a REACTION OF PARTIAL IDENTITY. The line for the immunogen (BSA) forms a SPUR over the line for the cross-reactive antigen (HSA). A few other examples of Ouchterlony patterns are also shown in Figure 3. Most are self-expla-natory. In pattern 3F, two lines are observed because the HSA, being at a high concentration, diffuses ahead of the BSA. The lower line is therefore due to the reaction of HSA with anti-BSA. Some of the anti-BSA molecules are, however, unreactive with HSA; they penetrate the HSA barrier and react with BSA to form the upper line. In pattern G, the BSA diffuses ahead of the HSA because of its high concentra-tion. All of the anti-BSA is stopped by the BSA barrier and does not reach the more slowly diffusing HSA; the result is a single line.

3. *Use in monitoring a purification procedure.* Consider an anti-genic substance that is to be isolated from a complex mixture. Assume further that antiserum had been prepared against the mixture. This antiserum will give multiple bands in an Ouchterlony test. If, how-ever, an antigen is successfully purified from the mixture, a single band will be observed despite the presence of multiple antibodies in the antiserum.

IMMUNOELECTROPHORESIS

A limitation of the Ouchterlony assay is its inability to resolve a complex mixture of antigens; the bands frequently overlap. Resolution of a mixture of antigens can be greatly improved by first subjecting the mixture to electrophoresis (Grabar and Williams, 1953). This is illustrated in Figure 4; the antigenic material here is a complex mix-ture, namely, human serum. The serum is first electrophoresed in agar gel in one dimension (to the left). This causes partial separation of the various antigenic components of serum according to their mo-

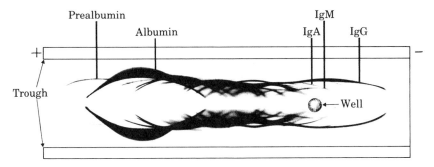

FIGURE 4. Immunoelectrophoretic pattern of human serum. A layer of agarose gel was first prepared on a microscope slide. A sample of human serum was placed in the small circular well cut into the agarose and electrophoresis was carried out at slightly alkaline pH. Most of the proteins migrated toward the anode (to the left). Rabbit antiserum directed against whole human serum was then placed in the two troughs and allowed to diffuse into the agar gel; after washing, the bands that formed were developed with a dye that stains proteins. The protein in an individual band is identified by comparison with a pattern developed by using a single antibody, specific for an individual protein; for example, antibody to IgG.

bility in the electric field. Antibody prepared against whole human serum is then placed in the two troughs, along the length of the agar. Precipitin bands will develop, as shown in Figure 4. The individual bands are identified from their location, i.e., by comparison with the location of bands obtained by using known antisera specific for individual components of serum.

RADIOIMMUNOASSAYS

The radioimmunoassay is a very sensitive technique that makes use of radiolabeled antigen or antibody to determine the amount of antibody or antigen in an unknown, unlabled preparation. To illustrate the principle, let us assume that one wishes to quantitate antigen X in a complex mixture, such as serum. First one obtains pure antigen X and radiolabels a small amount with, say, ^{125}I, which is a gamma emitter. A series of reaction tubes can then be set up, each containing a constant amount of antibody (anti-X) and a constant amount of ^{125}I-labeled, pure antigen X. The labeled antigen is usually present in slight excess over the antibody. Then, increasing amounts of the unknown serum are added to the series of tubes. For each tube, one measures the amount of radiolabeled antigen bound by antibody. Be-

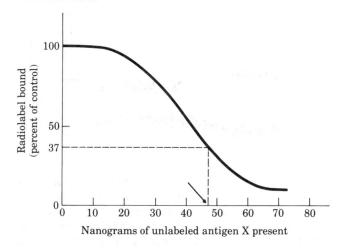

FIGURE 5. Effect of the addition of unlabeled antigen (antigen X) on the binding of radiolabeled pure antigen X by anti-X. Each assay tube contains a fixed amount of labeled X and of antibody. The amount of label bound in the absence of unlabeled X (control experiment) is taken as 100%. Suppose that in the presence of an unknown sample 37% of the maximum amount of radiolabel is bound (see dashed lines in the figure). By using this standard curve, one ascertains that the sample tested contains 47 ng of antigen (arrow).

cause the capacity of the antibody to bind antigen is limited, addition of serum containing *unlabeled* antigen will cause a decrease in the amount of *labeled* antigen that is bound. To quantify antigen X in serum, a "standard curve" is required. This curve is constructed by using a sample of unlabeled serum (or unlabeled pure antigen) whose antigen concentration is known. A graph is then constructed (Figure 5) showing percentage of *labeled* X bound as a function of the amount of *unlabeled* X present. (The amount of labeled X bound in the absence of any inhibitor can arbitrarily be taken as 100%.) Once such a standard curve is constructed, one can use it to read off the amount of unlabeled antigen in any unknown serum tested. A sample calculation is described in the legend of Figure 5.

A general rule of radioimmunoassays is that the radiolabeled substance (antigen or antibody) must be quite pure. However, as indicated above, such assays can then be used to quantify an unlabeled antigen (or antibody) in a complex mixture, such as blood serum. Another general consideration is that the sensitivity of a radioimmunoassay is limited by the affinity (K_A) of the antibodies used: the higher the affinity of the antibody, the lower the concentration of antigen that can be detected. Besides ^{125}I, the most commonly used radiolabels are ^{14}C or ^{3}H, which emit beta rays (electrons). Radioimmunoassays are widely used in research and clinical laboratories. Over 100 radioim-munoassay "kits" for substances of clinical interest are commercially available. A few examples are listed in Table 2. Monoclonal antibodies (Chapter 10), which have recently become available, have increased the versatility and reliability of the technique.

So far we have not specified how the amount of radiolabel bound was determined experimentally. There are various ways to do this, a few of which will now be described.

"DOUBLE ANTIBODY" ASSAYS

Assume that one wishes to quantify an antigen (antigen X) in a complex mixture such as human serum. The following materials can be utilized: radiolabeled *pure* X; an antiserum (e.g., from a rabbit) that contains anti-X; and goat antiserum reactive with rabbit immu-noglobulin. A very small amount—say, 10 ng (10×10^{-9} g) — of labeled antigen may be used in each assay—although assays of greater sensitivity exist. If the labeled antigen is mixed with the rabbit antibody, an antigen–antibody complex will form. However, the amount of complex is far too small to form a precipitate. (Microgram quantities are needed for precipitation to occur in a reasonable length of time.) Next, a small amount of "normal" rabbit serum (not containing anti-X) is added to provide bulk. Finally, one adds sufficient goat antiserum to precipitate *all* of the rabbit immunoglobulin present. This precipi-

TABLE 2. Partial list of clinically important substances for which radioimmunoassay kits are commercially available.[a]

Insulin	Tobramycin
Total human IgE	Gentamycin
Prolactin	Follicle stimulating hormone
Vitamin B_{12}	Luteinizing hormone
Thyroxin	Growth hormone
Testosterone	Parathyroid hormone
Cortisol	Renin
Estriol	Carcinoembryonic antigen
Digoxin	Thyrocalcitonin

[a] Kits contain all components required for the assay, with the exception of the unknown sample.

tate will include the very small amount of X–anti-X complex present. The radioactivity of the washed precipitate is then determined.

To assay for *unlabeled* antigen X in an unknown serum, one adds some of the unknown sample to the rabbit antibody prior to the labeled X. Because the assay is deliberately set up by using a minimal amount of rabbit anti-X, unlabeled antigen will compete with labeled antigen for the limited number of anti-X combining sites present, i.e., unlabeled antigen will diminish the amount of radioactivity that is bound by the antibody. Quantitation of antigen is accomplished by using a standard curve, as described earlier and illustrated in Figure 5. To construct the standard curve, one needs a sample having a known concentration of unlabeled antigen.

RADIOIMMUNOASSAYS WITH IMMOBILIZED ANTIBODY OR ANTIGEN

The principle of this type of assay, which quantitates small amounts of antigen, is similar to that of the "double-antibody" procedure just described; however, antibody or antigen is irreversibly attached to an insoluble support. As will be seen, this makes the use of a second antibody unnecessary.

A commonly used procedure is to attach the antibody covalently to Sepharose beads. These are very small spheres of crosslinked dextran. The beads play no role in the antigen–antibody reaction other than to serve as an insoluble support. Radiolabeled antigen will be bound by the antibody on the beads and the amount bound can be determined by centrifuging, washing the beads, and measuring their radioactivity. If unlabeled antigen is mixed with the labeled antigen before exposure to the beads, the amount of radioactivity bound will decrease as a result of the competition of the unlabeled antigen for the limited amount of antibody present. A standard inhibition curve can be constructed and unknown samples assayed for antigen, as already described. The unknown sample can, again, be a complex mixture; the labeled antigen must be quite pure.

If pure labeled *antibody* is available, the following method can be used. Unlabeled antigen is first attached to the beads; the amount attached can vary considerably. The labeled antibody will then be bound by the conjugated beads, and the binding will be inhibited by unlabeled antigens. The amounts of antigen in unknown samples can then be quantified through their ability to prevent the uptake of the labeled antibody. Again a standard curve must first be constructed, using a sample of known antigen content.

Another popular way of immobilizing antigens or antibodies is to attach them to the surface of small plastic test tubes. Hydrophobic plastics such as polystyrene or polyvinyl chloride will irreversibly bind small amounts of proteins. For example, if one simply adds 0.5 ml of a 1 mg/ml solution of almost any protein to such a test tube, a small amount (perhaps 5–50 ng) will become irreversibly bound within a few hours. The mechanism probably involves denaturation of a small amount of protein and exposure of its hydrophobic interior to the test tube, permitting the formation of strong hydrophobic bonds. A large amount of irrelevant protein is then added to "saturate" the surface of the test tube. Suppose the protein added first is a solution of antibody. Radiolabeled antigen can then be bound to the test tube *via* combining sites of the antibody. The amount bound is determined by removing the supernatant fluid, washing the test tube, and putting it into a radiation counter. Unlabeled antigen will of course compete with the labeled antigen for the combining sites of the antibody, thus providing the basis for a quantitative assay. Once again, the labeled antigen should be pure or nearly so, but the competing, unlabeled antigen to be assayed can be present in a complex mixture.

A commonly used assay for *antibody* makes use of immobilized antigen. Suppose we wish to determine the amount of antibody directed against antigen X in, say, human serum. The antigen is immobilized on the test tube (or beads). Then the serum of unknown antibody content is added. The combination is incubated for a suitable period and then washed; next, purified, radiolabeled antibody (such as rabbit antibody) reactive with human immunoglobulin is added. The amount of radioactivity that will bind to the test tube is dependent on the concentration of anti-X present in the human serum being tested. To set up the standard curve, a sample with a known content of human anti-X is required. This assay is illustrated in Figure 6.

THE ELISA ASSAY

This acronym stands for "enzyme-linked immunosorbent assay." In principle, such assays are precisely the same as radioimmunoassays, but the antibody (or, less frequently, the antigen) is labeled by covalently attaching an enzyme rather than a radioactive molecule. The enzyme attached to the antibody is one that can react with a colorless substrate to give a colored product. The amount of product released in a fixed period of time depends on the concentration of enzyme, and this in turn is a measure of the amount of antibody present. Alkaline phosphatase and *p*-nitrophenyl phosphate are examples of the enzyme and substrate, respectively. A product of the reaction is *p*-nitrophenol, which has a strong yellow color; the amount

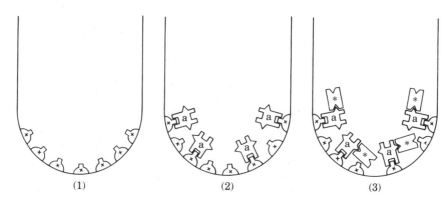

(1)   (2)   (3)

FIGURE 6. Example of a radioimmunoassay using antigen immobilized on a polystyrene test tube. (1) A small polystyrene test tube is exposed to a solution of antigen X overnight. A small amount of X adheres irreversibly. (2) The tube is washed and human serum containing an unknown amount of antibodies against antigen X is added to the tube. The anti-X antibodies are labeled "a." Such antibodies will adhere to antigen X on the tube. (3) The tube is washed again and specifically purified, radiolabeled rabbit antibody (labeled with an asterisk) directed against human IgG is added. The amount of radio-label that adheres is a measure of the amount of anti-X (of the IgG class). Normally, between steps (1) and (2) a concentrated solution of an irrelevant protein is added to saturate the surface of the tube. In assays of this type the wells of a polystyrene or polyvinylchloride tissue culture plate are commonly used in place of test tubes.

of product formed is determined in a spectrophotometer. In a typical assay, the amount of antibody (with enzyme attached) bound to an immobilized antigen is determined by washing, then adding p-nitrophenyl phosphate solution. The amount of colored product released in a fixed period of time—say, 30 minutes—is a measure of the amount of antibody bound. Virtually the same permutations can be applied to ELISA as to radioimmunoassays. Specialized spectrophotometric equipment is available for rapid reading of optical densities.

The principal advantages of ELISA are that it eliminates the hazard and precautions required in handling radioactive substances, that the equipment needed is somewhat less expensive, and that the final readings can be made more quickly than determinations of radioactivity.

COMPLEMENT FIXATION

This method was at one time widely used but has been largely supplanted by other assays. It is quite sensitive and still quite useful for certain types of antigens for which radioimmunoassays are not readily available.

Complement (Chapter 11) is a complex system of serum proteins. One of its properties is the ability to cause lysis (rupture) of erythrocytes in the presence of antibodies reactive with the erythrocytes. Both antibody and complement are required for the lysis to occur. A second factor that is important in the assay to be described is that complement activity is depleted if it is present during an antigen–antibody reaction. The depletion of activity is called COMPLEMENT FIXATION.

Suppose we wish to know whether antigen is present in an unknown sample. The test is carried out in two stages (Figure 7). First, the unknown is mixed with the appropriate antibody in the presence of serum containing complement. If antigen is indeed present, an antigen–antibody reaction will take place and the complement in the serum will be inactivated ("fixed"). Thus, determining whether or not complement was inactivated tells us whether or not antigen was present in the unknown sample.

To ascertain whether complement has been inactivated, the above mixture is tested as a potential source of complement in a second stage, namely, lysis of red blood cells coated with antibody. If the coated red cells are not lysed when the test mixture is added, complement must have been inactivated and the antigen in question must have been present during the first stage. The evidence for lysis is release of hemoglobin, which is red, into the medium. Quantitation of antigen is achieved by determining how far the solution containing antigen can be diluted before it loses the capacity to fix complement. A "standard" containing a known amount of antigen is required for

Mixture A	Mixture B
Solution containing unknown amount of virus V + Antibody to virus V (from a rabbit, human etc.) + Guinea pig complement	Rabbit antibody to sheep red blood cells (depleted of complement by heating at 56 degrees for 30 minutes) + Sheep red blood cells
Add A to B. If V is present in the unknown, the complement in mixture A will be inactivated and lysis will not occur in B. If lysis does occur, the unknown sample lacked V. Lysis is indicated by release of hemoglobin from the red blood cells.	

FIGURE 7. Complement fixation as a test for the presence of a specific virus (V). Quantitation is discussed in the text.

comparison. Controls must be included for nonspecific lysis of red cells and for nonspecific inactivation of complement by factors other than the antigen–antibody complex. Preliminary tests are needed to determine optimal amounts of complement and of antibodies to be used.

PLAQUE ASSAY FOR ANTIBODY FORMATION BY CELLS

This assay (Jerne et al., 1963) has had a great impact on immunological research and applications. It permits the enumeration of cells producing antibody of a given specificity. The assay is based on the fact that an antibody-producing cell, such as a plasma cell or lymphoblast, will continue to secrete antibody for a day or two when placed in an agar gel containing nutrients. Suppose the antibody in question is a mouse antibody specific for sheep red blood cells (SRBC). One mixes SRBC with the leukocytes to be tested for antibody production and incorporates them both into agar on a Petri dish or microscope slide. SRBC that are in the vicinity of an antibody-secreting cell will become coated with antibody. If, after a few hours, one overlays the agar with guinea pig complement, lysis of red cells coated with IgM antibody will take place and this will be visible as a cloudy circular area in the relatively clear background. Each IgM-forming cell will lie in the center of such a cloudy circle, or "plaque." Plaques may range in diameter from that of a pinpoint to a millimeter or two. The antibody-producing cells must be at a concentration that is low enough to prevent excessive overlap of plaques.

IgG-producing cells are poor plaque formers because IgG does not lyse red cells efficiently. However, such cells can be identified by using a second antibody specific for the IgG (in this case, rabbit anti-mouse IgG) together with the complement. The additional crosslinking that then takes place at the red cell surface greatly enhances the activation of complement.

The method is not limited to SRBC as an antigen. One can covalently attach various haptens or, with greater difficulty, proteins to the red cells and then use the method for enumerating anti-hapten or anti-protein antibody-forming cells.

PURIFICATION OF ANTIBODIES

We will consider two types of purification procedures. In the first, a fraction of serum that contains antibodies of all specificities is separated from other serum proteins. This will be referred to as the isolation of an immunoglobulin fraction. The second procedure deals with the isolation from serum of those antibodies that are reactive with a particular antigen. Antibodies isolated in this way are "SPECIF-ICALLY PURIFIED" or "AFFINITY-PURIFIED" antibodies.

ISOLATION OF AN IMMUNOGLOBULIN FRACTION

The following example illustrates one of a variety of procedures that can be used. A useful first step in the procedure is to add ammonium sulfate or sodium sulfate solution to the serum. Enough ammonium sulfate is generally added to yield a final concentration equal to 33–40% of a saturated solution. Sodium sulfate may be added to a final concentration of 16–18% (w/v). Either of these reagents will precipitate the globulins of serum, leaving serum albumins in the supernatant fluid. Because albumins constitute about two-thirds of the serum protein, this step results in considerable enrichment of the antibodies (which are globulins and are precipitated). Further purification of the precipitated material can be carried out by ion-exchange chromatography, e.g., with diethylaminoethyl (DEAE)-cellulose. Proteins can be eluted from DEAE-cellulose with a salt gradient at neutral pH; high salt concentrations overcome the electrostatic forces that cause binding to the positively charged DEAE-cellulose; alternatively, gradients of pH can be used. Fortuitously, the IgG fraction of serum has the lowest affinity of the serum proteins for DEAE-cellulose at neutral pH; it passes through the column at a very low salt concentration, whereas other proteins are retained.[1] IgA and IgM will be eluted at higher salt concentrations and will generally be contaminated with other serum proteins. Nevertheless, considerable enrichment of IgA or IgM is achieved by this procedure; they can be further purified by gel filtration and electrophoresis. Also, IgM is quite insoluble at very low salt concentrations, a property that can be used for additional purification.

SPECIFIC PURIFICATION OF ANTIBODIES (AFFINITY CHROMATOGRAPHY)

Antibodies specific for a given ligand (hapten or antigen) can be isolated by immobilizing the ligand on a solid support, allowing the antibodies to bind to the ligand, washing thoroughly, and then treating with a reagent that releases the antibody. Almost any protein antigen or protein–hapten conjugate can be covalently bound to bromoacetyl-cellulose powder, or to beads of Sepharose (crosslinked dex-

---

[1] IgG is quite heterogeneous; the most negatively charged fraction of the IgG may be retained more avidly and eluted at higher salt concentration, together with other serum proteins.

tran) that have been activated with cyanogen bromide. Other solid supports have also been used.

A chromatography column is prepared with the antigen-conjugated cellulose or Sepharose, and the solution of antibody to be purified (frequently serum) is passed slowly through the column. The column is then washed with buffer and the antibody is eluted by applying a reagent that breaks the noncovalent antigen–antibody bonds. Whether a reagent is effective for a given antigen–antibody pair must be determined by trial and error. Frequently used reagents are glycine buffer, pH 2.5 to 3; 1 M acetic or propionic acid; 2 to 3 M KSCN; 8 M urea; or 5 M guanidine HCl. The latter reagent is very effective but is a strong denaturing agent for proteins and must be removed quickly; some denaturation of antibody may nonetheless result. Each of the reagents can be removed from the antibody by dialysis or gel filtration. Antibodies to haptens, adsorbed to an immobilized protein–hapten conjugate, can be eluted by using a concentrated solution of the free hapten. The eluate will of course contain hapten as well as antibody; the hapten is removed by repeated dialysis. It may, however, be difficult to remove hapten completely from antibodies of high affinity.

AUTORADIOGRAPHY

The following is an example of a procedure utilizing autoradiography. We have already mentioned that the IgG fraction of serum is very heterogeneous. One way to demonstrate this is by isoelectric focusing, which separates proteins according to ISOELECTRIC POINT (the pH at which the net charge on the protein is zero). Isoelectric focusing in a gel breaks up the IgG fraction into many separate bands, which can be visualized by staining with an appropriate dye (Figure 8). Suppose an animal has been immunized with antigen X and one wishes to ascertain which of the IgG bands contains anti-X antibodies. One can overlay the gel, after isoelectric focusing, with ^{125}I-labeled antigen X. Upon standing, the antigen will form complexes with antibodies present in the gel. If the gel is then washed, the complexes will remain, whereas the remainder of the labeled antigen will be washed away. The complexes containing radiolabeled antigen can be identified by overlaying the gel in the dark with X-ray film for several hours to several days, then developing the film to localize radioactive bands. This identifies the bands that contain anti-X antibodies. A photograph of such a gel is shown in Figure 8. The method provides a powerful approach to the question of the degree of heterogeneity of antibodies of a given specificity in an antiserum.

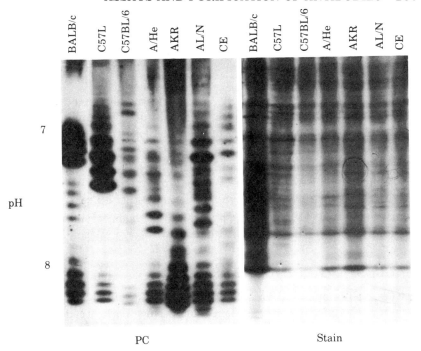

FIGURE 8. Method for identifying immunoglobulins that bind a particular antigen. Antisera were prepared against the phosphorylcholine (PC) hapten group in the seven strains of mice designated at the top of the figure. The antisera were subjected to isoelectric focusing in a polyacrylamide gel; each sample was run in duplicate on the same gel slab. The section of the gel shown includes proteins having isoelectric points of approximately 6.5 to 8.3; this range includes most of the immunoglobulins. The right half of the figure shows the pattern obtained when all of the protein was stained with a dye (Coomassie Brilliant Blue R). The portion of gel on the left was exposed to a solution containing ^{125}I-labeled phosphorylcholine conjugated to a protein. After washing to remove unbound labeled material, the left hand section of the gel was placed in contact with X-ray film for about a day; the film was then developed. The bands that are seen in the left-hand section thus contained antibodies that bind phosphorylcholine. Notice that there are many fewer bands on the left, corresponding only to those antibodies that bind the hapten. Other conclusions that one can draw are that the antibodies that bind the hapten are quite heterogeneous, showing multiple bands, but that some of the same bands are repeated in the patterns for different strains of mice; this suggests that closely related antibodies against PC are present in various strains, but that there are also intrastrain differences. (Courtesy of J. Latham Claflin. For a complete description of the method, see Claflin and Cubberley, 1978.)

LITERATURE CITED

Claflin, J. L. and Cubberley, M. (1978). Clonal nature of the immune response to phosphocholine. Molecular uniformity of a single idiotype among BALB/c mice. *J. Immunol. 121,* 1410.

Grabar, P. and Williams, C. A. (1953). Méthode permettant l'étude conjuguée des propriétés électrophorétiques et immunochimiques d'un mélange de protéines. Application au sérum sanguin. *Biochim. Biophys. Acta 10,* 193.

Jerne, N. K., Nordin, A. A. and Henry, C. (1963). The agar plaque technique for recognizing antibody-producing cells. *Cell-Bound Antibody,* p. 109. Philadelphia, Wistar Institute Press.

Ouchterlony, Ö. (1958). Diffusion-in-gel methods for immunological analysis. In P. Kallos, Ed., *Progress in Allergy.* Basel, Karger.

SUGGESTED ADDITIONAL READING

Chase, M. W. and Williams, C. A., Jr. (1971) *Methods in Immunology and Immunochemistry,* Vols. I and II, New York, Academic Press.

Garvey, J. S., Cremer, N. E. and Sussdorf, D. H. (1977). *Methods in Immunology,* 3rd ed. Menlo Park, CA, W. A. Benjamin.

Heidelberger, M. (1969). Quantitative absolute methods in the study of antigen-antibody reactions. *Bact. Revs. 3,* 49.

Kabat, E. A. and Mayer, M. M. (1961). *Experimental Immunochemistry,* 2nd ed. Springfield, IL, C. C. Thomas.

Weir, D. M., Ed. (1978). *Handbook of Experimental Immunology.* 3rd ed. Oxford, Blackwell Scientific Publications.

10

MONOCLONAL ANTIBODIES
PRODUCED BY HYBRIDOMAS

OVERVIEW

By fusing an antibody-producing B cell with an appropriate myeloma tumor cell, it is possible to produce an immortal cell line that secretes antibody characteristic of the B cell. The line can be maintained in tissue culture or by successive passages *in vivo*. Mouse, rat, and human tumor lines suitable for the production of hybridomas are available. The secreted product of the fused cell line is a homogeneous, "monoclonal" antibody. Cell lines producing antibodies of almost any specificity, and in virtually unlimited amounts, can be obtained. Monoclonal antibodies can be prepared even when purified antigen is not available; an important example is the production of monoclonal antibodies against individual antigens on cell membranes. Monoclonal antibodies have found a wide range of applications in biology and biochemistry, some of which are described.

*   *   *

A report published by G. Köhler and C. Milstein in 1975 has had an enormous impact on immunology and on applications of antibodies to a great variety of biological problems. The method they described makes it possible to produce virtually unlimited amounts of homogeneous, MONOCLONAL ANTIBODIES against desired antigens or haptens. In the case of a macromolecular antigen, each monoclonal antibody is specific for an individual antigenic determinant (epitope) on the antigen molecule.

PRINCIPLE OF THE METHOD

Monoclonal antibodies are produced by cell hybrids called HYBRIDOMAS. The agents that can induce fusion of the cells are Sendai virus

169

or polyethylene glycol; the latter is used in hybridoma technology. The two cell types involved in the fusion are a myeloma tumor cell, from a line that has been adapted so that it grows in tissue culture, and an antibody-producing B cell from an animal immunized against the desired antigen. The fused cells retain the immortality of the myeloma cell line but continue to secrete the antibody produced by the B cell. (Cultured B cells ordinarily have a very limited lifespan.) The fused cells can be maintained indefinitely in tissue culture or, in the case of a mouse or rat hybridoma, by passage as a tumor in animals.

Most of the work reported so far has involved mouse myelomas, which can fuse with mouse or rat B cells. Appropriate rat tumor lines have also been produced. In the case of human antibodies, one or two myeloma tumor lines suitable for the production of hybridomas have been developed but not yet widely distributed; the methodology is less versatile than that applied to the mouse or rat because of restrictions on deliberate immunization of humans. Human hybridomas are prepared by using white blood cells from the peripheral blood of individuals who happen to have been exposed to the antigen in question or have been purposefully immunized with an acceptable antigen. From the clinical standpoint, human hybridomas may prove to be of great importance.

Because both the myeloma and the B cell normally synthesize immunoglobulin, the fused cell produces two different H chains and two different L chains. The H and L chains combine in the cell, apparently at random, to produce 10 different molecular species, one of which is the desired bivalent antibody—say, H_1L_1–H_1L_1—and three of which are monovalent forms of the desired antibody—H_1L_1–H_2L_2, H_1L_1–H_1L_2, and H_1L_1–H_2L_1.[1] For the mouse, mutant myeloma tumors are now available that do not secrete H or L chains but that do retain the immortality of the myeloma cell and the capacity to undergo a productive fusion. When such a cell line is used, a single homogeneous antibody is secreted after fusion.

In tissue culture, antibodies are secreted into the medium and are collected from the cell supernatant fluid. For passage *in vivo,* mice or rats are first primed intraperitoneally with a liquid hydrocarbon called Pristane (2,6,10,14-tetramethylpentadecane). When the fused cells are subsequently injected, they grow as a suspension in the peritoneal cavity. The surrounding fluid, called ASCITIC FLUID, contains the secreted antibody; the antibody is also present in the serum of the mouse, but the volume of ascitic fluid can considerably exceed the volume of serum. The growing tumor, which is lethal, can be trans-

---

[1] Heavy chains of different classes (e.g., γ and μ) will not self-assemble into a single molecule; however, γ_{2a}, γ_{2b}, and γ_1 chains can form "mixed" molecules.

ferred to another mouse, returned to tissue culture, or stored in liquid nitrogen ($-196°$ C) for future use. In tissue culture, the concentrations of antibody obtainable are generally in the range of 10 to 50 μg/ml. In ascitic fluid or serum, concentrations of 10 mg/ml are often achieved, although this is highly variable.

SELECTION AND SCREENING OF FUSED CELLS

To select cells that have undergone fusion, culture conditions are chosen such that the fused cells, but neither of the two parental cells, will survive. Of the two parental cell types, the B cell has a short lifespan in culture, but a myeloma cell line can survive indefinitely. A mutant of the myeloma cell is therefore developed that will die in a medium that permits a fused cell to survive. The principle is as follows (see also Figure 1).

1. Prepare a mutant of the myeloma that lacks the enzyme hypoxanthine–guanine phosphoribosyltransferase (HGPRT). Use this mutant cell line for the fusion.

2. After fusion, the medium used to select for fused cells contains hypoxanthine, aminopterin, and thymine (HAT medium).

3. The aminopterin will kill the mutant myeloma cells because it blocks *de novo* synthesis of purines and pyrimidines, which the myeloma cells require to survive.

4. The aminopterin will *not* kill fused cells because they can utilize the hypoxanthine and thymine in the HAT medium in an alternative pathway for synthesis of purines and pyrimidines; this pathway requires the enzyme HGPRT, which the mutant myeloma lacks. However, the fused cells do contain HGPRT because the required genes are derived from the parental B cell.

5. Any B cells that have not undergone fusion will die simply because they are short-lived cells. Thus, only fused cells survive.

These methods are described in detail by Kennett (1979).

In practice, after fusion one transfers small aliquots of the cells to a large number of wells in a tissue culture plate and, after a few days, inspects the wells to see if they contain growing colonies. The next step is to screen the cell supernatant fluids in such wells for the presence of the desired antibody. (For this discussion we will assume that we are working with mouse antibodies.) Because the concentration of antibody is of the order of micrograms per milliliter, screening

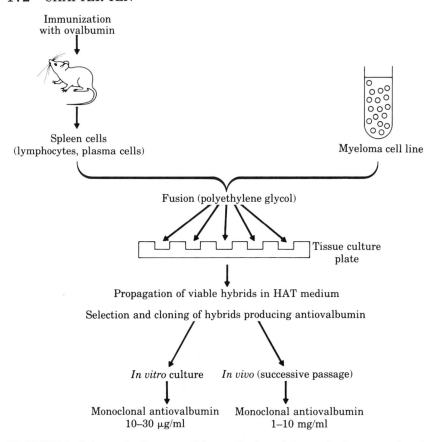

Immunization
with ovalbumin

Spleen cells
(lymphocytes, plasma cells)

Myeloma cell line

Fusion (polyethylene glycol)

Tissue culture
plate

Propagation of viable hybrids in HAT medium

Selection and cloning of hybrids producing antiovalbumin

In vitro culture   *In vivo* (successive passage)

Monoclonal antiovalbumin
10–30 μg/ml

Monoclonal antiovalbumin
1–10 mg/ml

FIGURE 1. Schematic diagram of the method used for producing monoclonal antibodies.

is often carried out by a radioimmunoassay or by the ELISA technique (Chapter 9). In a typical assay, the antigen in question (antigen X) is coated onto the surface of wells in a polyvinyl chloride tissue culture plate. The surface is next saturated with an irrelevant protein. A supernatant fluid to be tested for antibody against antigen X is then added to each well. The plate is washed and purified rabbit anti-mouse Fab is added; the rabbit antibody is labeled with ^{125}I or conjugated to an enzyme suitable for the ELISA assay. If the supernatant fluid contained anti-X, the labeled rabbit antibody will be bound to the surface of the well.[2] Many variations of this procedure have been

[2] The principle of this assay is illustrated in Figure 6, Chapter 9. In that example, antibody from a rabbit, rather than a mouse, is being assayed.

employed. Because a well containing fused cells may contain more than one hybridoma, the next step is to "clone" the cells. This is done by preparing a very dilute suspension of cells in agar or agarose made up in tissue culture medium; the mixture is poured into a Petri dish and allowed to solidify. The separate colonies that now grow in the agar are products of one or a very small number of cells. The colonies are transferred individually to wells in a tissue culture plate, grown up, and their supernatant fluids again analyzed for the desired antibody. Such antibody may now be homogeneous; this can be established by isoelectric focusing of the antibody product. If more than one protein is seen, the cloning procedure is repeated.

Alternatively, cells can be cloned without the use of agar by the method of "limiting dilution." A cell suspension is pipetted into each well in a volume such that a significant number of wells contain no cells at all.[3] After cell growth and selection for the desired property the process is repeated until monoclonality is virtually a mathematical certainty. In addition, tests are carried out to determine whether the final antibody product is homogeneous. Having established a monoclonal line, it can be maintained indefinitely as already described. (As indicated earlier, a single product will be obtained only if a nonsecreting myeloma line is used. Useful products can nonetheless be obtained with secreting myeloma tumor lines. In this case, the isoelectric focusing pattern of the secreted protein will, of course, exhibit some heterogeneity, even when the cells are monoclonal.)

When hybridomas are grown *in vivo,* the host must have histocompatibility antigens corresponding to those on the hybridoma cells; otherwise, the hybridoma will be rejected. The murine myeloma lines currently available are from the BALB/c strain. If BALB/c spleen cells are fused with such a line, the hybridoma can be grown in BALB/c mice. If another strain of mouse—say, C57BL—is used as the source of spleen cells, the hybridoma is grown in F_1(BALB/c × C57BL) mice.

APPLICATIONS OF MONOCLONAL ANTIBODIES

Monoclonal antibodies have been applied to so many different problems that a complete description is not feasible. Some of the more important uses will be listed and a few specific examples cited.

1. The hybridoma technique can be used to obtain large amounts of antibody that would otherwise be available only in small quantities.

---

[3] According to the Poisson distribution, when an average of 1 viable cell per well is pipetted, approximately 37% of the wells will on the average contain zero viable cells, 37% will contain 1 cell, and 26% more than one cell. About 30% of the wells will contain 1 cell and 9% more than one cell if an average of 0.5 cells/well are introduced.

This applies to antibody directed against almost any antigen that is difficult to obtain in large amounts.

2. By the hybridoma technique, one can obtain antibodies, all of which are directed to a single epitope on an antigen molecule. For complex antigens, this is otherwise very difficult to achieve; also, conventional antibodies directed against a single epitope, such as a hapten, are heterogeneous.

3. The procedure can be used to obtain pure antibodies against antigens that cannot be purified. (From a conventional immune serum, one isolates antibodies of a given specificity by adsorption to and elution from insolubilized antigen, such as antigen conjugated to Sepharose; this requires reasonable amounts of purified antigen, which may not be available.)

An important class of antigens that are difficult to isolate are molecules present in cell membranes. Antibodies can be elicited by inoculation of whole membrane material, but they will obviously be very heterogeneous. With the hybridoma technique, however, one can obtain monoclonal antibodies to a given antigen by screening clones made with spleen cells of an animal immunized with unfractionated membrane. Monoclonal antibodies have been prepared that are specific for a variety of membrane components, such as histocompatibility antigens and antigens specific to particular cell types, including macrophages, red blood cells, various subsets of lymphocytes, or tumor cells. Monoclonal antibodies have also been prepared against clinically important antigens present on infectious agents such as bacteria, viruses, and parasitic organisms. Monoclonal antibodies are of particular value for this purpose because of the difficulty of isolating individual cell surface antigens, free of other surface components, for use in immunization. To obtain monoclonal antibodies against a component of a cell surface, one immunizes a mouse with a whole cell preparation, fuses, and screens a large number of fused cells until one is found that secretes the desired antibody.

4. Monoclonal antibodies can be used to identify or isolate cells by virtue of antigens present on the surface. Identification is accomplished by using monoclonal antibody conjugated with a fluorescent substance or with an electron-dense protein such as ferritin, thus permitting its visualization in the light microscope or electron microscope, respectively. One can isolate subpopulations of cells by each of several techniques that utilize antibodies directed to cell-surface components.

5. Not only can one obtain pure antibody with an impure antigen, but the monoclonal antibody thus obtained can be used to purify the

antigen. The antibody, which is obtainable in large quantity, can be conjugated to an insoluble support, such as Sepharose, and the antigen can be purified by adsorption to the bound antibody, followed by elution at low pH or with a high concentration of a salt such as potassium thiocyanate.

6. Monoclonal antibodies are in widespread use for studies of the biochemical and biological properties of homogeneous antibodies of a given specificity. Insight into the size of the antibody repertoire has been obtained by studying the diversity of monoclonal antibodies directed against a single hapten.

7. The method provides a permanent source of antibodies with invariant properties for quantitative immunological assays of a variety of antigens. This is important, for example, in routine radioimmune or ELISA assays carried out in clinical laboratories. Well over 100 such assays are in use, some of which already make use of monoclonal antibodies.

8. Antibodies of high affinity are needed for assaying very low concentrations of antigens, e.g., hormones in blood. After a fusion, one can set up the screening procedure so as to select for monoclonal antibodies of high affinity.

In the following sections, a few specific examples of applications of monoclonal antibodies are discussed. These represent a very small fraction of the applications that could be cited.

Studies of cellular mechanisms in the immune response

The availability of monoclonal antibodies has greatly facilitated research on the roles of various cell types in the immune response. For example, helper T cells have surface antigens that distinguish them from suppressor T cells. Macrophages, B cells, and other leukocytes also have characteristic surface antigens. Specific antibodies can be used for the direct isolation of such cells or to eliminate a given type of cell by killing with antibody and complement. One can study the effect of killing particular cells on a given biological function and thus can ascribe that function to a particular class of white cell. Before the advent of monoclonal antibodies, it was very difficult to isolate the relevant antibodies or to obtain them in sufficient quantity for practical use.

Isolation of Interferons

Monoclonal antibodies (MA) have been used for the purification of human interferon. Interferons are being intensively investigated because of their potential as antiviral and, with less supporting evidence, as antitumor agents. Their purification by conventional means is a tedious and expensive process. Secher and Burke (1980) reported on the preparation of MA directed against one of the interferons from human leukocytes and its use in a purification procedure. The pure MA was conjugated to Sepharose; interferon was bound to this adsorbent and eluted in an active form at pH 2. By this procedure, crude interferon was purified 5000-fold in a single step; also, a partially purified preparation was brought to a stage of apparent homogeneity. This appears to be the method of choice for large scale purification of interferons.

Monoclonal antibodies as a "magic bullet"

MA are being used in an effort to kill tumor cells by attacking them with an antibody that is specific for the tumor and to which a highly toxic molecule is conjugated. The antibody would, in principle, localize to the tumor *in vivo*; the attached toxic agent would then kill the tumor cells. This approach is still in the experimental stage, although interesting results have been obtained *in vitro*.

Papers by Krolick et al. (1980) and Gilliland et al. (1980) provide specific examples of the method. Both investigations made use of monoclonal mouse antibody directed against a tumor: in one case the tumor was a human colorectal carcinoma; in the other, a mouse B-cell lymphoma. Monoclonal antibodies were prepared that would interact quite specifically with each tumor. Each monoclonal antibody was then conjugated with a toxic molecule (the A chain of ricin or of diphtheria toxin). The high degree of toxicity of these substances is indicated by the fact that a single molecule can kill a cell. Although both A chains are very cytotoxic, neither is capable of penetrating a cell in the absence of the other fragment (the B chain) of the toxin molecule. In both sets of experiments, however, the antibody–toxin conjugate was capable of killing target tumor cells *in vitro*. It appears that the antibody becomes attached to the membrane of the cell, then is internalized, at which point the attached toxin fragment becomes lethal. Each of the anti-tumor antibodies tested has a high degree of specificity, but it has not yet been proved that such antibodies will bind to *no* other tissues *in vivo*. This and other technical problems remain to be resolved.

Monoclonal antibodies to histocompatibility antigens

The histocompatibility (H) antigens, present on the membranes of virtually all tissues, are of great importance from the standpoint of transplant rejections, the capability of responding to particular antigens, and cooperation of different cell types during the immune response (Klein, 1975). Such antigens are being investigated in various animal species, including man, mouse, rat, and chicken. In each species there is a great variety of H antigens that can be distinguished with antisera on the basis of their antigenic determinants. Because H antigens represent only a small fraction of the contents of a cell, they are difficult to purify. It has taken many years to develop the antisera needed for typing the H antigens on cells. It is particularly difficult to obtain an antibody preparation that is reactive with a single epitope. In addition, antisera prepared in different laboratories often differ in their fine specificities and cross-reactivities. With the hybridoma technique, monoclonal antibodies are currently being developed that are specific for individual H antigens. Because the antibodies can be obtained in large amounts, they can be distributed to various laboratories; this should eventually result in standardization of typing for H antigens throughout the world. The use of monoclonal antibodies has also permitted the identification of previously unknown H antigens.

As in the case of the interferons, monoclonal antibodies to H antigens have great potential for use in purification of the antigens.

Classification of microorganisms

Monoclonal antibodies are increasingly being used for classification of bacteria, viruses, and parasitic organisms. The reasons for their utility are the availability of large amounts of antibody directed to a single epitope, the reproducibility of results over a long period of time, and the ability to select monoclonal antibodies that are active against a particular organism and that show minimal cross-reactivity with other organisms.

Passive immunization

The possibility of obtaining very large quantities of human monoclonal antibodies directed against microorganisms adds a new dimension to PASSIVE IMMUNIZATION (inoculation of antibody, as contrasted to immunization with antigen). This may prove to be applicable to ongoing infections by certain bacteria or parasites that remain accessible to serum antibodies during an infection. (Infections by viruses, which are sequestered in cells, may be less susceptible to such an approach.) If, for example, we had available a battery of human monoclonal antibodies directed against the various infectious forms of pneumococci, these might well be useful in limiting the extent of a pneumococcal infection. The utility of passive immunization is illustrated by a report of prolonged remission of a human B cell lymphoma after administration of monoclonal mouse antibody directed against the idiotype of an immunoglobulin present on the surface of the lymphoma cells.

An interesting report by Potocnjak et al. (1980) demonstrated that inoculation of monoclonal antibodies directed against a surface component of the sporozoite form of a malarial parasite that infects mice (*Plasmodium berghei*) protected the mice against an otherwise lethal dose of the parasites. Although, in humans, passive immunization of the general population against malaria is not feasible because of the short half-life of antibodies, the possibility of preparing protective antibodies suggests that such antibodies might be used to isolate an antigen that would be useful for long-term immunization.

Studies of the diversity of antibodies

The most definitive method for studying antibody diversity is by determining the variability of amino acid sequences. One approach is to determine the sequences of an array of antibodies that are from an inbred strain of mice and that are directed against the same antigen or hapten. From the practical standpoint, this requires the availability of homogeneous antibodies, because sequencing of a heterogeneous mixture is difficult or impossible and because antibodies, even against a single hapten, are heterogeneous. One can, however, induce antibodies against the antigen or hapten in question in an inbred mouse and use the hybridoma technique to generate homogeneous antibodies, specific for that antigen, for use in amino acid sequencing.

An example of this approach is the work of Schilling et al. (1980), who prepared a variety of monoclonal antibodies against dextran in the BALB/c strain of mouse. For sequencing, they selected monoclonal anti-dextran antibodies that shared a common idiotype. Thus, the antibodies they sequenced were selected, not only for anti-dextran activity, but for the presence of a related structure in the region of the antigen-binding site (i.e., a related idiotype). Despite this selection process, a large number of anti-dextran antibodies were found to differ slightly in the amino acid sequences of their V_H regions. (Their results were described in detail in Chapter 8.) Studies of this kind have been used to demonstrate the diversity of mouse antibodies that have a number of different antigen-binding specificities.

T-CELL HYBRIDOMAS

Hybridomas have been prepared by fusing T cells with a T-cell lymphoma that grows in continuous culture and that has undergone a mutation such that it lacks the enzyme HGPRT. Whereas such hybridomas, as expected, do not secrete antibodies, they are useful for

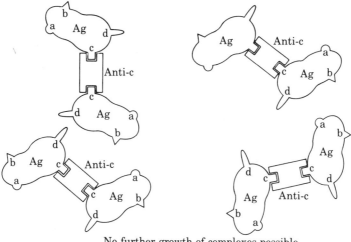

No further growth of complexes possible

(A)

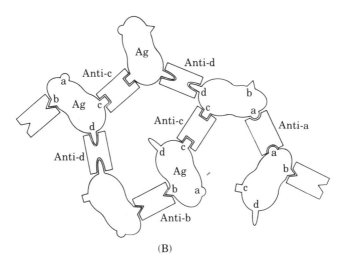

(B)

FIGURE 2. (A) Interaction of an antigen that has epitopes a, b, c, and d with a monoclonal antibody directed against epitope c. Each antibody molecule can combine with two antigen molecules, but no further growth of complexes is possible. (B) A conventional antiserum contains antibodies with combining sites directed against each of the epitopes on the antigen. Indefinite growth of complexes, with crosslinking, is possible. A mixture of monoclonal antibodies directed against two or more different epitopes on the same antigen can precipitate the antigen by a similar mechanism.

studying receptors of T cells or biologically active molecules (called "factors") synthesized by T cells. Such molecules include factors that augment or suppress an immune response. T-cell hybridomas may also serve as a homogeneous source of various messenger RNA molecules that can be used to probe the organization of genes controlling proteins of biological importance synthesized by these cells.

UNUSUAL PRECIPITATING PROPERTIES OF MONOCLONAL ANTIBODIES

Insight into the mechanism of the precipitin reaction was obtained when it was observed that monoclonal anti-protein antibodies often fail to precipitate the protein antigen. The reason for this failure is illustrated in Figure 2. If the antigen molecule has only one epitope reactive with the monoclonal antibody, a large polymer cannot be produced. Conventional antibody, which is a mixture of antibodies reactive with different epitopes on the same antigen molecule, can, in contrast, form a crosslinked polymer, which precipitates. The validity of this concept is supported by experiments in which mixtures of different monoclonal antibodies directed against the same antigen were found to precipitate the antigen, whereas individual monoclonal antibodies were ineffective.

LITERATURE CITED

Gilliland, D. G., Steplewski, Z., Collier, R. J., Mitchell, K. F., Chang, T. H. and Koprowski, H. (1980). Antibody-directed cytotoxic agents: use of monoclonal antibody directs the action of toxin A chains to colorectal carcinoma cells. *Proc. Natl. Acad. Sci. USA 77*, 4539.

Kennett, R. H. (1979). Cell fusion. *Methods Enzymol. 58*, 345.

Klein, J. (1975). *Biology of the Mouse Histocompatibility-2 Complex: Principles of Immunogenetics Applied to a Single System.* New York, Springer-Verlag.

Köhler, G. and Milstein, C. (1975). Continuous cultures of fused cells secreting antibodies of predefined specificities. *Nature 256*, 495.

Krolick, K. A., Villemez, C., Isakson, P., Uhr, J. W. and Vitetta, E. S. (1980). Selective killing of normal or neoplastic B cells by antibodies coupled to the A chain of ricin. *Proc. Natl. Acad. Sci. USA 77*, 5419.

Potocnjak, P., Yoshida, N., Nussenzweig, R. S. and Nussenzweig, V. (1980). Monovalent fragments (Fab) of monoclonal antibodies to a sporozoite surface antigen (Pb44) protect mice against malarial infection. *J. Exp. Med. 151*, 1504.

Schilling, J., Clevinger, B., Davie, J. M. and Hood, L. (1980). Amino acid sequence of homogeneous antibodies to dextran and DNA rearrangements in heavy chain V-region gene segments. *Nature 285*, 35.

Secher, D. S. and Burke, D. C. (1980). A monoclonal antibody for large-scale purification of human leukocyte interferon. *Nature 285*, 446.

SUGGESTED ADDITIONAL READING

Hoogengrad, N., Helman, T. and Hoogengrad, J. (1983). The effect of preinjection of mice with pristane on ascites tumor formation and monoclonal antibody production. *J. Immunol. Methods 61*, 317.

Kennett, R. H., McKearn, T. J. and Bechtol, K. B., Eds. (1980). *Monoclonal Antibodies*. New York, Plenum Publishers.

Melchers, F., Potter, M. and Warner, N. L., Eds. (1978). Lymphocyte Hybridomas. *Curr. Topics Microbiol. Immunol.* Volume 81.

Milstein, C. (1980). Monoclonal antibodies. *Sci. Amer. 243*, No. 4, 66.

Moyle, W. R., Lin, C., Corson, R. L., and Ehrlich, P. H. (1983). Quantitative explanation for increased affinity shown by mixtures of monoclonal antibodies; importance of a circular complex. *Molec. Immunol. 20*, 439.

Yelton, D. E. and Scharff, M. D. (1981). Monoclonal antibodies; a powerful new tool in biology. *Ann. Rev. Biochem. 50*, 657.

11

MECHANISMS OF ACTION IN THE COMPLEMENT SYSTEM

OVERVIEW

The complement system is a group of serum proteins that plays an important role in defense against pathogenic microorganisms. Activated complement can bring about lysis of certain gram-negative bacteria, parasites, virus-infected cells, or red blood cells. The complement system also includes molecules that can enhance phagocytosis (opsonins) or that are chemotactic for phagocytic leukocytes. Individuals with a hereditary deficiency of one of the key components of complement are subject to recurrent, serious infections. Before causing lysis of cells, complement must undergo a series of reactions called activation; these reactions also generate the opsonins and chemotactic agents. During activation, several components are converted to active proteolytic enzymes and, as such, act on other components in a precise manner. One pathway of activation, the classical pathway, is initiated by the formation of complexes of antigen with human IgG1, IgG2, IgG3, or IgM antibodies. A second pathway, called the alternative pathway, can be triggered by various microorganisms in the absence of antibody or by aggregated human antibody of any class. The alternative pathway is also triggered by, and thereby amplifies, reactions of the classical pathway. Complement can have deleterious as well as beneficial effects; it is involved in the damage of tissues that takes place after deposition of antigen–antibody–complement complexes or during autoimmune reactions.

*   *   *

COMPLEMENT, or the COMPLEMENT SYSTEM, are terms used to denote a group of 18 serum proteins that have a number of important biological functions. The system was discovered in the 1890s by investigators who noted its capacity to cause lysis of red blood cells (RBC) or certain gram-negative bacteria in the presence of antibodies directed against the cells. In the absence of complement, the antibodies may agglutinate the cells but do not disrupt them. That at least two components of serum are required for lysis was first demonstrated by heating the antiserum at 56°C for 30 minutes (Bordet, 1896). This destroyed the lytic capability of the serum, but it could be restored by adding fresh nonimmune serum (lacking antibodies). The heat-sensitive component that is present in nonimmune serum was referred to as alexin and, later, as complement.

Lysis of RBC is readily observed and quantified because of the release of hemoglobin, a protein with an intense red color. It is now known that before lysis can occur, the complement system must undergo a series of reactions, referred to as ACTIVATION OF COMPLEMENT. Many of the components of complement are precursors of enzymes (zymogens) that acquire activity as proteolytic enzymes during the activation process.

The conjoint action of complement and antibody directed to antigens present on cell surfaces can kill many types of cells, including most varieties of cells of animal origin and some parasites. Other important targets of this lytic action are gram-negative bacteria; gram-positive bacteria and some gram-negative strains are resistant. Recent evidence indicates that some virus-infected cells can be killed through the action of antibody and complement. This may well be of significance in recovery from viral infections, although T cells are considered to be more important.

Complement also plays an essential role in the enhancement of phagocytosis of bacteria, virus-infected cells, or parasites. The combination of antibody and complement is generally more effective than antibody alone in promoting the engulfment of microorganisms by phagocytic leukocytes. The enhancement of phagocytosis is referred to as OPSONIZATION of the microorganism. Some microorganisms can be opsonized by complement components in the absence of antibody. Opsonization can occur with particles that are either resistant or susceptible to lysis and may be more significant than lysis from the standpoint of immunity.

Complement also participates in defense mechanisms by mediating CHEMOTAXIS. Certain components of complement, or breakdown products of components, are chemotactic for phagocytic leukocytes, i.e., the cells will migrate in the direction of higher concentrations of these substances. This mechanism is important in attracting phagocytic cells to the site of tissue injury.

The degree to which the body relies on complement for protection against disease has been elucidated by studying individuals with hereditary deficiencies of individual components of the complement system (see below).

Complement can also mediate effects that are harmful to the animal. A sequel of many types of prolonged infection is the appearance of antigen–antibody complexes in the serum. Such complexes, which are often deposited in the kidney, are found to contain complement as well as antigen and antibody. They can induce inflammatory responses and destruction of tissue (nephritis). Deposition of injurious complexes has also been observed in the lung, joints, spleen, and other tissues. Complement is, in addition, involved in injury to tissues associated with autoimmune diseases, in which the individual makes antibodies that react with his own tissues.

STUDY OF THE COMPLEMENT SYSTEM THROUGH HEMOLYSIS OF ERYTHROCYTES

HEMOLYSIS OF ERYTHROCYTES (lysis with the release of hemoglobin) is historically the basic assay system for studying mechanisms of activation of complement and lysis of a target cell. The overall process can be summarized as:

$$RBC + Ab + C \rightarrow lysis \text{ (liberating hemoglobin)}$$

where Ab is an IgG or IgM antibody directed against the red blood cell (RBC) and where C represents the various components of complement that are active in the process. Lysis is not brought about by either Ab or C acting alone. In an assay of this type, it is not necessary that the antibody and C be derived from the same species. A typical assay involves the use of sheep RBC, rabbit antibody to the RBC, and guinea pig or human C. For simplicity most of this discussion will pertain to human C. Most of our detailed information on the complement system has come from studies of human or guinea pig C.

As previously indicated, there are 18 components of the complement system. One group of components is designated C1, C2, . . . , C9. Lysis of target cells is brought about by a complex consisting of C5b, C6, C7, C8, and C9. C5b, which has a molecular weight of about 180,000, is produced by proteolysis of C5 (mol. wt. 190,000). The actual lesion in the cell membrane is caused by a tubular structure consisting of 12 to 16 molecules of C9 (total mol. wt., $\sim 1 \times 10^6$ daltons). Such tubules form channels in the phospholipid layer of the cell membrane, render the membrane leaky, and allow the external medium to enter the cell and cause osmotic lysis (Podack et al., 1982). The polymerization of C9 is induced by a C5b, C6, C7, C8 complex. The C5b that is required is produced from C5 by two different sequences of events, referred to as the CLASSICAL and ALTERNATIVE PATHWAYS.

Reactions of antibodies with simple antigens, such as proteins or carbohydrates, may activate the complement system, even though lysis is obviously not involved. The activation results in loss of complement activity from the serum. The loss of activity is a sensitive indicator of the occurrence of an antigen–antibody reaction and can be exploited to monitor for the presence of small amounts of antibody or antigen (Chapter 9).

THE CLASSICAL PATHWAY

The name given to this pathway derives from the fact that it was the first to be identified and studied. Eleven components of complement, all of which are proteins, participate. A serum protein that acts as an inhibitor (C1INH) is also generally included as a member of the system. The components are numbered C1, . . . , C9, where C1 is a complex of three proteins, C1q, C1r, and C1s, bound by calcium ions. The molecular weights and approximate serum concentrations of the various components are shown in Table 1. The sequence of events that takes place on the RBC surface in the classical pathway will be described next. Some of the proteolytic cleavages that occur are schematically illustrated in Figure 1.

Step 1

$$\text{Ag,Ab complex} + \text{C1q,C1r,C1s} \xrightarrow{\text{Ca}^{2+}} \text{Ag,Ab(C1q,C1r,C1s)}$$

Ag refers to an epitope on the surface of the RBC and Ab is an antibody specific for that epitope.

C1q, C1r, and C1s exist as a trimolecular complex that is stabilized by calcium ions. Binding of this group of components to an antigen–antibody complex occurs through the interaction of C1q with IgM or IgG present in the complex. C1q has multiple binding sites with specificity for the $C_\gamma 2$ domain of IgG or the $C_\mu 4$ domain of IgM. The binding of C1q to monomeric IgG is very weak; the greater avidity for IgG in complexes is due to the interaction of a single C1q molecule with two or more adjacent IgG molecules. In contrast, C1q can interact well with a single IgM molecule because IgM is pentameric, i.e., C1q can simultaneously combine with more than one monomeric unit in the pentameric IgM molecule. A structural diagram of C1q is shown in Figure 2.

TABLE 1. Properties of proteins in the complement system.

Component	Approx. serum concentration ($\mu g/ml$)	Mol. wt.	Chain structure
Components of classical pathway			
C1q	150	410,000	6 × 24,000
			6 × 23,000
			6 × 22,000
C1r	50	83,000	1 chain
C1s	50	83,000	1 chain
C2	15	110,000	1 chain
C3	1300	190,000	1 × 115,000
			1 × 75,000
C4	400	206,000	1 × 93,000
			1 × 78,000
			1 × 33,000
Late-acting components			
C5	80	190,000	1 × 115,000
			1 × 75,000
C6	60	95,000	1 chain
C7	55	120,000	1 chain
C8	80	163,000	1 × 83,000
			1 × 70,000
			1 × 10,000
C9	160	79,000	1 chain
Components of alternate pathway			
D	1	24,000	1 chain
B (C3 Proactivator)	200	93,000	1 chain
P (Properdin)	25	220,000	4 × 55,000
Inhibitors			
C1INH (C1 inhibitor)	180	100,000	1 chain
H	500	150,000	1 chain
I (C3b inactivator)	35	88,000	1 × 50,000
			1 × 38,000

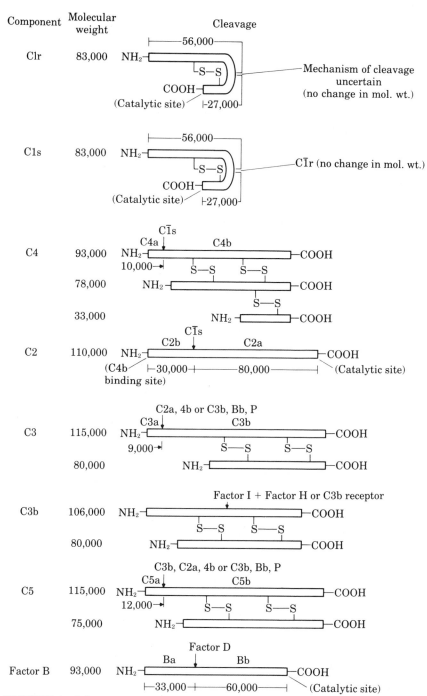

FIGURE 1. Schematic diagram of cleavages that occur during activation of the human complement system.

188

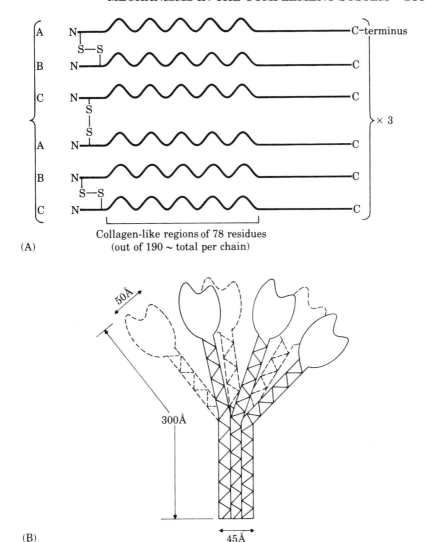

Collagen-like regions of 78 residues
(out of 190 ~ total per chain)

(A)

(B)   45Å

FIGURE 2. Structure of the C1q component of human complement. (A) The molecule consists of 18 chains: 6 A chains, 6 B chains, and 6 C chains, each with an approximate molecular weight of 23,000. Each A chain is disulfide-bonded to a B chain, and each C chain is disulfide-bonded to another C chain. (B) Probable arrangement of the subunits in C1q. Each of the six subunits consists of one A chain, one B chain, and one C chain. Each wavy line designates a triple helix involving one of each of the three chains. The structure of this helix is similar to that found in collagen, and this portion of the molecule can be digested by the enzyme collagenase. The upper portion of

(continued)

Step 2

$$Ag,Ab(C1q,C1r,C1s) \rightarrow Ag,Ab(C1q,\overline{C1r},\overline{C1s})$$

The horizontal bars over C1r and C1s designate activated forms of these components, which can function as proteolytic enzymes. Subsequent to the initial binding reaction (Step 1) C1r, which is a single polypeptide chain, undergoes a conformational change that somehow results in an internal cleavage, which yields two polypeptides that are linked by a disulfide bond. As a result of this internal cleavage, C1r acquires proteolytic activity and cleaves C1s, which is initially a single chain, to form $\overline{C1s}$, which also consists of two disulfide linked chains. The process of cleavage activates C1s, which in turn acquires proteolytic activity (Figure 1).

Step 3

$$Ag,Ab(C1q,\overline{C1r},\overline{C1s}) + C4 \rightarrow C4a + C4b(Ag,Ab)(C1q,\overline{C1r},\overline{C1s})$$

The next step is a cleavage (catalyzed by $\overline{C1s}$) of C4 into two fragments. The smaller fragment (C4a) has a molecular weight of approximately 10,000. The remainder of the C4 molecule (C4b) has a molecular weight of approximately 195,000. It becomes bound to the antigen–antibody complex at a location separate from the site of binding of the C1 components. Any C4b that is not bound to complexes is rapidly inactivated.

Step 4

$$C2 + C4b(AgAb)(C1q,\overline{C1r},\overline{C1s}) \xrightarrow{Mg^{2+}}$$

$$(C2a,C4b,C2b)(AgAb)(C1q,\overline{C1r},\overline{C1s})$$

C2 is cleaved by $\overline{C1s}$, yielding C2a (mol. wt. 80,000) and C2b (mol. wt. 30,000). C2a,C4b has the capacity to cleave C3; the enzymatic site is in the C2a molecule. The C4b binds C3 in such a way as to render

---

FIGURE 2. (continued)
each of the six subunits has a structure characteristic of a globular (non-fibrous) protein. These upper portions are responsible for binding to the $C_\gamma2$ domain of IgG or to the $C_\mu4$ domain of IgM. To initiate the classical pathway, it is necessary that a single C1q molecule bind to more than one immunoglobulin molecule. (The precise minimum number is uncertain.) A single C1q molecule can, under optimal conditions, bind as many as 12 antibody molecules. (After Porter and Reid, 1979.)

it more susceptible to cleavage. The C2a is gradually lost from the complex and is immediately inactivated; it can, however, be replaced by cleavage of additional C2. The C2a,C4b enzyme complex is referred to as C3 CONVERTASE. A single C1q,C$\bar{1}$r,C$\bar{1}$s complex can generate multiple C2a,C4b complexes. This amplification process enables a single C1q, C$\bar{1}$r, C$\bar{1}$s complex to produce numerous openings in the membrane, thereby causing lysis of the cell.

Step 5

C3 + (C2a,C4b,C2b)(AgAb)(C1q,C$\bar{1}$r,C$\bar{1}$s) →
    C3a + (C3b,C2a,C4b,C2b)(AgAb)(C1q,C$\bar{1}$r,C$\bar{1}$s)

The C3 convertase cleaves C3 into C3a (mol. wt. ~9,000) and C3b (180,000). When the larger fragment (C3b) is bound, the complex can initiate the terminal phase of the complement sequence by cleaving C5. The C3b,C2a,C4b unit is called C5 CONVERTASE of the classical pathway. The active catalytic site is in the C2a component.

Step 6

Cleavage of C5; binding of C6, . . . , C9

C5 convertase cleaves C5 into C5a (mol. wt. ~12,000) and C5b (180,000). The remaining components of the sequence are then linked to C5b on the membrane; the complex contains one molecule each of C5b, C6, C7, and C8, and several molecules of C9. This complex induces the formation of channels in the membrane, thus causing osmotic lysis. The C5b–C8 complex can penetrate the membrane partially, but C9 is needed to produce a complete channel. Note that the formation of C5b is the last step in the sequence that requires proteolysis.

THE ALTERNATIVE PATHWAY

The existence of an alternative pathway of complement activation was proposed in 1954 by Louis Pillemer and his colleagues at Western Reserve University. They observed that complement could be activated, without antibody, in the presence of properdin (a serum protein) and zymosan (a crude preparation of yeast cell walls). Varying explanations were proposed by others, and it was not until the late 1960s that the mechanism was firmly established and gained wide acceptance.

The sequence of events in the alternative pathway does not involve antibody or components C1q,r,s, C2, or C4. It provides an alternative method for producing C3b from C3. The C3b in combination with other components can then initiate a lytic event by generating C5b from C5. Of equal significance is the fact that C3b enhances phagocytosis of microorganisms through its interaction with C3b receptors on phagocytic cells.[1] The alternative pathway also yields C3a and C5a, both of which act as ANAPHYLATOXINS; in addition, component C5a has CHEMOTACTIC activity. (Anaphylatoxins and chemotaxis will be discussed later.)

Of major importance is the fact that the alternative pathway can be triggered by many microorganisms in the absence of specific antibody as well as by an antibody-dependent mechanism. Thus, the complement system alone is able to cause lysis or induce phagocytosis of many, although not all, strains of bacteria, as well as certain parasites, viruses, or virus-infected cells. Also, when antibody is present, the alternative pathway can greatly enhance the efficiency of lysis or phagocytosis by supplying increased amounts of C3b.

The alternative pathway is initiated in the absence of antibody by the interaction of four serum proteins: C3, B, D, and properdin (P)(Table 1). Factor B is sometimes called C3 PROACTIVATOR. Factor D is a proteolytic enzyme.

Step 1

$$B + C3 \xrightarrow{Mg^{2+}} C3,B \xrightarrow{D} C3,Bb + Ba$$

Component B, present as a complex with C3, is cleaved by D to yield C3,Bb + Ba. The molecular weights of Bb and Ba are 60,000 and 33,000, respectively. C3,Bb has weak proteolytic activity and slowly digests C3.

Step 2

$$C3 \xrightarrow{C3,Bb} C3b + C3a$$

A small amount of C3b is generated by this reaction, which is catalyzed by C3,Bb and takes place in the fluid phase. The steps that follow produce much larger amounts of C3b, but only if they occur on an appropriate surface, where C3b is protected against the degradation that would otherwise be caused by components H and I (see later). The surfaces of many types of bacteria and of certain parasites and mammalian erythrocytes afford this protection and thus permit functioning

---

[1] For some organisms both antibody and complement are required to induce phagocytosis; others are susceptible in the presence of either antibody or activated complement. The interaction with antibody is mediated by Fc receptors on phagocytic leukocytes.

of the alternative pathway. Such microorganisms and erythrocytes can serve as targets for lysis or phagocytosis. Protection against degradation is also provided by zymosan, which was used in Pillemer's original experiments.

Step 3

$$C3b + B \longrightarrow C3b,B \xrightarrow{D} C3b,Bb + Ba$$

Step 4

$$C3b,Bb + P \rightarrow C3b,Bb,P$$

C3b,Bb is a proteolytic enzyme that cleaves C3. C3b,Bb is much more effective than C3,Bb in catalyzing this reaction. Properdin (P) stabilizes the complex by decreasing the rate at which Bb spontaneously dissociates from C3b.

Step 5

$$C3 \xrightarrow{C3b,Bb,P} C3a + C3b$$

Note that the system exhibits autocatalytic properties. The initial generation of a small amount of C3b in Step 2 permits formation of an effective proteolytic enzyme, C3b,Bb. This enzyme cleaves C3, yielding additional C3b. This system is unusual in that a product of C3 degradation becomes a subunit of the enzyme, C3b,Bb, which cleaves additional C3.

Through these mechanisms, the alternative pathway can operate in the absence of antibody. It can also enhance the activity of the classical pathway, which is initiated by antibody; C3b generated through the classical sequence can participate in the generation of additional C3b by the above autocatalytic process, involving components of the alternative pathway. The pathway that generates additional C3b is known as the AMPLIFICATION LOOP.

An enzyme that effectively cleaves C5 into C5a and C5b is formed from an assemblage of one molecule of Bb and two or more molecules of C3b, in the presence of P, on the surface of the activating particle. The active site of the enzyme is present in the Bb subunit. As in the classical pathway, C5b can initiate a lytic event.

Sketches summarizing the two pathways are shown in Figure 3.

BINDING SPECIFICITY OF C3b

This component is remarkable with respect to the number of different binding specificities it expresses. Substances with which it in-

(A) Classical pathway

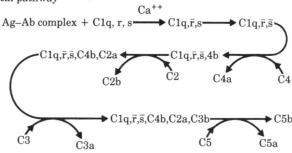

(B) Alternative pathway

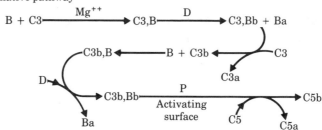

(C) Amplification loop for increasing yield of C3b

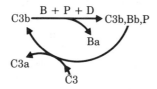

FIGURE 3. Outlines of the classical and alternative pathways for production of C5b and of the amplification loop for increasing the yield of C3b. (A) The classical pathway is initiated when C1q binds to antibody present in an antigen–antibody complex. Most subsequent events take place on the surface of the aggregate. (B) The alternative pathway is initiated by the interaction of later complement components with an appropriate activating surface. Once C5b is formed, it can, by acting in concert with C6, C7, C8, and C9, cause the lysis of RBC or of many gram-negative bacteria. (C) The amplification loop enhances the yield of C3b produced by the classical or alternative pathway.

teracts include cells and microorganisms, with discrimination for activators and nonactivators of the alternative pathway; C3b receptors on phagocytic cells and B cells; factor H; properdin; and factor B. In addition, C3b acts as a substrate for the C3b inactivator, factor I.

C3b undergoes interactions through noncovalent or covalent bonding. When C3 is converted to C3b the thioester group (Figure 4) is exposed and becomes reactive, permitting C3b to combine with the antigen in an antigen–antibody complex. Such complexes can then interact with phagocytic cells, which have receptors for C3b. The latter interaction is mediated by noncovalent bonds.

DIRECT ACTIVATION OF THE ALTERNATIVE PATHWAY BY IMMUNOGLOBULINS

Certain immunoglobulins directly activate the alternative pathway without the participation of C1, C2, or C4. These include guinea pig IgG1, aggregated human IgG4, IgA, or IgE, or F(ab')$_2$ fragments of IgG. None of these immunoglobulins can initiate the classical pathway. The Fab region is probably responsible for activation in each case; in contrast, Fc regions initiate the classical pathway. It is probable that Fab regions of any class are active when aggregated.

REGULATORS OF COMPLEMENT PATHWAYS

Normal serum contains proteins that interfere with certain steps in the complement sequence and thus regulate the overall process. They are designated C1INH (C1 inhibitor); I (formerly called C3b inactivator or C4b inactivator); H (formerly β1H); and S protein.

C1INH

This component regulates the rate of the classical pathway by inhibiting C$\overline{1}$r and C$\overline{1}$s. Thus, it retards the formation of C1s through its effect on C$\overline{1}$r, and reduces the rates of cleavage of C4 and C2 by C$\overline{1}$s.

Factor I

Factor I inactivates C3b, forming iC3b, by removal of a small polypeptide from the α chain (Figure 4). For this to occur the presence of a cofactor is essential. Factor H (Table 1) or a C3b receptor, CR1, present on certain cell surfaces, can act as cofactors for the inactivation reaction. CR1 is a glycoprotein with an approximate molecular weight of 220,000 that is found on erythrocytes, lymphocytes, and various types of phagocytic cells. Since CR1 is bound to cell surfaces it acts as a cofactor for the degradation only of cell-bound C3b.

Factor I can also inactivate C4b by a proteolytic process; this requires the participation of a cofactor, called C4-binding protein, which is present in serum.

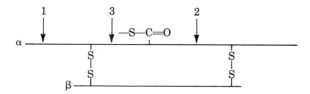

FIGURE 4. Proteolytic degradation of human C3. Cleavage number 1 is carried out by the C3 convertase of the classical or alternative pathway (C4b, 2a, or C3b, Bb, P, respectively). This cleavage generates C3a (mol. wt. 9000 daltons) and C3b (mol. wt. 186,000). Additional proteolysis (cleavage 2) removes a small segment (mol. wt. 3000) from the α chain, inactivating C3b. This cleavage is accomplished by factor I in the presence of a cofactor, which can be factor H or a C3b receptor on cells. The inactivated product is designated iC3b. Cleavage number 3 and a subsequent undefined cleavage of the remaining larger segment (possibly by serum proteolytic enzymes) yields C3e, whose precise structure is not yet known. The —S—C=O structure is a thioester that becomes exposed after cleavage 1 and allows C3b to form covalent bonds with antigen–antibody complexes. The thioester reacts with hydroxyl or amino groups.

Factor H

Factor H interferes with the alternative pathway by several mechanisms. It binds to C3b and inhibits its combination with B; it causes dissociation of the C3b,Bb complex; and, as already discussed, it is a cofactor for the proteolytic inactivation of C3b by factor I.

As mentioned earlier, the susceptibility of C3b to factor I depends on the surface to which C3b is bound. Protective substances include many gram-negative bacteria, zymosan, and rabbit erythrocytes. Sheep erythrocytes, frequently used as an antigen in laboratory experiments, are nonprotective. In general, microorganisms and RBC that bind C3b and that also provide this protection against proteolysis can activate the alternative pathway.

S Protein

This serum protein may interact with the C5b–C9 complex and prevent its uptake by cell membranes, thus protecting the membranes from lysis. At present, its importance is somewhat uncertain.

Properdin

The four regulators listed above all retard the activation of complement. Properdin, in contrast, is a positive regulator whose presence is required for efficient functioning of the alternative pathway.

In the following sections we will consider aspects of the complement system that were not included in the outlines of the classical and alternative pathways.

ROLE OF C3b IN PHAGOCYTOSIS

As indicated above, phagocytic cells—monocytes, macrophages, polymorphonuclear leukocytes—possess membrane receptors that are specific for C3b. Thus, when C3b is bound to antigen–antibody complexes, it mediates binding of the complexes to phagocytic cells and enhances phagocytosis. C3b can also promote phagocytosis of certain bacteria in the absence of antibody.

PRESENCE OF C3b RECEPTORS ON OTHER CELL TYPES

The glomeruli of the kidney possess receptors for C3b that are in part responsible for the uptake of antigen–antibody–complement (Ag-Ab-C) complexes. Such complexes can initiate tissue damage by attracting phagocytic cells, which release lysosomal enzymes that damage surrounding tissue. B lymphocytes also have receptors that bind C3 or C3b. These receptors may possibly play a role in initiating the immune response, by enhancing the avidity of interaction of B cells with Ag-Ab-C complexes.

ANAPHYLATOXINS

C3a and C5a, the smaller fragments released upon proteolysis of C3 and C5, respectively, are not bound to the antigen–antibody complex. These polypeptides can, however, induce dilation and increased permeability of blood vessels and spasmodic contractions of smooth muscle. On the basis of these properties, C3a and C5a are referred to as ANAPHYLATOXINS. These substances affect tissues directly and also cause mast cells and basophilic leukocytes to degranulate, releasing histamine and other mediators of immediate hypersensitivity, which are largely responsible for the symptoms noted. (Histamine is also released as a consequence of interactions of antigens and IgE antibodies on the surface of mast cells or basophils, Chapter 4.)

The anaphylatoxins have other important biological effects, which have been reviewed by Hugli and Müller-Eberhard (1978).

CHEMOTAXIS

In addition to possessing activity as an anaphylatoxin, C5a attracts phagocytic and basophilic leukocytes, which migrate in the direction of higher concentrations of C5a. The effect is known as CHEMOTAXIS.

C5a also causes the membranes of phagocytic cells to become "sticky"; this in turn causes them to deposit in tissues where they may degranulate, releasing enzymes that destroy tissue. A soluble complex containing C6, C7, and inactivated C5b also has some chemotactic activity.

DEGRADATION PRODUCTS OF C3b

Some of the steps involved in the formation and further breakdown of C3b are illustrated in Figure 4. One of the products, C3e, has the important property of mobilizing the release of neutrophils from bone marrow.

A partial list of cell surface receptors for these and other components of complement is presented in Table 2.

TABLE 2. Cell types bearing complement receptors (partial list)[a]

Receptor for	Cell type	Cellular response
C1q	Neutrophil	Respiratory burst
	Monocyte	?
	Null cell	Enhanced ADCC[b]
	B lymphocyte	?
C4a, C3a	Mast cell	Secretion
C3b	Neutrophil	Enhanced phagocytosis; adsorptive endocytosis
	Monocyte/Macrophage	Same as neutrophil
	Eosinophil	Enhanced phagocytosis
	Erythrocyte	Production of C3bi and C3d
	B lymphocyte	?
	T lymphocyte	?
C3e	Neutrophil	Release of neutrophils from bone marrow
C5a	Mast cell	Secretion; leukotriene synthesis?
	Neutrophil	Chemotaxis; increased stickiness; secretion; increased C3b receptor expression
	Monocyte/Macrophage	Chemotaxis; secretion; spreading; leukotriene synthesis?
Factor H	B lymphocyte	Secretion of factor I; mitogenesis
	Monocyte	Respiratory burst
	Neutrophil	?

[a] Adapted from Fearon and Wong (1983)
[b] Antibody-dependent cell-mediated cytotoxicity

INHERITED COMPLEMENT DEFICIENCIES

A congenital deficiency of a complement component is found in a very small percentage of the population. In general, persons with deficiencies of the early components of the classical pathway—C1, C2, or C4—are not exceptionally prone to bacterial infections. A few cases have been reported in which C2 deficiency was accompanied by recurrent infections; however, some of these individuals also had reduced levels of factor B of the alternative pathway. It appears that, in most cases, other elements of the immune system, including the alternative pathway, can provide adequate protection against infections in the absence of a functional classical pathway.

Deficiencies in the early components of complement (most commonly a C2 deficiency) are associated with a high incidence of immune complex diseases in which antigen–antibody complexes are deposited in tissues. It is believed that complement is required for the normal elimination of immune complexes or helps to maintain them in a soluble state.

Deficiencies of components C5, C6, or C8 have also been described in a limited number of cases. The percentage of such individuals with meningococcal or gonococcal (*Neisseria*) infections has been high enough to indicate a causal relationship, which is attributable to impaired bactericidal capacity.

The most striking observation is that most individuals who are deficient in C3 have repeated, serious bacterial infections. The sera of such individuals have a decreased capacity for opsonization of bacteria. These findings strongly support the view that the alternative pathway is a major defense mechanism.

An inherited deficiency of the complement inhibitor C1INH is associated with a serious illness: hereditary angioneurotic edema. Recurrent swelling occurs in various parts of the body, inducing a variety of symptoms. Patients with a hereditary deficiency of factor I—a rare disease—have recurrent bacterial infections because of rapid catabolism of C3, through the amplification loop shown in Figure 3, caused by a high concentration of C3b.

LITERATURE CITED

Bordet, J. (1896). Sur le mode d'action des sérums préventifs. *Annal. Inst. Pasteur 10*, 193.

Fearon, D. T. and Wong, W. W. (1983). Complement ligand-receptor interactions that mediate biological responses. *Annu. Rev. Immunol. 1*, 243.

Hugli, T. E. and Müller-Eberhard, H. J. (1978). Anaphylatoxins: C3a and C5a. *Adv. Immunol. 26*, 1.

Pillemer, L., Blum, L., Lepow, I. H., Ross, O. A., Todd, E. W. and Wardlow, A. C. (1954). The properdin system and immunity: I. Demonstration and isolation of a new serum protein, properdin, and its role in immune phenomena. *Science 120*, 279.

Podak, C. R., Tschoop, J. and Müller-Eberhard, H. J. (1982). Molecular organization of C9 within the membrane attack complex of complement. *J. Exp. Med. 156*, 268.

Porter, R. R. and Reid, K. B. M. (1979). Activation of the complement system by antibody–antigen complexes: the classical pathway. *Adv. Prot. Chem. 33*, 1.

SUGGESTED ADDITIONAL READING

Fearon, D. T. and Austen, K. F. (1977). Activation of the alternate complement pathway due to resistance of zymosan-bound amplification convertase to endogenous regulatory mechanisms. *Proc. Natl. Acad. Sci. USA 74*, 1683.

Fine, D. P. (1981). *Complement and Infectious Diseases*. Boca Raton, FL, CRC Press.

Mayer, M. M. (1973). The complement system. *Sci. Amer. 229*, No. 5, 54.

Müller-Eberhard, H. J. and Schreiber, R. D. (1980). Molecular biology and chemistry of the alternative pathway of complement. *Adv. Immunol. 29*, 2.

Reid, K. B. M. and Porter, R. R. (1981). The proteolytic activation systems of complement. *Ann. Rev. Biochem. 50*, 433.

12

MOLECULES ENCODED BY THE MAJOR HISTOCOMPATIBILITY COMPLEX

OVERVIEW

Glycoprotein molecules encoded by the major histocompatibility complex (MHC) are present on nearly all mammalian cell surfaces and play an important role in the immune response. They are responsible in large part for rejection of tissue transplants and, in general, for allowing discrimination between "self" and "nonself." They are also involved directly in recognition by T cell receptors; they help to determine the repertoire of antigens against which an animal can mount an immune response; and they are associated with susceptibility to certain diseases. The molecules encoded by the MHC can be divided into 3 classes, each of which is associated with particular biological functions. This chapter focuses on the structures of class I and class II human and mouse MHC-encoded molecules, and on the organization of genes within the MHC. Information on these topics has been increasing rapidly since 1980, owing to the application of methods of molecular genetics.

*   *   *

The term "major histocompatibility complex" refers to a linked set of genes located on chromosome 17 in mice and on chromosome 6 in humans. The MHC is also referred to as the HLA (human leukocyte antigen) complex in humans, and it includes the H-2 (H for histocompatibility) and Tla complexes in the mouse. Molecules encoded by these genes play an important role in the immune response. They are present on cell surfaces and are largely responsible for recognition of the foreign nature of tissues transplanted from one individual to another of the same species (hence the term "histocompatibility antigen"). Thus, one person will not accept a skin graft from another unless the

201

donor is an identical twin. Similarly, grafts cannot be exchanged among inbred mice of different strains if the strains differ at the MHC. The genes that encode the antigens recognized as nonself are principally localized in the MHC, although there are other, minor, histocompatibility loci. When lymphocytes from different human individuals, or from genetically different mice, are mixed *in vitro* they proliferate. This is referred to as the MIXED LYMPHOCYTE REACTION, or MLR.

Within an individual animal, molecules encoded by the MHC are intimately involved in recognition of antigens by T cells. For example, cytotoxic T cells (killer cells) can destroy cells infected by a virus. In doing so a receptor on the T cell must interact with an epitope on the virus and, at the same time, with a product of the MHC localized on the surface of the cell that is to be destroyed. It has not been established whether there are two separate types of receptor on the T cell—one for the viral epitope and one for the MHC-encoded protein—or whether a single receptor on the T cell recognizes a single epitope to which structures from the virus and the MHC product both contribute. Current evidence favors the latter hypothesis; this would imply that the MHC-encoded antigen must be in intimate contact with the viral antigen. Products of the MHC are also directly involved in the activity of helper T cells; again, the receptor on the helper T cell recognizes a foreign antigen in association with an MHC product. The foreign antigen and the MHC product are brought into contact with the helper T cell by an "antigen-presenting" cell, such as a macrophage.

The MHC is also associated with immunological responsiveness. Inbred strains of mice, or individual humans, vary with respect to their capacity to respond to certain antigens. The immune response or "Ir" genes that are responsible have been localized to the MHC. In addition, the probability of contracting certain diseases is associated with the presence of particular genes in the MHC. Although the same set of genes that controls immune responsiveness is also associated with susceptibility to those diseases, it has not been proved that the two phenomena are directly related. A partial list of human diseases that correlate to varying degrees with the presence of particular genes in the MHC is shown in Table 1.

CLASSES OF MOLECULES ENCODED BY THE MHC

Products of the MHC are divided into three major classes, designated I, II, and III. Class I antigens are the molecules that, together with the viral antigen, are recognized by cytotoxic T cells that kill virus-infected cells. They are also the histocompatibility antigens that are the principal targets of leukocytes or antibodies during graft re-

TABLE 1. Association of diseases with human HLA antigens (partial list).

Disease	Population	Antigen	Relative risk[a]
Multiple sclerosis	Caucasian	DR2	4.8
Multiple sclerosis	Arab	DR2	13
Pernicious anemia	Caucasian	DR2	3.3
Tuberculoid leprosy	Caucasian	DR2	8.1
Autoimmune thyroiditis	Caucasian	DR3	3.4
Type I diabetes	Caucasian	DR3	5.7
Type I diabetes	Japanese	Dw3	29
Rheumatoid arthritis	Caucasian	DR4	6.0
Myasthenia gravis	Caucasian	HLA-B8	4.4
Dermatitis herpetiformis	Caucasian	DR3	56
Ankylosing spondylitis	Caucasian	HLA-B27	90
Reiter's syndrome	Caucasian	HLA-B27	36

[a] The term relative risk refers to the relative probability that individuals possessing or lacking the gene in question will acquire the disease.

jection. The ability to respond to certain antigens, and the association with susceptibility to certain diseases, are associated with molecules of class II. Class II molecules also induce the mixed lymphocyte reaction and are the structures, in conjunction with antigen, recognized by helper T cells. Class III molecules comprise some of the components of the complement system. The molecules are not involved in T cell recognition, and are designated as products of the MHC simply because the genes controlling them are located physically within the boundaries of the MHC.

Molecules of class I are found on the surface of virtually all nucleated cells in the body. Class II molecules are much more restricted in their distribution. They are most abundant on B cells, activated T cells, monocytes, macrophages, and certain other phagocytic cells; i.e., molecules of class II are found principally on cells that are active in the immune response.

Within an animal species there are multiple alleles at each locus controlling class I and class II molecules. Since there are multiple loci, and many alleles associated with each locus, the potential for variation among individuals is very large. In the case of inbred mice, each strain has a characteristic set of histocompatibility antigens. There are, however, groups of strains that share the same set of alleles (Table 2). In addition, laboratory strains of mice have been bred that differ from

TABLE 2. *H-2* types of various strains of mice.

Prototype strain	Other strains (partial list)	*H-2* haplotype	Subregion				
			K	A	E	S[b]	D
A	A/He, A/Sn, A/Wy, AL/N, B10.A[a]	a	k	k	k	d	d
C57BL/10	C57BL/6, C57L, DW/J	b	b	b	b	b	b
DBA/2	BALB/c, NZB, SEA/GnJ, SEC/1Gn	d	d	d	d	d	d
CBA	AKR, CE, C3H/He, C3H/St., C57BR, RF/J, 101	k	k	k	k	k	k
DBA/1	AU/SsJ, SWR/J	q	q	q	q	q	q
	A.TL[c]	t1	s	k	k	k	d
	B10.A(3R)[c]	i3	b	b	k	d	d

[a] B10.A is a congenic strain in which the *H-2* locus of strain A is present on a C57BL/10 background.

[b] The *S* locus encodes class III molecules (components of complement).

[c] Note tne multiple alleles represented in the subregions of A.TL and B10.A(3R). These resulted from crossovers in laboratory breeding studies. Such strains are very useful for inducing antibodies directed against the product of a single locus or a small number of loci.

one another at the MHC but are otherwise identical. Such a pair of strains, differing only at one genetic locus, is referred to as a CONGENIC PAIR.

A detailed discussion of the genetics of the MHC is beyond the scope of this book. Useful references are Klein (1975), Dorf (1981), and Volume 66 of *Immunological Reviews* (1982).

SEROLOGICAL ANALYSIS

Histocompatibility antigens were discovered through tissue grafting experiments but have been investigated in greater detail by serological methods; i.e., with antibodies that react with cell-surface antigens encoded by the MHC or by means of the mixed lymphocyte reaction. The production of antibodies specific for individual histocompatibility antigens (monospecific antibodies) has engaged many laboratories, starting with the discovery of these antigens by P. A. Gorer in 1936. In mice, the work has been simplified by the existence of inbred strains. If one inoculates mice of one strain with cells from another that differs at the MHC, antibodies will be produced against

MHC products. Antibodies will also be produced, however, against other cell-surface antigens that differ in the two strains. The problem was simplified although not completely solved by the production of congenic strains that differ from one another only at the MHC. Such strains are developed by crossing, say, strain A with strain B, where A and B differ genetically at the MHC. The F_1 offspring are backcrossed to strain B. Those offspring of the backcross that express MHC products characteristic of A are selected and backcrossed again to B. This process is repeated many times, selecting at each generation offspring that express the MHC of strain A and backcrossing them to B. Eventually, congenic mice are produced that have the MHC genes of strain A (and other genes of strain A that are closely linked to the MHC) but whose other genes are derived from strain B. Pairs of congenic mice are then mated to produce offspring that are homozygous for the MHC of A and for genes of strain B at all other loci. If cells, such as leukocytes, from such congenic mice are inoculated into mice of strain B, the antibodies formed will be directed almost exclusively against MHC products of strain A.

Unfortunately, even these antibodies will not be monospecific because there are multiple loci within the MHC. The process has been further refined by developing strains of mice that differ from the parental strain at only one or two loci within the MHC. This is done by breeding studies, using MHC-congenic mice, in which one searches for crossovers within the MHC itself. Since the frequency of such crossovers is low, particularly for two adjacent loci, the production of mice differing at only one locus is a tedious process. Nevertheless, many such pairs of strains have been developed and are generally available. They have been very useful for the production of antibodies directed against individual histocompatibility antigens.

In humans, antibodies used for serological analysis can be obtained from the sera of women who have been pregnant several times and have developed antibodies against paternal antigens present on cells of the fetus. Ocassionally such sera contain antibodies against one or a small number of MHC products.

A major improvement in the production of antisera used for typing histocompatibility antigens has occurred with the advent of monoclonal antibodies. Such antibodies are gradually replacing conventional (polyclonal) antibodies and are being used almost exclusively for antigens encoded by certain recently discovered loci in the MHC, such as the *DC* locus that encodes class II antigens in humans (see below).

An alternative method that is widely used for studying human histocompatibility antigens of class II is the LYMPHOCYTE PROLIFERA-

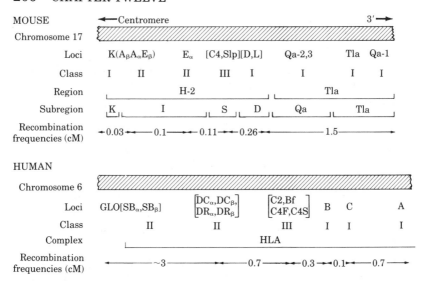

FIGURE 1. Arrangement of genes in the MHC, on chromosome 17 of the mouse or chromosome 6 of humans (Hood et al., 1983). Recombination frequencies among the loci are given in centimorgans (cM). Note that in the mouse MHC the E_β gene is closely linked to A_β and A_α, rather than to E_α. Also, in the mouse MHC (but not in the human MHC or in that of several other species studied), the class I loci are separated into two segments. A class I molecule also contains a β_2-microglobulin chain, which is encoded on chromosome 2 of the mouse and on human chromosome 15. The class III molecules are members of the complement system. The *GLO* locus in humans encodes an enzyme, glyoxylase, which is not part of the MHC but which serves as a marker for the location of the MHC. It is estimated that the length of the mouse MHC is between 2×10^6 and 5×10^6 base pairs; the I region is about 2×10^5 base pairs in length.

TION TEST (mixed lymphocyte reaction). Lymphocytes from two individuals who differ with respect to class II antigens of the MHC will proliferate when mixed *in vitro*. Proliferation can be quantified by measuring the uptake of labeled thymidine or by other methods. This property has been used for classifying many human class II antigens. Details of the methodology are given by van Rood et al. (1981).

GENETIC MAP OF THE MOUSE MHC

Figure 1 shows a genetic map of the mouse MHC. Note that the genes encoding class I molecules are not contiguous. As indicated in the figure, this contrasts with the human MHC, and with the MHC of several other species that have been studied, in which the class I genes are in a single cluster; the separation in the mouse probably reflects a series of recombination events during evolution. Each class I or class II gene encodes a glycosylated polypeptide (a histocompatibility antigen) that is embedded in the cell surface membrane. These polypeptide antigens have been extensively investigated by serological methods, and multiple alleles of class I and class II molecules have been identified. Table 2 presents a partial list of alleles associated with various strains of inbred mice. The list is greatly abbreviated; there are, for example, over 50 known alleles of K and D molecules. Also absent from the list are many congenic strains of mice, artificially bred so as to differ from another strain only at the MHC, or with respect to a part of the MHC.

There are multiple genes at some of the individual loci designated in Figure 1, as shown by studies of mouse, human and pig DNA. The most detailed investigations have been carried out with BALB/c (H-2^d) mice. A total of 36 class I genes, spread out over 840,000 base pairs (840 kb pairs) of DNA, were identified on chromosome 17 (Steinmetz et al., 1982). Five of the genes are present in the K, D or L regions ($2K$, $2L$ and $1D$). Whether both K and both L genes are functional is not yet known. (We know from serological tests that at least one K and one L gene are active.) The remaining 31 genes were localized in the Qa-$2,3$ or Tla regions (Figure 1). One cluster in the Qa-$2,3$ region occupies about 190 kb pairs and contains 7 genes. For many of these 36 genes, it is not yet known whether the corresponding polypeptide is actually expressed. We also do not yet know whether other strains differ significantly from BALB/c with respect to the organization of their class I genes. Research in this area is very active, and answers to these questions should soon be available. One interstrain difference that is already apparent is the absence of L genes from mice of the C57BL (H-2^b) and AKR (H-2^k) strains.

PROPERTIES OF MOUSE CLASS I MOLECULES

Class I molecules in the mouse are glycoproteins designated K, D, L, Qa and Tla. The subregion of the MHC that stretches from K to L in Figure 1 is called the H-2 complex; the subregion that includes the Qa and Tla genes is designated Tla. The K, D and L antigens are present on nearly all cells of the mouse and are responsible in large part for graft rejection. The Tla antigens are present on thymus cells, and on leukemic cells in some but not all types of mouse leukemia. The Qa antigens are found in the spleen and lymph nodes as well as the thymus. Both Tla and Qa molecules are present on multipotential stem cells. Thus, the Qa and Tla antigens are restricted to lymphoid and hematopoetic cells. They are designated class I molecules because of their close similarity in structure to the K, D and L proteins. All of the class I molecules probably arose from a common precursor during evolution. The K, D and L antigens show much greater inter-strain variation (polymorphism) than the Qa and Tla antigens; i.e., there are many fewer alleles of *Tla* and *Qa* genes then of *K, D* and *L*. The genetics of the *Tla* region has been reviewed by Flaherty (1981).

A class I molecule consists of two polypeptide chains (mol. wt. 44,000 and 12,000 daltons) linked by noncovalent bonds. The larger, 44K, chain contains approximately 350 amino acid residues, the smaller 99. Only the larger chain is encoded in the MHC (on chromosome 17). The gene for the smaller polypeptide, which is designated β_2-microglobulin or β_2M, is on mouse chromosome 2. The 44K chain is highly polymorphic and accounts for the antigenic differences of class I molecules among strains. Nevertheless, the various 44K chains exhibit substantial homology of amino acid sequence to one another and are probably very similar in their three-dimensional structures. All have the capacity to combine noncovalently with β_2M. β_2M is invariant within a strain and exhibits very minor interstrain variation.

STRUCTURE OF β_2M

The amino acid sequence of β_2M from four species is shown in Figure 2. As indicated in the figure, β_2M from the BALB/c (H-2^d) and C57BL (H-2^b) strains of mice differ only at position 85, where BALB/c has aspartic acid and C57BL has an alanine group. Each of the molecules contains 99 amino acid residues and lacks carbohydrate. There is considerable evidence suggesting that β_2M and the immunoglobulins had a common evolutionary ancestor. For example, the length of the β_2M chain is similar to that of a single immunoglobulin domain. Also, β_2M has an intrachain disulfide bond joining half-cystine residues at positions 25 and 80. (In the mouse V_κ domain a disulfide bond joins positions 23 and 88.) Finally, there is a significant degree of amino acid sequence homology (as high as 30%) between mouse β_2M and individual domains of constant regions of various immunoglobulins.

Figure 2 also presents the amino acid sequences of guinea pig, rabbit and human β_2M. There is a substantial degree of homology, exceeding 55%, between any pair of sequences. All four polypeptides have the same length and a disulfide bond linking positions 25 and 80.

```
                     10              20                30
Mouse       I Q K T P Q I Q V Y S R H P P E N G K P N I L N C Y V T Q F H P P H I

Guinea Pig  V L H A   R V ——————————— A ——————— Q — F I ——————— S G ——————— Q —

Rabbit      V — R A — N V ——————————— A ——————————— F ——————————— S G ——————— Q —

Human       —— R —— K ——————————————— A ——————— S — F ——————————— S G —————— S D —


                     40              50                60              70
Mouse       E I Q M L K N G K K I P K V E M S D M S F S K D W S F Y I L A H T E F

Guinea Pig  — V E L ——————————————— D N ——————————— L ——————————— T — L — V — A A —

Rabbit      D — E L ——————— V — E N — Q — L —————— N ——————————— L — V —————————

Human       — V D L ——————— E R — E —————— H — L ——————————————— L — Y Y —————————


                     80                90               99
Mouse       T P T E T D T Y A C R V K H A S M A E P K T V Y W D R D M
                                        D
Guinea Pig  —— N D S — E — S ——————— S — I T L S ————— I — K —— P N K

Rabbit      ——— N N K N E — S ——————————— V T K L — M — K ——————— Y

Human       ———————— K — E ——————————— N — V T L S Q —— I — K ———————
```

FIGURE 2. Sequences of β_2-microglobulin from four species. Solid lines represent identities with the uppermost (mouse) sequence. The alternative sequences for the mouse protein at position 85 represent two strains of mice: C57BL, which has alanine, and BALB/c, which has aspartic acid at that position. A disulfide bond is formed between the half-cystine groups at positions 25 and 80. The single letter code and references are in Appendices I and III, respectively.

PRIMARY STRUCTURE OF THE 44K CHAIN OF MOUSE CLASS I MOLECULES

Information on the primary structure (amino acid sequence) of these molecules has been obtained by sequencing either the protein or the corresponding DNA. Sequences have thus far been worked out for only a few of the extremely large variety of class I molecules. Nevertheless many important general structural features are now evident.

Investigations of a class I molecule from C57BL mice (H-2K^{b}) led to the conclusion that the 44K chain consists of 5 domains, as shown in Figure 3 (Coligan et al., 1981). The two carbohydrate side chains and β_2M are also indicated in the figure. Three of the domains, labeled α1, α2 and α3, protrude from the membrane of the cell surface in which the molecule is embedded; the N-terminus of the chain is in the

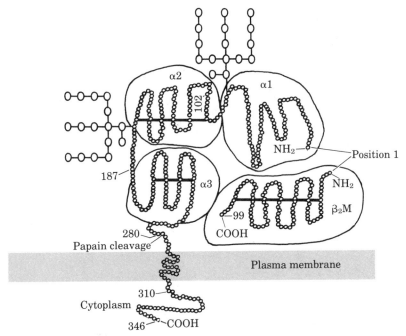

FIGURE 3. A schematic representation of the primary structure of the mouse H-2K^b, class I transplantation antigen (slightly modified from Coligan et al., 1981). Each bead represents one amino acid. (The sequence is given in Figure 4.) Solid bars represent intrachain disulfide bonds and open ellipses are carbohydrate groups. The evidence that β_2M makes contact only with the α3 domain is not yet conclusive. Note that papain cleaves the molecule just above the transmembrane region; β_2M is not affected by the enzyme. There are 346 amino acid residues in the heavy (44K) chain and 99 in β_2M.

α1 domain. These three domains are cleaved from the rest of the molecule as a single unit when cells are treated with papain, a proteolytic enzyme. The fourth domain, labeled TM for transmembrane, comprises approximately 25 amino acid residues and is embedded in the membrane, a fact consistent with the presence of many hydrophobic amino acids in the domain (which makes it compatible with the hydrophobic lipid membrane). Immediately following the membrane-binding stretch of amino acids are several basic amino acids (lysine and arginine groups). These may help to anchor the chain through interactions with the negatively charged phosopholipids present in the membrane. The fifth, C-terminal segment (CYT, ≈38 residues) extends into the cytoplasm where it may serve to communicate signals received from the exterior of the cell. Since the first three domains protrude from the cell surface, the antigenic variability associated with recognition by antibodies or T cells would be expected to be associated with that region of the molecule, and considerable evidence supports this conclusion. In Figure 3, β_2M is shown as making contact with the α3 domain. This is based on studies of binding of β_2M to peptide fragments from various regions of the 44K polypeptide chain. β_2M is evidently not linked directly to the cell membrane.

As already mentioned, β_2M shows significant homology of amino acid sequence with the immunoglobulins. It is of interest that the sequence of the α3 domain, which interacts with β_2M, also exhibits weak but significant homology with β_2M and with immunoglobulins. Furthermore, α3 has a length of about 90 amino acid residues and an intrachain disulfide bond, both characteristic of an immunoglobulin domain. The possibility of a common ancestry of the α3 domain, β_2M, and immunoglobulins is suggested. Although the α2 domain is similar to α3 in size, and in its possession of an intrachain disulfide bond, its amino acid sequence is not demonstrably related to sequences of β_2M or immunoglobulins.

Although there are similarities between class I molecules and immunoglobulins, major differences also exist. For example, there is no evidence for a rearrangement of gene segments comparable to the V–C joining that occurs in immunoglobulin genes, or for any substantial amount of somatic mutation. There is extensive polymorphism of K and D antigens among strains, but the structure of a given gene product within a strain shows little variability, although mutations do occur at a low frequency.

AMINO ACID SEQUENCES OF 44K CHAINS OF CLASS I MOLECULES

Figure 4 shows the complete amino acid sequence of a mouse H-2K^b, 44K polypeptide, and partial sequences for H-2D^b and H-2K^d chains. Also shown in the figure is the almost complete sequence of a human class I antigen, designated HLA-B7, and partial sequences of HLA-A2 and HLA-A28 chains. The degree of sequence homology among these sequences is summarized in Table 3.

For the allelic gene products H-2K^b and H-2K^d, the degree of homology is 76%. As compared to many other proteins that are encoded by allelic genes this extent of homology is quite low; it indicates a rapid evolution of the H-2K antigens. Another point that emerges from these and other data is that the mouse H-2K antigens are no more closely related to one another than they are to D antigens (and

```
            10        20        30        40        50        60        70
            |         |         |         |         |         |         |
H-2Kᵇ   GPHSLRYFVTAVSRPGLGEPRYMEVGYVDDTEFVRFDSDAENPRYEPRARWMEQEGPEYWERETQKAKGN

H-2Dᵇ   ____M_E_____E__IS____NK_____P_____Q

H-2Kᵈ   _____FIA_____Q_____D_A_F____P_____EQ_RV_SQ

HLA-B7  _S_M__Y_S____R___FIS_____Q_____AS_E___P_I_____D_N__IY_AQ

HLA-A2  _S_M__F_S____R___FIA_____Q_____ASQ_M___P_I_____D___V_AH

HLA-A28 _S_M__Y_S____R___FIA_____Q_____ASQ_M___P_I_____D_N_RNV_AQ


            80        90        100       110       120       130       140
            |         |         |         |         |         |         |
H-2Kᵇ   EQSFRVDLRTLLGYYNQSKGGSHTIQVISGCEVGSDGRLLRGYQQYAYDGCDYIALNEDLKTWTAADMAA

H-2Dᵇ   __W__S_N____A____L_QM___

H-2Kᵈ   __W__ST_AQR_____F_RMF___

HLA-B7  A_TD_ES__N_R____EA___L_SMY_D_P_____HD_____K_____RS____T_

HLA-A2  AHTV____G_R_____EA___L_RMY_                         __

HLA-A28 S_TD___G_R_____EA_____MY_D_____F__R_D____K____K___S_____ _


            150       160       170       180       190       200       210
            |         |         |         |         |         |         |
H-2Kᵇ   LITKHHKWEQAGEAERLRAYLEGTCVEWLRRYLKNGNATLLRTDSPKAHVTHHSRPDDKVTLRCWALGFYP

HLA-B7  Q__QR__A_R__QR_____E_____E_KDK_E_A_P_T_____PIS_HEA_____

HLA-A2  T_____A_HV__Q_____E__E_Q__A_T_H__AVS_HEA_____

HLA-A28 QT_____AAHV____ _____ _E__KE_Q__A____ __AVS_HEA_____


            220       230       240       250       260       270       280
            |         |         |         |         |         |         |
H-2Kᵇ   ADITLTWQLNGEELIQDMELVETRPAGDGTFQKWASVVVPLGKEQYYTCHVYQQGLPQPLTLRWDEPPST

HLA-B7  _E_____RD__DQT_T_____R_E__A___S_E__R_____QHE__K_____EPSSQS

HLA-A2  _E_____RD__DQT_T_____E__A___S_Q__R_____QHE__K_

HLA-A28 _E_____D__DQT_T_____VA___S_Q__R_____QHE__K_


            290       300       310       320       330       340
            |         |         |         |         |         |
H-2Kᵇ   VSNMATVAVLVVLGAAIVTGAVVAFVMKMRRRATGGKGGDYALAPGSQTSDLSLPDCKVMVHPPHS

HLA-B7  TVP_VG_VAG_AV__VV_____A__C___KSS_____S_SQ_AC_DSAQG_DVSLTA

HLA-A2                          W___KSSDR___S_SQ_AS_DSAZG_DVSLTA
```

FIGURE 4. Amino acid sequences (partial or complete) of the 44K chain of three mouse (H-2) and three human (HLA) class I histocompatibility antigens. All of the data were obtained by sequencing the proteins rather than the corresponding DNA. Solid lines represent identity with the H-2K^b sequence. Blank spaces are undetermined amino acids. The domain structures in the mouse and human proteins, deduced from the sequences, are very similar. Note that up to position 340, no artificial insertions or deletions are needed to maintain the homology between mouse and human sequences. Intrachain disulfide bonds are formed between half-cystines at positions 101 and 164 in the α2 domain, and 203 and 259 in the α3 domain of mouse and human 44K chains. References for the sequences are in Appendix III.

vice versa). For example, the degree of sequence homology between H-2K^b and H-2D^b is 84% (Table 3). Hood et al. (1983) propose that this lack of "K-ness" or "D-ness" suggests that "there is a rapid exchange of information between K and D genes so that they fail to evolve independent characteristics." One mechanism that could permit such exchange of information is gene conversion, which is well established in yeast (Baltimore, 1981). That gene conversion has played a role in the evolution of class I sequences has been suggested by other investigators on the basis of comparisons of structures of various human HLA antigens, or of spontaneously arising mutants of mouse H-2 antigens. Some of these mutants have altered sequences resembling those of nearby genes. An alternative mechanism would involve a high frequency of crossovers at nonhomologous positions (unequal crossovers).

TABLE 3. Percentage of homology among pairs of amino acid sequences of class I 44K chains.[a]

	H-2D^b	H-2K^d	HLA-B7	HLA-A2	HLA-A28
H-2K^b	84	76	65	67	74
H-2D^b		75	73	69	68
H-2K^d			69	69	71
HLA-B7				86	86
HLA-A2					95

[a] The sequences (partial or complete) that are compared are those in Figure 4. Designations H-2 and HLA apply to mouse and human class I sequences, respectively.

It is evident that there is a great deal of homology among mouse and human proteins which, however, decreases markedly after position 275, a region that includes the transmembrane segment of the protein (residues 282-308) and the cytoplasmic region (309 to the C-terminus). In contrast, the high degree of homology among human class I antigens includes the cytoplasmic region.

There are numerous positions in the amino acid sequence that are relatively invariant: 68 of the first 98 positions are the same in the 3 mouse sequences, and 55 of these 68 positions are also identical in the 2 human proteins. These invariant amino acids may be vital to the structural integrity of the molecule. Many of the sequence differences up to position 98 of the two mouse H-2K proteins are located between position 62 and 83 in the N-terminal, α1 domain, suggesting that this region plays a role in determining antigenic variability. By analogy with sequences of human class I antigens, it would be predicted that other regions of variability will be found when additional data are accumulated on the mouse proteins. One report indicates that cytotoxic T lymphocytes (CTL) recognize determinants in the mouse α2 and α3 domains. An important recognition site for CTL on human HLA antigens has been localized to the α2 domain.

ORGANIZATION OF EXONS AND INTRONS IN GENES ENCODING MOUSE CLASS I HISTOCOMPATIBILITY ANTIGENS

Figure 5 shows the organization of a gene that encodes a single mouse class I 44K chain. Also represented are the genes for β2M and for 2 class II polypeptides (which will be discussed later). The black rectangles represent exons, the white spaces between them introns, and the hatched rectangles 3′ untranslated regions. The latter regions are transcribed into mRNA but are not translated into polypeptide. Note that both the β2M and the 44K genes have a short leader sequence (L) encoding a polypeptide segment that is cleaved from the molecule before its incorporation into the membrane. (Leader sequences are also present in the immunoglobulins; Chapter 6.) The α1, α2, and α3 segments of the 44K chain are encoded by separate exons. This strongly reinforces the conclusion, derived earlier from amino acid sequencing and studies of proteolytic cleavage, that α1, α2, and α3 should be considered separate domains (Figure 3). Although X-ray crystallographic data are not yet available, one would predict that the domain structure will be apparent in the three-dimensional structure, as it is in the immunoglobulins (Chapter 5). After α1, α2, and α3 the next exon encodes the hydrophobic domain (TM) that spans the cell

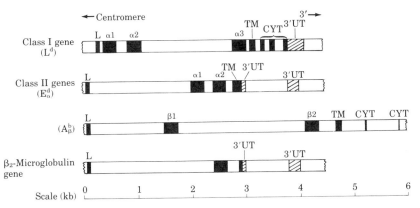

FIGURE 5. Diagram showing the arrangement of exons (dark areas) and introns (white spaces between the dark areas) in a mouse class I gene, two class II genes, and β_2M. The abbreviation 3'UT (hatched areas) refers to a region that is transcribed into RNA, is not translated into polypeptide, but remains in the mRNA after the splicing that removes introns. Other abbreviations: L, leader sequence (removed from the final polypeptide by enzymatic cleavage); TM, transmembrane sequence; CYT, portion of the sequence that is present in the cytoplasm. Note that separate domains in the protein are in general encoded by one or more separate exons. However, for E_α^d the exon labeled TM also includes the cytoplasmic region. The data used for the A_β^b structure are from Larhammar et al. (1983). Other structures are from Hood et al. (1983).

membrane, and the last 3 exons encode the single cytoplasmic domain. The β_2M gene comprises 2 exons in addition to that which controls the leader sequence.

HUMAN CLASS I HISTOCOMPATIBILITY ANTIGENS

The heavy chains of these molecules are encoded by loci designated *HLA–A, HLA–B,* and *HLA–C* (Figure 1). As already noted, the class I genes are in a single cluster in the human genome, in contrast with those of the mouse. Whether each *HLA* locus comprises a single gene or, as in the mouse, more than one gene, is not yet established, but this should be clarified in the near future. Table 4 shows a partial list of alleles of human histocompatibility antigens that have been identified by serological testing, using antibodies or mixed lymphocyte reactions.

As in the mouse, a human class I molecule is made up of two polypeptide chains: a 44K chain (the heavy chain) and β_2M. The

TABLE 4. Specificities of human HLA antigens.[a]

Class I

HLA-A	A1, A2, A3, A9[b], A10, A11, Aw19[c], Aw23, Aw24, A25, A26, A28, A29, Aw30, Aw31, Aw32, Aw33, Aw34, Aw36, Aw43.
HLA-B	Bw4, Bw6, B5, B7, B8, B12, B13, B14, B15, Bw16, B17, B18, Bw21, Bw22, B27, Bw35, B37, Bw38, Bw39, B40, Bw41, Bw42, Bw44, Bw45, Bw46, Bw47, Bw48, Bw49, Bw50, Bw51, Bw52, Bw53, Bw54.
HLA-C	Cw1, Cw2, Cw3, Cw4, Cw5, Cw6, Cw7, Cw8.

Class II

HLA-D[d]	Dw1, Dw2, Dw3, Dw4, Dw5, Dw6, Dw7, Dw8, Dw9, Dw10, Dw11, Dw12.
HLA-DR	DR1, DR2, DR3, DR4, DR5, DRw6, DR7, DRw8, DRw9, DRw10, DRw13.
HLA-DC	DC1, DC2, DC3.
HLA-SB	SB1, SB2, SB3, SB4, SB5.

---

[a] Adapted from van Rood et al. (1981).

[b] Specificity A9 has been split into Aw23 plus Aw24; and A10 into A25 and A26. Bw4 and Bw6 each include several other specificities listed under HLA-B.

[c] The letter "w" signifies that the specificity has been reported at a workshop but that an antibody that identifies the specificity is not generally available.

[d] Specificities at the *D* and *SB* loci were identified by mixed lymphocyte reactions. More recently, anti-SB antibodies have also been used. Many or all of the D specificities may be present on the same molecules that express known DR specificities; i.e., they may be controlled by the *DR* locus. The DR specificities are identified with antibodies, as are the DC and the class I specificities.

sequence of $\beta_2 M$ is shown in Figure 2. The two polypeptides are encoded on human chromosomes 6 and 15, respectively. Whereas the mouse class I 44K chains studied so far are glycosylated at 2 positions, 86 and 176, the human class I antigens that have been investigated have a single carbohydrate group, at position 86. The degree of sequence homology of the 44K chains from mouse and human is indicated in Table 3. A comparison of the sequences in Figure 4 indicates that the two molecules encoded by the *HLA–A* locus, HLA-A28 and HLA-A2, show 95% homology (Table 3). The degree of homology between each of the two *HLA–A* products and HLA-B7 is 86%. The differences that do exist occur mainly between positions 43 and 195, and are clustered between residues 65–80, 106–116, and 117–194 in the α1 and α2 domains. As we have seen, the more limited data for the mouse indicate that positions 62–83 constitute one region of variability. It seems very probable that these variable regions contribute to the epitopes on the surface of the molecule that are responsible for the antigenic variability of class I histocompatibility antigens.

STRUCTURE OF MOUSE CLASS II HISTOCOMPATIBILITY ANTIGENS

Class II molecules are glycoproteins encoded by genes in the I-A and I-E subregions of the mouse MHC (Figure 1). Genes in the I region are also called IMMUNE RESPONSE GENES, or Ir genes, because they determine the ability of an animal to respond to certain antigens. Each class II molecule consists of 2 chains, designated α and β, which are held together by noncovalent bonds.[1] A class II molecule has the structure $A_\alpha A_\beta$ or $E_\alpha E_\beta$. It is of interest that the E_β gene is localized in the I-A rather than the I-E subregion. All strains studied so far express I-A; some strains, however (H-2 alleles b, f, q, and s), do not produce I-E molecules.

The α and β subunits have molecular weights of 34,000 $\pm$1000 and 29,000 $\pm$1000, respectively. Although the two polypeptide chains do not exhibit substantial homology of amino acid sequence, they are very similar in size and structural organization. The difference in molecular weight is largely attributable to a difference in carbohydrate content; the α chain has two attached carbohydrate groups and the β chain only one.

In their general structural organization, the class II polypeptides resemble the 44K chain of mouse class I, with a major exception: the class II molecules have only two external domains (domains situated outside the cell membrane) rather than three. Both classes have transmembrane and cytoplasmic domains, and the corresponding domains are similar in size in the two classes. Note, however, that a class II molecule has two transmembrane and two cytoplasmic segments, as compared to one in a class I molecule.

Amino acid sequence analyses and studies by serological methods (using mixed lymphocyte reactions or antibodies specific for the products of various alleles) have indicated that the β chains of I-A and I-E molecules are more polymorphic (i.e., exhibit more variation among strains) than the α chains. However, the α chains also exhibit significant variability; some of the relevant amino acid sequence data will be presented below.

Figure 6 shows a schematic diagram of a mouse class II molecule

---

[1] Class II molecules present in the cytoplasm of mouse and human cells also contain a third polypeptide chain (mol. wt. $\approx$33,000) which appears invariant but has not yet been well characterized. The invariant chain is removed from the molecule before it is finally embedded in the membrane.

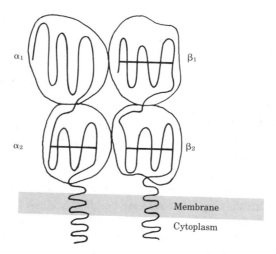

FIGURE 6. Sketch of the probable arrangement of domains in a mouse or human class II molecule. Note that each chain has 2 external domains as well as a transmembrane and a cytoplasmic domain. The solid bars represent intrachain disulfide bonds (locations inexact).

and its possible orientation with respect to the cell membrane. The proposed arrangement of the domains ($\alpha 1$, $\alpha 2$, etc.) is not firmly established but is supported by indirect evidence. Three of the 4 domains that are external to the cell—$\alpha 2$, $\beta 1$ and $\beta 2$—have intrachain disulfide bonds similar to those in immunoglobulins. Since each external domain contains about 90–95 amino acid residues, a resemblance to immunoglobulin domains and to $\beta_2 M$ is evident. The transmembrane and cytoplasmic regions contain about 30 and 15 residues, respectively.

Amino acid sequences of a number of mouse class II molecules have been obtained by sequencing either DNA that is isolated from cells and then cloned ("genomic DNA") or cDNA (which is complementary to mRNA and is produced enzymatically). Sequencing of DNA is far more rapid and efficient than the earlier methods, which required isolation and sequencing of the corresponding polypeptides. As a consequence, new data are accumulating rapidly. The following generalizations can be made from the published sequences. (The sequences of A_α^k and E_α^k are shown in Figure 7.)

1. There is very little sequence homology between α and β subunits.

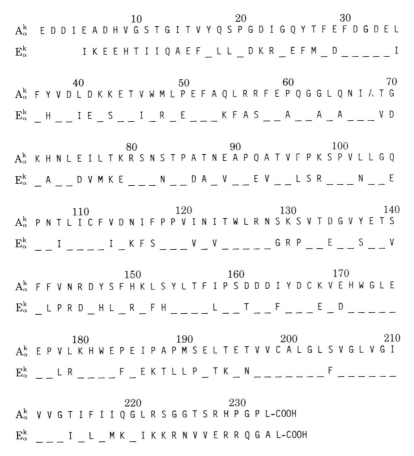

$$
\begin{array}{l}
\quad\quad\quad\quad\quad 10\quad\quad\quad\quad\quad\quad\quad 20\quad\quad\quad\quad\quad\quad\quad 30\\
A_\alpha^k\quad E\ D\ D\ I\ E\ A\ D\ H\ V\ G\ S\ T\ G\ I\ T\ V\ Y\ Q\ S\ P\ G\ D\ I\ G\ Q\ Y\ T\ F\ E\ F\ D\ G\ D\ E\ L\\[4pt]
E_\alpha^k\quad\quad\quad I\ K\ E\ E\ H\ T\ I\ I\ Q\ A\ E\ F\ \_\ L\ L\ \_\ D\ K\ R\ \_\ E\ F\ M\ \_\ D\ \_\ \_\ \_\ \_\ \_\ I
\end{array}
$$

$$
\begin{array}{l}
\quad\quad\quad 40\quad\quad\quad\quad\quad\quad 50\quad\quad\quad\quad\quad\quad 60\quad\quad\quad\quad\quad\quad 70\\
A_\alpha^k\quad F\ Y\ V\ D\ L\ D\ K\ K\ E\ T\ V\ W\ M\ L\ P\ E\ F\ A\ Q\ L\ R\ R\ F\ E\ P\ Q\ G\ G\ L\ Q\ N\ I\ /,\ T\ G\\[4pt]
E_\alpha^k\quad \_\ H\ \_\ \_\ I\ E\ \_\ S\ \_\ \_\ I\ \_\ R\ \_\ E\ \_\ \_\ \_\ K\ F\ A\ S\ \_\ \_\ A\ \_\ \_\ A\ \_\ A\ \_\ \_\ \_\ V\ D
\end{array}
$$

$$
\begin{array}{l}
\quad\quad\quad\quad 80\quad\quad\quad\quad\quad\quad 90\quad\quad\quad\quad\quad\quad 100\\
A_\alpha^k\quad K\ H\ N\ L\ E\ I\ L\ T\ K\ R\ S\ N\ S\ T\ P\ A\ T\ N\ E\ A\ P\ Q\ A\ T\ V\ F\ P\ K\ S\ P\ V\ L\ L\ G\ Q\\[4pt]
E_\alpha^k\quad \_\ A\ \_\ \_\ D\ V\ M\ K\ E\ \_\ \_\ \_\ N\ \_\ \_\ D\ A\ \_\ V\ \_\ \_\ E\ V\ \_\ \_\ L\ S\ R\ \_\ \_\ \_\ N\ \_\ \_\ E
\end{array}
$$

$$
\begin{array}{l}
\quad\quad 110\quad\quad\quad\quad\quad 120\quad\quad\quad\quad\quad 130\quad\quad\quad\quad\quad 140\\
A_\alpha^k\quad P\ N\ T\ L\ I\ C\ F\ V\ D\ N\ I\ F\ P\ P\ V\ I\ N\ I\ T\ W\ L\ R\ N\ S\ K\ S\ V\ T\ D\ G\ V\ Y\ E\ T\ S\\[4pt]
E_\alpha^k\quad \_\ \_\ I\ \_\ \_\ \_\ \_\ I\ \_\ K\ F\ S\ \_\ \_\ \_\ V\ \_\ V\ \_\ \_\ \_\ \_\ \_\ G\ R\ P\ \_\ \_\ E\ \_\ \_\ S\ \_\ \_\ V
\end{array}
$$

$$
\begin{array}{l}
\quad\quad\quad 150\quad\quad\quad\quad\quad 160\quad\quad\quad\quad\quad 170\\
A_\alpha^k\quad F\ F\ V\ N\ R\ D\ Y\ S\ F\ H\ K\ L\ S\ Y\ L\ T\ F\ I\ P\ S\ D\ D\ D\ I\ Y\ D\ C\ K\ V\ E\ H\ W\ G\ L\ E\\[4pt]
E_\alpha^k\quad \_\ L\ P\ R\ D\ \_\ H\ L\ \_\ R\ \_\ F\ H\ \_\ \_\ \_\ \_\ L\ \_\ \_\ T\ \_\ \_\ F\ \_\ \_\ \_\ E\ \_\ D\ \_\ \_\ \_\ \_\ \_
\end{array}
$$

$$
\begin{array}{l}
\quad\quad\quad 180\quad\quad\quad\quad\quad 190\quad\quad\quad\quad\quad 200\quad\quad\quad\quad\quad 210\\
A_\alpha^k\quad E\ P\ V\ L\ K\ H\ W\ E\ P\ E\ I\ P\ A\ P\ M\ S\ E\ L\ T\ E\ T\ V\ V\ C\ A\ L\ G\ L\ S\ V\ G\ L\ V\ G\ I\\[4pt]
E_\alpha^k\quad \_\ \_\ L\ R\ \_\ \_\ \_\ \_\ F\ \_\ E\ K\ T\ L\ L\ P\ \_\ T\ K\ \_\ N\ \_\ \_\ \_\ \_\ \_\ \_\ \_\ F\ \_\ \_\ \_\ \_\ \_\ \_
\end{array}
$$

$$
\begin{array}{l}
\quad\quad\quad 220\quad\quad\quad\quad\quad 230\\
A_\alpha^k\quad V\ V\ G\ T\ I\ F\ I\ I\ Q\ G\ L\ R\ S\ G\ G\ T\ S\ R\ H\ P\ G\ P\ \text{L-COOH}\\[4pt]
E_\alpha^k\quad \_\ \_\ \_\ I\ \_\ L\ \_\ M\ K\ \_\ I\ K\ K\ R\ N\ V\ V\ E\ R\ R\ Q\ G\ A\ \text{L-COOH}
\end{array}
$$

FIGURE 7. Complete amino acid sequences, deduced from DNA sequences, of mouse A_α^k and E_α^k polypeptide chains. A solid line represents identity with the A_α^k sequence. The degree of homology between A_α^k and E_α^k is 114 out of 229 positions or 49.8%. The E_α^d sequence (not shown) differs from that of E_α^k in only 3 out of 230 positions. Each polypeptide also has a leader sequence of 25–29 amino acid residues that is removed by enzymatic cleavage within the cell. The one-letter code and references are in Appendices I and III.

2. In contrast there is considerable homology of sequence when one compares A_α with E_α, or A_β with E_β. For A_α^k versus E_α^k (Figure 7), the degree of homology is 50%.

3. Among A_α proteins that are the products of 6 allelic genes (from 6 different inbred strains), the degree of sequence homology between any pair of polypeptides is 90 to 95%. Figure 8 shows the differences

	11	14	15	28	35	44	46	48	53	56	57	59
k	Ser	Ile	Thr	Phe	Leu	Glu	Val	Met	Ala	Arg	Arg	Glu
d	Phe	Thr	—	His	—	Lys	—	Arg	Gly	Ile	Leu	—
b	Thr	—	Ser	—	—	—	—	—	Gly	Ala	Ser	Asp
f	Phe	—	Ser	—	Trp	—	—	Arg	Gly	Thr	Ser	Asp
u	—	—	Val	—	—	—	Ile	—	—	—	Ser	Asp
q	—	—	Val	His	Trp	—	—	—	Gly	Thr	Ser	Asp

	66	69	70	75	76	77	83	133	142	147	175	229
k	Asn	Thr	Gly	Glu	Ile	Leu	Ser	Thr	Phe	Tyr	Glu	His
d	—	Ala	Glu	Gly	—	—	Phe	—	Leu	His	—	—
b	Glu	Val	Val	Gly	Val	—	—	Ala	—	—	—	—
f	—	—	—	Gly	—	—	Phe	—	Leu	His	—	—
u	—	—	—	Gly	Val	—	—	Ala	—	—	—	—
q	—	—	—	Gly	Gly	Trp	Phe	—	Leu	His	Asp	Pro

FIGURE 8. Positions that exhibit variability in the amino acid sequences of 6 mouse A_α polypeptide chains controlled by 6 alleles (*k, d, b, f, u* and *q*). A dash indicates identity with the uppermost amino acid in that column. All of the sequences were deduced from the corresponding DNA sequences. There are 233 amino acid residues in each sequence and the 6 alleles are identical except for the 24 positions listed above. Note that many of the substitutions are clustered between positions 44 and 83, in the N-terminal, or $\alpha1$, domain. The complete sequence of A_α^k is shown in Figure 7. (From Benoist et al., 1983.)

that exist among 6 products of alleles of A_α. All 6 proteins are identical at the remainder of the 233 positions in the sequence. Most of the differences that do exist are localized in the N-terminal, $\alpha1$ domain (~90 residues). The polypeptides encoded by two E_α alleles that have been sequenced, E_α^k and E_α^d, differ in only 3 positions out of 230; the 3 differences are in the $\alpha2$ and transmembrane regions.

4. Sequences of three alleles of A_β, namely, A_β^b, A_β^d and A_β^k demonstrate more than 90% homology between any pair, with nearly all of the variability occurring between positions 1 and 90 in the β_1 domain.

5. Based on serological as well as biochemical data, the consensus emerging is that there is a moderate degree of polymorphism in A_α, A_β and E_β, and that E_α is highly conserved.

CLASS II GENES OF THE HUMAN HLA REGION

Human histocompatibility antigens of class II are encoded in the D region of the MHC on chromosome 6. This region includes loci

designated *SB, DR* and *DC* (Figure 1). (Some authors use the designation *DS* instead of *DC*.) The *SB* locus is on the 5′ side (centromeric
side) of *DR* and *DC*, but the order of *DC* and *DR* is not yet known.
The existence of the *DR* locus was known for a number of years before
DC and *SB* were discovered; DR antigens have therefore been studied
more exhaustively. The DR and DC antigens have been investigated
by using specific antibodies, the SB antigens by means of mixed lymphocyte reactions and, more recently, with antibodies as well. The
human D region corresponds in many respects to the I region of the
mouse and some authors are now using the symbol I for both species.
Despite the similarities it appears that the human D region is considerably more complex than the mouse I region. Also, the human class
II loci are not as well defined as those of the mouse, and many uncertainties still exist. It is possible, for example, that there are loci in
addition to *SB, DR* and *DC* (Figure 1). Also, it is not yet known
precisely how many genes are associated with each locus. For α chains,
one DR_α, three or four DC_α and one SB_α gene have been identified in
the genome so far (Auffray et al., 1983).

A list of alleles of human histocompatibility antigens is shown in
Table 4. In addition to *SB, DR* and *DC*, Table 4 lists alleles of the *D*
series. These antigens have been identified and classified by the mixed
lymphocyte reaction. They are not assigned a separate locus because
many if not all of these antigens are present on the same molecules
as the DR antigens that are identified with antibodies.

As in the mouse, a human class II antigen consists of an α-chain
(mol. wt. 33,000 daltons) and a β-chain (mol. wt. 28,000). An invariant
chain with an approximate molecular weight of 33,000 is also present
in the molecule after synthesis but is removed before insertion into
the cell membrane. Depending on the locus, a class II molecule has
the structure $DR_\alpha DR_\beta$, $SB_\alpha SB_\beta$, or $DC_\alpha DC_\beta$. The biological functions
of the human class II antigens are virtually identical to those of the
mouse, discussed earlier: they are involved in presentation of antigen
to helper T cells and in mixed lymphocyte reactions, and are associated
statistically with the incidence of certain diseases (Table 1). In addition, the capacity to respond to certain antigens correlates with the
presence of specific genes of class II.

This close resemblance between human and mouse class II antigens
extends to the molecular structure. Within either species, a molecule
consists of an α-chain and a β-chain linked by noncovalent forces. For
each chain, the molecular weights and domain structures in the two
species are very similar. In the α or β chain of either species there are
two external domains which protrude from the cell surface, as well as
a transmembrane and an intracellular domain. In the human and
mouse proteins, there is a small but significant degree of homology

between the second (α2 or β2) domain of the α and β chains, and also between these domains and the constant regions of immunoglobulins and β_2M. In either species, the β chains are more polymorphic (show greater variation within the species) than the α chains. In the human MHC, DR_β exhibits a moderate degree of polymorphism, whereas DR_α (like E_α in the mouse) is highly conserved. DC_α, while more restricted than DC_β, does show some variability of structure, principally in the N-terminal (α1) domain.

CORRESPONDENCE BETWEEN MOUSE AND HUMAN CLASS II SUBREGIONS

Data on amino acid sequences indicate that molecules encoded by the human *DR* locus correspond to those encoded by the *I-E* locus of the mouse. More limited evidence strongly suggests that *DC* corresponds to the mouse *I-A*. So far, a counterpart of the human *SB* locus has not been identified in mice.

LITERATURE CITED

Auffray, C., Kuo, J., DeMars, R. and Strominger, J. L. (1983). A minimum of four human class II α-chain genes are encoded in the HLA region of chromosome 6. *Nature 304,* 174.

Baltimore, D. (1981). Gene conversion: Some implications for immunoglobulin genes. *Cell 24,* 592.

Benoist, C. O., Mathis, D. J., Kanter, M. R., Williams, V. E. and McDevitt, H. O. (1983). Regions of allelic variability in the murine A_α immune response gene. *Cell 34,* 169.

Coligan, J. E., Kindt, T. J., Uehara, H., Martinko, J. and Nathenson, S. G. (1981). Primary structure of a murine transplantation antigen. *Nature 291,* 34.

Dorf, M. E., Ed. (1981). *The Role of the Major Histocompatibility Complex in Immunobiology.* New York, Garland STPM Press.

Flaherty, L. (1981). The TLA region antigens. In M. E. Dorf, Ed., *The Role of the Major Histocompatibility Complex in Immunobiology,* New York, Garland STPM Press, p. 33.

Gorer, P. A. (1936). The detection of a hereditary antigenic difference in mouse erythrocytes by the employment of immune sera. *Brit. J. Exp. Pathol. 17,* 42.

Hood, L., Steinmetz, M. and Malissen, B. (1983). Genes of the major histocompatibility complex. *Annu. Rev. Immunol. 1,* 529.

Klein, J. (1975). *Biology of the Mouse Histocompatibility-2 Complex.* New York, Springer-Verlag.

Larhammar, D., Hammerling, U., Denaro, M., Land, T., Flavell, R. A., Rask, L. and Peterson, P. A. (1983). Structure of the immune response I-A_β locus; sequence of the I-A_β gene and an adjacent β-chain second domain exon. *Cell 34,* 179.

Steinmetz, M., Winoto, A., Minard, K. and Hood, L. (1982). Clusters of genes encoding mouse transplantation antigens. *Cell 28,* 489.

van Rood, J. J., de Vries, R. R. P. and Bradley, B. A. (1981). Genetics and biology of the HLA system. In M. E. Dorf, Ed., *The Role of the Major Histocompatibility Complex in Immunobiology.* New York, Garland STPM Press.

SUGGESTED ADDITIONAL READING

Benacerraf, B. and McDevitt, H. O. (1972). Histocompatibility-linked immune response genes. *Science 185,* 273.

Immunological Reviews, Volume 66. (1982). Structure and function of HLA-DR. A collection of 6 review articles.

Immunological Reviews, Volume 70. (1983). HLA and disease susceptibility. A collection of 9 review articles.

Klein, J. (1981). The major histocompatibility complex of the mouse. *Science 203,* 516.

13

ANTIGEN-SPECIFIC RECEPTORS
OF T CELLS

OVERVIEW

The specificity of reactions of cellular immunity is mediated by thymus-derived lymphocytes (T cells), which have antigen-specific receptors embedded in the cell membrane.[1] To interact effectively with the receptor an antigen must be presented together with a product of the MHC. Although T cell receptors were first isolated with the aid of antiidiotypic antibodies, their amino acid sequences, as well as the organization of receptor-specific genes, have been deduced by application of the methods of molecular genetics. The mouse or human T cell receptor consists of two nonidentical glycosylated polypeptide chains (T_α and T_β) with molecular weights of 40,000–50,000 daltons. Each chain contains a variable (V) and a constant (C) region and has many structural features in common with the immunoglobulins. For example, the variable region contains a D and a J segment as well as a V domain similar in size to immunoglobulin domains. The C region comprises a C domain, a small hingelike segment, a hydrophobic transmembrane segment and a short, hydrophilic, cytoplasmic segment. For T_β, there are 2 C genes, multiple V genes, about 12 J genes, and a small but uncertain number of D genes. The corresponding information should soon be available for T_α. Variations in specificity are mediated by pairing of different T_α and T_β chains; by the use of different combinations of V, D and J segments; by variations in the precise locus of joining of V and D or D and J genes; by insertions of nucleotides at these junctions; and probably by somatic mutations. In humans and mice a molecule designated T3 is intimately associated with the T cell receptor. T3 may be involved in the transmission of signals to the interior of the cell.

*　　　*　　　*

[1] The presentation in this chapter is based on the assumption that the student is familiar with the content of Chapter 6.

225

T cells, together with phagocytic and natural killer cells, are the principal mediators of cellular immunity. Although functionally heterogeneous, T cells share a common origin in the bone marrow and undergo subsequent maturation in the thymus gland. The mature cells are exported into peripheral lymphoid compartments (spleen, lymph nodes, etc.) where they participate directly in the elimination of microorganisms from the body by helping to activate macrophages, by killing cells that are infected with viruses or other pathogens, and by secreting γ-interferon, which increases the resistance of cells to viral infection and activates natural killer cells. In addition, there are classes of T cells that regulate the activity of other T cells and the production of antibodies by B cells; helper or suppressor T cells provide a positive or negative stimulus, respectively, to immune responses. These functions can be carried out by soluble molecules ("factors") released from the corresponding T cells. Limited progress has been made in characterizing such factors biochemically. There is general agreement that they are proteins with molecular weights between 30,000 and 70,000, but their precise structures have not yet been worked out, due to the extremely small amounts of material available. It appears that the determination of the structures of helper and suppressor factors may require the isolation and sequencing of the genes that encode them.

T cells are responsible for the antigenic specificity of the reactions of cellular immunity. The specificities of T cells are determined by receptors, which are glycoprotein molecules embedded in the cell membrane. In common with a B cell, an individual T cell has a single specificity—that is, all of its antigen-binding receptor molecules are the same. There is, however, an aspect of specificity in which T cells differ markedly from antibodies. The significant interactions of T cells take place with molecules on cell surfaces rather than with molecules in solution; and to combine effectively the T cell must recognize not only the antigen presented on the surface of a macrophage or B cell, but also and at the same time a molecule on the target cell surface encoded by the major histocompatibility complex (MHC). T cells will recognize antigen only in the context of an MHC product. This point is illustrated in Figure 1, which includes two possible models for the interaction. In the first (A), the T cell receptor interacts with a single epitope, which is formed by the noncovalent interaction of antigen with the MHC product. In this model only a single T cell receptor is involved. An alternative possibility (B) is that the T cell has two receptors, one for the antigen and one for the MHC product. Current evidence favors a single receptor model (Berzofsky, 1983). Although it is not easy to understand how a large number of different MHC prod-

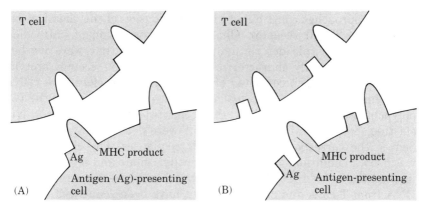

FIGURE 1. Alternative models for the interaction of T cells with an antigen or fragment of antigen on the surface of an antigen-presenting cell (such as a macrophage or B cell). (A) A single receptor interacts with a determinant formed by the noncovalent interaction of the antigen (or fragment of antigen) and MHC product. (B) The T cell has two separate receptors, one for antigen and one for a product of the MHC. The weight of current evidence favors the model shown in (A).

ucts can interact successfully with an enormous variety of antigenic structures (generally fragments of antigen) on cell surfaces, the evidence that this indeed occurs is quite strong.

The requirement for dual recognition of antigen and an MHC product is referred to as the MHC restriction of T cells. The nature of the restriction differs for different classes of T cells. Cytotoxic T cells (CTL) generally "see" antigen in the context of a class I MHC molecule (K or D antigen in the mouse; HLA-A, HLA-B or HLA-C in the human), although class II-restricted CTL also occur. Helper and inducer T cells are normally restricted by MHC antigens of class II (I-A or I-E antigens in the mouse; DR, SB or DC antigens in the human). Despite this distinction recent evidence indicates that cytotoxic and helper T cells utilize the same repertoire of genes that encode the receptors.

The specificity of T cells was attributed to the presence of antigen-specific receptors for many years before the chemical nature of the receptor was elucidated. During this interval the structure of the T cell receptor was one of the most important, interesting and frustrating open questions in immunology. The difficulty in elucidating the structure arose from the small amounts of receptor available for study. In contrast to antibodies, which are often available in substantial quantities, T cell receptors are not secreted in detectable amounts, and the amounts present on cell surfaces are very small.

Two approaches contributed to the elucidation of the chemical nature of the T cell receptor. One was the production of antibodies, specific for idiotypic determinants on receptors, that were used to isolate and partially characterize small amounts of receptor protein. The second approach consisted of the isolation and cloning of cDNA complementary to mRNA responsible for synthesis of each of the two polypeptide chains, T_α and T_β, that constitute a T cell receptor. Nucleotide sequences of the cloned cDNA were determined and used to deduce the corresponding polypeptide sequences. The cloned cDNA was used, in addition, as a probe to identify, isolate and sequence DNA in the genome of the cell; lengthy stretches of the relevant cellular DNA from T cells and other cell types have been sequenced. In both species, T_α has been localized to chromosome 14 which, in the human, also contains the H locus. The human T_β gene has been localized to chromosome 7 and is therefore (like mouse T_α) not linked to the H, κ, λ or MHC loci (see page 92). In the mouse the T_β gene is on chromosome 6, which also contains the κ-chain locus.

ISOLATION OF T CELL RECEPTORS BY THE USE OF ANTI-IDIOTYPIC ANTIBODIES

This approach has been used to isolate receptors of mouse and human T cells. Monoclonal antibodies are produced by immunization of mice with a homogeneous T cell preparation (a cloned T cell line, a T lymphoma, or a T hybridoma) and screened for the property of reacting uniquely with the cell line used for immunization, i.e., for idiotypic specificity. In a number of instances the target of such antiidiotypic antibodies has proven to be the T cell receptor (Allison et al., 1982; Haskins et al., 1983; Reinherz et al., 1983). The receptor is then isolated by radiolabeling cell surface molecules, solubilizing them, and precipitating with the monoclonal anti-Id antibody.

In the mouse, the molecule on the T cell surface with which such antibodies reacted was found to have a molecular weight of ~85,000. It is made up of two nonidentical glycosylated polypeptide chains, T_α and T_β, each with a molecular weight of 40,000–44,000, that are linked by a disulfide bond and noncovalent bonds. The T_β chain is somewhat more basic than T_α, that is, it has a higher isoelectric pH.

A similar approach led to the isolation of the human T cell receptor. The T cell clone, against which anti-Id antibodies were initially prepared, was from a cell line maintained in culture by repeated stimulation with antigen (rather than a lymphoma or hybridoma). The antibodies were then used to isolate small amounts of the human T cell receptor. As in the mouse, the receptor comprises two glycosylated polypeptide chains. The molecular weights are 49,000—51,000 (α chain) and 41,000–43,000 (β chain).

An interesting feature of the human or mouse T cell receptor is that it is intimately associated on the cell surface with a protein, designated T3, that is found on virtually all mature T cells. Whether protein T3 should be considered as an integral part of the receptor or as an associated molecule has not yet been established. T3 is discussed in more detail below.

ISOLATION OF cDNA CLONES ENCODING THE T CELL RECEPTOR

More detailed information on the chemical structure of the T cell receptor was obtained by determining nucleotide sequences of cDNA (complementary to mRNA) and genomic DNA. The initial studies were carried out by Hedrick et al. (1984) and Yanagi et al. (1984). Data on this topic are now accumulating rapidly.

The novel and ingenious approach that broke the impasse is exemplified by the work of Hedrick et al. with the mouse. They made the initial assumptions that mRNA encoding the polypeptides of the T cell receptor should be found in activated T cells but not in B cells, and that it ought to be present on membrane-bound polysomes, since the receptors find their way to the cell membrane after they are synthesized. They therefore prepared radiolabeled cDNA from membrane-bound polysomal mRNA of a T cell hybridoma. Next they hybridized this cDNA with mRNA from B cells and removed ("subtracted") all of the hybridized cDNA sequences. What remained was largely cDNA that is complementary to the mRNA of T cells but not B cells. This cDNA was used as a probe to screen a library of cloned cDNA that had been prepared from mRNA of the same T hybridoma and similarly subtracted. Those clones that hybridized were analyzed to determine whether they would, in turn, hybridize with genomic DNA that had undergone rearrangement in mature T cells (as compared to other cells). (The assumption here was that the genes encoding T cell receptors would be subject to a rearrangement analogous to that of V and C genes of immunoglobulins.)[2] By this strategy they isolated a cDNA clone that corresponded to mRNA having the following properties: (1) the mRNA is expressed in T cells but not in B cells;

---

[2] To look for hybridization with rearranged genes, Southern blots (see page 98) were prepared with the DNA of T cell tumors and of non-T cells. The cloned cDNA described above was then allowed to hybridize with the various separated bands. By this method Hedrick et al. identified cDNA clones that hybridized with two bands in DNA from non-T cells but with only one band in DNA from the T cell tumors.

(2) it is present on membrane-bound polysomes; and (3) it is encoded by DNA that undergoes rearrangement in T cells but not in other cell types. (The normal arrangement, present in non-T cells, is referred to as the germ line configuration.) The DNA identified by Hedrick et al. proved to be that encoding the β chain of the receptor of helper T cells. This was established by comparing the amino acid sequence, deduced from the DNA sequence, with limited sequence data available for the protein, which had been isolated by using antiidiotypic antibodies.

At about the same time a somewhat different approach was used by Yanagi et al. (1984) to identify mRNA that encodes the β chain of a human T cell receptor. They used a T cell leukemia as the source of mRNA, prepared cDNA and used the cDNA to generate 10,000 independent clones in *E. coli*. They then screened the clones and found four that hybridized with the mRNA of the human T cell leukemia but not with the mRNA of a human B cell line or several other non-T cell lines. One of the four clones was studied further and proved to correspond to the human T_β chain.

Similar methods were subsequently used to identify and clone cDNA and genomic DNA corresponding to the T_α chain (Chien et al., 1984; Saito et al., 1984). For example, Chien et al. "subtracted" cDNA, prepared from a T-helper hybridoma (T_{H1}), with cDNA from a different T-helper hybridoma (T_{H2}) and with cDNA from a T-like lymphoma. The remaining cDNA was used to screen a library of cDNA prepared from the T_{H1} hybridoma. This approach eventually yielded a cDNA clone, specific for V-region sequences, that hybridized with genes that encoded the T_α chain. Because the T_α genes were isolated about a year later than T_β, more detailed data are available at this time for T_β, particularly with respect to its diversity and gene organization. Considerable information has been obtained, however, for both chains.

STRUCTURAL FEATURES OF MURINE T_α AND T_β CHAINS

Although there is only a small degree of homology of sequence between murine T_α and T_β, the two chains are strikingly similar with respect to their general architecture (Figures 2, 3 and 4), which in important respects also resembles the architecture of immunoglobulins. Both chains are glycosylated, with 3 or 4 sites of attachment for carbohydrate, which comprises about one-third of the mass of each chain. The T_α and T_β chains contain approximately 250 and 280 amino acid residues, respectively. Each has a hydrophobic N-terminal leader sequence, 18–20 residues in length, that is cleaved from the mature chain. The next ~110 residues comprise the variable (V) region and

```
                                      -1 +1              V Region ——————→ 20
            Leader                        |
Tβ1  - - - - - - - - V V L C F L G T G L V|D M K V T Q M S R Y L I K R M G E N V L
Tβ2  M S C R L L L L Y V S L C L V E T A L M|N T K I T Q S P R Y L I L G R A N K - S

                                                                            58
Tβ1  L E [C] G Q D M S H E T M Y W Y R Q D P G - L G L Q L I Y I S Y D V D S N S E G
Tβ2  L E [C] E Q H L G H N A M Y W Y K Q S A E K P P E - L M F L Y N L K Q L I R N E  [CHO]

                                                [CHO]                         96
Tβ1  D I P K G Y R V S R K K R E H F S L I L D S A K T N Q T S - V Y F [C] A Q G A P
Tβ2  T V P S R F I P E C P D S S K L L L H I - S A V D P E D S A V Y F [C] A S S H G

     J Region                        110   [CHO]      C Region ——————→ 130
Tβ1  - - - - - E Q Y F G P G T R L T V L E D L R N V T P P K V S L F E P S K A E I
Tβ2  Q G V S G T L Y F G E G S R L I V V E D L R N V T P P K V S L F E P S K A E I
                                              [CHO]
                                                                           169
Tβ1  A N K Q K A T L V [C] L A R G F F P D H V E L S W W V N G R E V H S G V S T D P
Tβ2  A N K Q K A T L V [C] L A R G F F P D H V E L S W W V N G K E V H S G V S T D P

     [CHO]                                                                 208
Tβ1  Q A Y K E S N Y S Y C L S S R L R V S A T F W H N P R N H F R [C] Q V Q F H G L
Tβ2  Q A Y K E S N Y S H C L S S R L R V S A T F W H N P R N H F R [C] Q V Q F H G L

     [CHO]                            [CHO]                                 247
Tβ1  S E E D K W P E G S P K P V T Q N I S A E A W G R A D C G I T S A S Y H Q G V
Tβ2  S E E D K W P E G S P K P V T Q N I S A E A W G R A D C G I T S A S V Q Q G V
                                         [CHO]
     |256          Transmembrane                              |  CYT 282
Tβ1  L S A T I L Y E|I L L G K A T L Y A V L V S G L V L M A M V|K K K N S
Tβ2  L S A T I L Y E|I L L G K A T L Y A V L V S T L V V M A M V|K R K N S
```

FIGURE 2. Amino acid sequences of two murine T_β chains, deduced from sequences of cDNA clones. (For the single-letter code see Appendix I.) Note the near identity of sequences in the C region (positions 110 to the C terminus) and the very limited homology in the V region. Cysteine groups involved in intrachain disulfide bonds are boxed. The cysteine at position 236 probably participates in an interchain disulfide bond to the T_α chain. Amino acid triplets suitable for attachment of carbohydrate are labeled CHO. Hyphens represent gaps artificially introduced to maximize homology. ($T_\beta 1$ from Saito et al., 1984, *Nature 309,* 757; $T_\beta 2$ from Hedrick et al., 1984, *Nature 308,* 153.)

the remainder of the chain constitutes a constant (C) region. The V region and the first segment of the C region each have an intrachain disulfide bond, spanning 50–68 residues—a feature very reminiscent of immunoglobulin domains. The V region of the T_β chain also contains hypervariable regions (see below), three of which correspond in location to those found in immunoglobulin V regions. These striking similarities indicate a common evolutionary origin of T cell receptors and

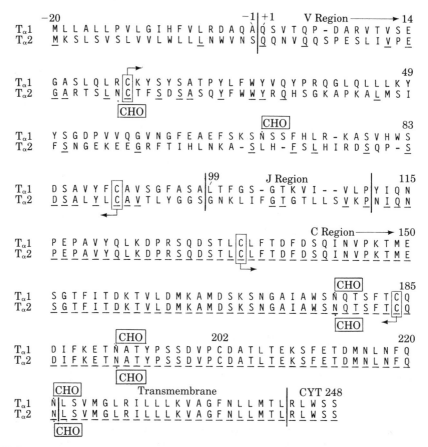

FIGURE 3. Amino acid sequences of two murine T_α chains, deduced from sequences of cDNA clones. Cysteine groups involved in intrachain disulfide bond formation are boxed. The cysteine at position 202 probably participates in an interchain disulfide bond to the β chain. Amino acid triplets suitable for attachment of carbohydrate are labeled CHO. (From Chien et al., 1984, *Nature 312*, 31; and Saito et al., 1984, *Nature 312*, 36.)

immunoglobulins, which is further supported by a limited but significant degree of homology of sequence.

Near the C termini of T_α and T_β are stretches of hydrophobic amino acids that are believed to be inserted into the cell membrane (designated "transmembrane" in Figures 2 and 3). These segments are similar in size, and in their hydrophobicity, to the transmembrane regions of Class I and Class II histocompatibility antigens, and of membrane-bound immunoglobulins. These segments are followed by short, polar

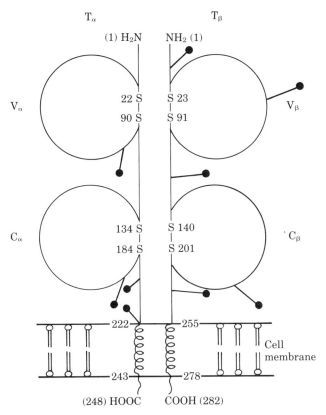

FIGURE 4. Schematic diagram of a T cell receptor. The numbers refer to positions in the amino acid sequence; they are slightly variable because of variations in length of V regions. The solid knobs indicate asparagine-linked carbohydrate groups attached to the chains. An interchain disulfide bond is thought to link Cys-202 in the α chain with Cys-236 in the β chain. The chains are also held together by noncovalent bonds.

segments at the C terminus, believed to be localized in the cytoplasm. The C region sequence of T_β is not totally invariant due to the presence of two C_β genes (see below) whose polypeptide sequences differ by 4 to 7 amino acids (of a total of 173). (The uncertainty in number of differences is due to slight variations in sequences reported from different laboratories.)

The C terminal portion of each V region contains a J segment, of limited diversity, preceded in T_β, and in all probability in T_α, by a short D segment. Studies of T_β gene organization, discussed below, indicate the presence of 12 functional J segments, several of which are expressed in the T$_\beta$ chains whose sequences have been reported so far, and at least two functional D segments. The J segments comprise 15 to 17 amino acids; the known D segments consist of 1 to 5 amino acids.

A schematic structure for the T cell receptor is shown in Figure 4.

From the sequences in Figures 2 and 3 it is evident that there is limited sequence homology in the V region sequences of the pair of T$_\alpha$ chains or in the pair of T$_\beta$ chains. Other data on V region sequences of T$_\beta$ chains (not shown) confirm that they show greater diversity than the V region sequences of a given class of immunoglobulin (V$_H$, V$_\kappa$ or V$_\lambda$). Figure 5 shows that T$_\alpha$ and T$_\beta$, despite their strikingly similar architecture, exhibit little sequence homology in either the V or C regions, an observation consistent with early divergence during evolution.

Variable region

```
         1                                                          35
T β      N T K I T Q S P R Y L I L G R A N K - S L E C E Q H L G H N A M - - - - Y W Y K
T α      Q Q N V Q Q S P E S L I V P E G A R T S L N C T F S D S A S Q Y F - - - W W Y R
λ1       Q A V V T Q E S A L T T S P G E T - V T L T C R S S T G A V T T S N Y A N W V Q

         36                                                         73
T β      Q S A E K P P - E L M F L Y N L K Q L I R N E T V P S R F I P E C P D S S K - L
T α      Q H S G K A P K A L M S I F S N G E K - E E G - - - - R F T I H L N K A S L H F
λ1       Q K P D H L F T G L T G G T N N R A P G V P A - - - - R F S G S L I G N K - - A

         74                                  98
T β      L L H I S A V D P E D S A V Y F C A S S H G Q G V
T α      S L H T R D S Q P S D S A L Y L C A V T L Y G G
λ1       A L T I T G A Q T E D E A I Y F C A L W Y S N H W
```

Constant region

```
         110                                                        148
T β      E D L R N V T P P K V S - L F E P S K A E I A N K Q K A T L V C L A R G F F P D
T α        N I Q N P E P A V Y Q L K D P R S Q D - - - - - - S T L C L F I D F D S Q
λ1         Q P K S S P S V T - L F P P S S E E L T E N K A - T L V C T I T D F Y P G

         149                                                        188
T β      H V E L S W W V N G R E V H S G V S T D P Q A Y K E S N Y S Y C L S S R L R V S
T α      I N V P K T M E S G T F I T D K T V L D M K A M D S K S N G A I A W S N Q T - -
λ1       V V T V D W K V D G T P V T Q G M E T T E P S K Q - S N N K Y M A S S Y L T L T

         189                                                        228
T β      A T F W H N P R N H F R C Q V Q F H G L S E E D K W P E G S P K P V T Q N I S A
T α      - - - - - - - - S F T C Q D I F K E T N A T Y P S S - - D V P C D A T L T E K
λ1       A R A W E R H S - S Y S C Q V T H E G H T V E K S L S - - R A D C S

         229                                                        268
T β      E A W G R A D C G I T S A S Y H Q G V L S A T I L Y E I L L G K A T L Y A V L V
T α      S F E T D - - - - - M N L N F Q - - N L S V M G L R - I L L L K V A G F N L L M

         269                  282
T β      S G L V L M A M - - - V K K K N S
T α      T L - - - - - - - - - R L W S S
```

FIGURE 5. Comparison of amino acid sequences of a mouse T$_\alpha$, T$_\beta$, and λ1 (immunoglobulin) chain.

Figure 5 also compares the amino acid sequence of a mouse λ1 chain with the sequences of T_α and T_β. J segments are omitted from the comparison. There is a moderate degree of sequence homology that includes highly conserved cysteine groups in both the V and C regions. In the C region the degrees of homology are: T_α versus λ1, 20%; T_β versus λ1, 35%; T_α versus T_β, 24%. The comparison of the constant region of T_α with that of either T_β or λ1 requires the artificial insertion of a number of gaps (hyphens) in T_α. Also, λ1, which lacks transmembrane and cytoplasmic segments, is considerably shorter than T_α or T_β. When comparisons are made of T_α or T_β with other mouse immunoglobulin sequences, such as those of κ or μ chains, significant sequence homology is similarly observed, although the closest resemblance is that to the λ chain.

AMINO ACID SEQUENCES OF J_β REGIONS

As we will see, there are two clusters of J_β genes, each containing 6 structural genes. The corresponding amino acid sequences of the 12 J_β regions are shown in Figure 6. We have underlined amino acids at each position that are represented 3 or more times in the 12 sequences.

Figure 7 shows a comparison of one J_β sequence with that of a J_α sequence and with selected J regions of mouse immunoglobulins (J_H,

$J_\beta 1$ N T E V F F G K G T R L T V V

$J_\beta 2$ N S D Y T F G S G T R L L V I

$J_\beta 3$ S G N T L Y F G E G S R L I V V

$J_\beta 4$ S N E R L F F G H G T K L S V L

$J_\beta 5$ Q P A P L F G E G T R L S V L

$J_\beta 6$ S Y N S P L Y F A A G T R L T V T

$J_\beta' 1$ N Y A E Q F F G P G T R L T V L

$J_\beta' 2$ N T G Q L Y F G E G S K L T V L

$J_\beta' 3$ S A E T L Y F G S G T R L T V L

$J_\beta' 4$ S Q N T L Y F G A G T R L S V L

$J_\beta' 5$ N Q D T Q Y F G P G T R L L V L

$J_\beta' 6$ C S Y E Q Y F G P G T R L T V L

FIGURE 6. Amino acid sequences of mouse J_β segments. The symbol J_β' is used to designate sequences encoded by the second (3′) cluster.

J$_\alpha$	S G N K L I F G T G T L L S V K
J$_\beta$1	N T E V F F G K G T R L T V V
J$_H$1	Y W Y F D V W G A G T T V T V S S
J$_\kappa$1	G G G T K L E I K R
J$_\lambda$1	F G G G T K L T V L

FIGURE 7. Amino acid sequences of selected J regions of the mouse. J$_\alpha$ and J$_\beta$ refer to the corresponding chains of the T cell receptor. J$_\alpha$ is not numbered because of insufficient information concerning the J$_\alpha$ gene cluster. The last three are sequences present in immunoglobulins.

J$_\kappa$, J$_\lambda$). It is evident that J region sequences have been significantly conserved in all of these molecular species.

ORGANIZATION OF T$_\beta$ GENES

Figure 8 illustrates the organization of genes encoding the T$_\beta$ polypeptide chain. There is an indeterminate number of V$_\beta$ genes and two clusters of J$_\beta$–C$_\beta$ genes, with each cluster containing 6 active J$_\beta$ and a single C$_\beta$ gene. The J–C region is spread out over 15 kilobases. A J$_\beta$ gene in the first (5′) cluster is expressed together with the first C$_\beta$ gene; those in the second cluster are expressed with the second C$_\beta$ gene, labeled C$_\beta'$. The number of J$_\beta$ genes exceeds the number of J$_H$, J$_\kappa$ or J$_\lambda$ immunoglobulin genes. Because of this larger number it has been suggested that the J$_\beta$ genes make a relatively important contribution to the diversity of specificities of T cell receptors. The existence of two clusters may reflect difficulties in achieving appropriate recombination with a given C gene when the number of J genes exceeds 6. The presence of two C$_\beta$ genes does not add significantly to the diversity of T cell receptors because the two differ at only 4 to 7 positions in the amino acid sequence. For reasons not understood, most T cell lines analyzed so far have been found to use the "3′-most" J–C cluster, i.e., J′–C′. The presence of J–C clusters is also seen in mouse λ genes (see page 97), but not in κ or H genes. For κ and H, any J gene can be expressed with any C gene.

As indicated in Figures 8 and 9, each of the two C$_\beta$ genes is made up of 4 exons, separated of course by 3 introns. These exons correspond to functional domains deduced from the amino acid sequence. The C$_\beta$1 exon encodes positions 115–239, which are external to the membrane. C$_\beta$2 encodes a hingelike stretch of 5 amino acids that includes a

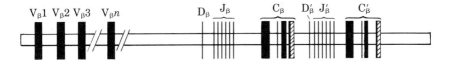

FIGURE 8. Organization of genes encoding the β chain of the mouse T cell receptor. The two *J–C* clusters occupy about 15 kb. The distance between the *J–C* and *V* genes is unknown. Additional but as yet unidentified *D* genes may be present. The hatched regions represent nucleotide sequences that are transcribed but not translated in the cell.

cysteine believed to be involved in the T_α–T_β linkage. $C_\beta 3$ encodes 35 amino acids that include the hydrophobic transmembrane segment; and $C_\beta 4$ encodes 6 amino acids, the last 5 of which make up the cytoplasmic tail of the molecule, plus an untranslated segment (UT).

D SEGMENTS IN MURINE T_β CHAINS

It has been observed that both mouse and human cDNA clones encoding the T_β chain contain several nucleotides in addition to those seen in germ line V_β and J_β gene segments. This finding is consistent with the presence of separate *D* genes. So far, two D_β genes, containing 12

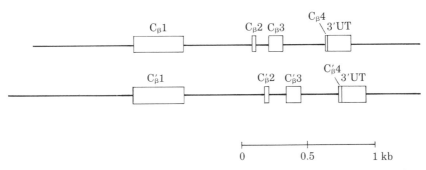

FIGURE 9. Arrangement of exons and introns in the two C_β genes of the murine T cell receptor. C'_β is located 3' to C_β. UT, untranslated (but transcribed) sequences in exons. (From Gascoigne et al., 1984, *Nature 310*, 387.)

and 14 nucleotides respectively, have been isolated; there is indirect evidence for the presence of D_α genes as well. One D_β gene is localized on the 5′ side of the first J_β cluster; the other is on the 5′ side of the second J_β cluster, designated J'_β (Figure 8). Recognition signals, required for recombination (see below), are found on the 5′ and 3′ sides of each gene. How many additional D_β genes may exist is uncertain. The joining of D to J in T_β, as in immunoglobulin V_H genes, takes place prior to the rearrangement of a V gene; that is, the sequence of recombination is: $D + J \rightarrow DJ;$ $V + DJ \rightarrow VDJ$.

NUCLEOTIDE SEQUENCES INVOLVED IN RECOMBINATION OF V_β, D_β AND J_β GENES

For the immunoglobulins we have seen that specific nucleotide sequences act as signals (probably to enzymes) that permit recombination of V, D and J genes (see page 102). A recognition signal consists of a palindromic nucleotide heptamer; a spacer of 11–12 or 22–23 nucleotides corresponding to one or two turns of the DNA helix; and an A–T rich nonamer. This is illustrated in Figure 10A. When recombination occurs a two-turn spacer is invariably joined to a one-turn spacer. For the immunoglobulins, this is illustrated schematically in Figure 10B. Figure 10C shows the corresponding arrangement of recognition sequences for the T_β gene. Note that the arrangement is somewhat different in T_β than in V_H, despite the fact that both possess a D segment. On the 5′ side of J_H there are two turns of the helix in the spacer, whereas there is only one turn on the 5′ side of J_β. This is compensated for in D_β which has two turns on its 3′ side so that the same $(2 + 1)$ rule of recombination is maintained. (In D_H there is a one-turn spacer on each side.) Note that in T_β direct recombination of V_β with J_β (omitting D) is possible without violating the "2 + 1 turn" rule. It is not yet known whether V–J joining is a physiologically important occurrence, although it has been observed.

The oligonucleotide heptamers and nonamers found adjacent to T_β gene segments are similar but not identical in sequence to those adjacent to immunoglobulin genes.

THE T_γ GENE

A gene designated T_γ is rearranged and transcribed in most cytotoxic T cell clones but infrequently in helper T cells and not at all in B cells (Kranz et al., 1985). The T_γ gene encodes a polypeptide sequence that is very similar in its architecture to T_α and T_β chains, and comprises a V, J, C, and, probably, a D segment. The nature of the rearrange-

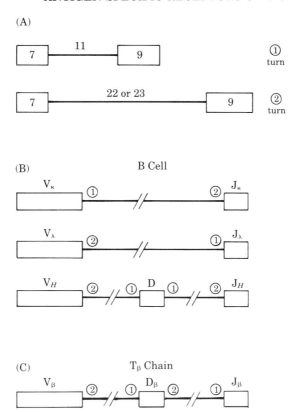

FIGURE 10. (A) Arrangement of nucleotides that constitute recognition signals for recombination of *V, D* and *J* genes. The numbers represent numbers of nucleotide base pairs. A spacer of 11 base pairs corresponds to approximately one turn of the DNA helix. Recombination requires the juxtaposition of nucleotide sequences containing spacers of one turn and two turns. (B) and (C) show the arrangement of recognition signals in immunoglobulins and T_β genes, respectively.

ment, as compared to the germ line configuration, is also virtually identical to that of T_α and T_β. T_γ differs from T_α and T_β in the very limited diversity of the *V* segments that are utilized in different cell lines and in the absence of appropriate sites of attachment for asparagine-linked carbohydrate. So far, the polypeptide itself has not been isolated and its presence is inferred from the presence of the corresponding mRNA. The high frequency of appearance of T_γ mRNA in cytotoxic T cell clones strongly implies a functional role, but so far this role has not been established. It has been suggested that the T_γ

polypeptide may participate in determining the specificity of cytotoxic T cells. When the T_γ mRNA was discovered, it was thought erroneously for a time that it encoded the T_α chain.

DIVERSITY OF T CELL RECEPTORS

Some of the factors responsible for the diversity of immunoglobulin sequences are also operative on T_β chains. (There is less information for T_α.) These include the presence of multiple V_β, J_β and, probably, D_β genes, capable of yielding a large number of different combinations. Preliminary data suggest that a relatively small number of germ line V_β genes (perhaps as few as 10) may account for most of the T cell response. The presence of additional V_β genes, that are poorly represented in T cell responses, has not been ruled out. V_β genes exhibit greater diversity of sequence than the V genes in a given family of immunoglobulins. The degree of homology among V_β amino acid sequences studied so far ranges from only 20% to about 50%. Diversity is also generated by imprecise recombination between V and D or D and J, generating variability in the amino acid sequence at the junction (page 111). Additional diversity arises from the addition of short new stretches of nucleotides (called N segments), not present in the germ line, at the junction of V_β and D_β or D_β and J_β. The extent to which somatic mutations operate on the V_β gene is uncertain at present, although there is some evidence that they occur; the frequency appears to be considerably lower than that observed in immunoglobulin V regions.

An unexpected feature of V_β amino acid sequences is that there are more regions of hypervariability (as many as 7) than are found in immunoglobulins. It has been suggested that these extra hypervariable regions are used to make contact with MHC-encoded determinants on the antigen-presenting cell; for example, the three hypervariable regions that correspond in location to those of immunoglobulins might form a pocket that interacts with the antigen, while the extra hypervariable regions might be localized on the surface of the receptors and make contact with an MHC product. There is as yet no direct support for this interesting conjecture.

DEGREE OF RESEMBLANCE OF T CELL RECEPTORS TO HEAVY AND LIGHT CHAINS OF IMMUNOGLOBULINS

In some respects, the polypeptide chains of the T cell receptor are more closely related to immunoglobulin heavy chains than to light chains. One similarity is the presence of a hydrophobic transmembrane sequence and a cytoplasmic tail, analogous to those found in the C_H region of membrane-bound immunoglobulins; another is the presence of D segments. The length of J_β segments (15 to 17 amino acids) also corresponds more closely to those of J_H; J_κ and J_λ are somewhat shorter.

On the other hand, the amino acid sequences of T cell receptors are somewhat more homologous to those of mouse λ chains than to those of H chains. The presence of J–C gene clusters is another feature shared by T_α, T_β and V_λ. Also in common with light chains, a molecule of T_β or T_α each has a single C domain. What seems quite certain is that the genes encoding T cell receptors and immunoglobulins have a common evolutionary origin. If the genes encoding T_α and T_β diverged from this line prior to the divergence of genes encoding H and L chains this would account for resemblances of T cell receptors to both H and L chains.

COMPARISON OF THE STRUCTURES OF HUMAN AND MOUSE T CELL RECEPTORS

Most of the foregoing discussion has dealt with the murine T cell receptor, for which somewhat more detailed information is currently available as compared to that of the human. However, the genomic organization and structural properties of receptors of the two species are remarkably similar. In both cases there are separate variable (V), diversity (D), joining (J), and constant (C) gene segments, that rearrange in T cells to give the final unified product. And in both species there are two J_β–C_β clusters with at least one D gene on the 5' side of the J cluster. In the human, as in the mouse, the sequences of the two C_β genes are very similar although not identical. In both species the C region includes a domain characterized by an intrachain disulfide bond as well as transmembrane and cytoplasmic segments. The degree of homology between mouse and human C_β amino acid sequences is 82%. By comparison the degree of homology between human and mouse C_κ is 60%. Thus the receptors of the two species are structurally very similar. Also, for recombination, the two genomes make use of very similar recognition sequences in the flanking regions of V, D, and J.

T3, T4 AND T8 GLYCOPROTEINS

These proteins, found on the surfaces of mature human T cells, receive their designation from the monoclonal antibodies that define them (anti-T3, etc.). A uniform supply of the monoclonal antibodies is available from commercial sources. T3 is closely associated with the receptor on human T cells; a closely related molecule is present on mouse T cells. It has been postulated that a function of the T3 molecule is to transmit signals to the interior of the cell after interaction of the receptor with its ligand. Supporting this view is the observation that both antibodies to T3 and antibodies to the receptor can cause a rapid increase in the cytoplasmic calcium ion concentration in T cells and help to stimulate proliferation. (The calcium ions are released from intracellular stores.) The expression of T3 is linked to that of the receptor; the two are almost invariably found together on the T cell surface. A possible mode of noncovalent linkage of the receptor with T3 is suggested by the presence of a positively charged lysine side chain in the otherwise hydrophobic transmembrane segments of T_α and T_β chains, and the presence of a negatively charged aspartic acid in the hydrophobic human T3 transmembrane region. Human T3 comprises three polypeptide chains, designated γ, δ and ϵ, each having a molecular weight of 20–25 kilodaltons; the γ and δ chains, but not the ϵ chain, are glycosylated. Genes encoding δ and ϵ have been cloned and sequenced; the sequences are not homologous to those of immunoglobulins, T cell receptors or major histocompatibility antigens. The structure of mouse T3 is at present not as well defined, but it will undoubtedly be worked out in the near future.

T4 and T8 are a single-chain and a two-chain glycoprotein, respectively, with molecular weights of 62,000 and 76,000. T4 molecules are present on the surface of T cells of the helper/inducer subset, on cytolytic T cells (CTL) that are restricted by MHC antigens of Class II, and (rarely) on Class I-restricted T cells. T8 is found on the surface of suppressor T cells and on Class I-restricted or, infrequently, Class II-restricted CTL. It appears homologous to the Lyt 2 antigen of mouse T cells. Neither T4 nor T8 is directly associated with the T cell receptor; however, an important role in cell lysis is suggested by the fact that anti-T4 or anti-T8 can block the cytolytic activity of the corresponding CTL.

LITERATURE CITED

Allison, J. P., McIntyre, B. W. and Bloch, D. (1982). Tumor specific antigen of murine T cell lymphoma defined with monoclonal antibody. *J. Immunol. 129,* 2293.

Berzofsky, J. (1983). Promising clues to receptor genes and molecules. *Immunol. Today 4,* 299.

Chien, Y. S., Becker, D. M., Lindsten, T., Okamura, M., Cohen, D. I. and Davis, M. M. (1984). A third type of murine T cell receptor gene. *Nature 312,* 31.

Haskins, K., Kubo, R., White, J., Pigeon, M., Kappler, J. and Marrack, P. (1983). The major histocompatibility complex-restricted antigen receptor on T cells. I. Isolation with a monoclonal antibody. *J. Exp. Med. 157,* 1149.

Hedrick, S. M., Cohen, D. I., Nielsen, E. A. and Davis, M. M. (1984). Isolation of cDNA clones encoding T cell-specific membrane-associated proteins. *Nature 308,* 149.

Kranz, D. M., Saito, H., Heller, M., Takagaki, Y., Haas, W., Eisen, H. N., Tonegawa, S. (1985). Limited diversity of the rearranged T cell γ gene. *Nature 313,* 28.

Reinherz, E. L., Meuer, S. C., Fitzgerald, K. A., Hussey, R. A., Hodgdon, J. C., Acuto, O. and Schlossman, S. F. (1983). Comparison of T3-associated 49 and 43 kilodalton cell surface molecules on individual human T cell clones. *Proc. Natl. Acad. Sci. USA 80,* 4104.

Saito, H., Kranz, D. M., Tagaki, Y., Hayday, H. C., Eisen, H. N. and Tonegawa, S. (1984). Complete primary structure of a heterodimeric T cell receptor deduced from cDNA sequences. *Nature 309,* 757.

Yanagi, Y., Yoshikai, Y., Legett, K., Clark, S. P., Aleksander, I. and Mak, T. W. (1984). A human T cell-specific cDNA clone encodes a protein having extensive homology to immunoglobulin chains. *Nature 308,* 145.

SUGGESTED ADDITIONAL READING

Allison, J. P., Ridge, L., Lund, J., Gross-Pelose, J., Lanier, L. and McIntyre, B. W. (1984). The murine T cell antigen receptor and associated structures. *Immunol. Revs. 81,* 145.

Zinkernagel, R. M. and Doherty, P. C. (1979). MHC-restricted T cells. *Adv. Immunol. 27,* 52.

APPENDIX I: ABBREVIATIONS USED FOR AMINO ACIDS

Amino acid	Three-letter abbreviation	Single-letter abbreviation
Alanine	Ala	A
Arginine	Arg	R
Asparagine	Asn	N
Aspartic acid	Asp	D
Cysteine or Half-cystine	Cys	C
Glutamic acid	Glu	E
Glutamine	Gln	Q
Glycine	Gly	G
Histidine	His	H
Isoleucine	Ile	I
Leucine	Leu	L
Lysine	Lys	K
Methionine	Met	M
Phenylalanine	Phe	F
Proline	Pro	P
Serine	Ser	S
Threonine	Thr	T
Tryptophan	Trp	W
Tyrosine	Tyr	Y
Valine	Val	V
Uncertainties		
Aspartic acid or asparagine	Asx	B
Glutamic acid or glutamine	Glx	Z

APPENDIX II: AMINO ACID SEQUENCES: HUMAN AND MOUSE C_κ AND HUMAN C_H REGIONS

These sequences are shown in Figures 1 and 2.

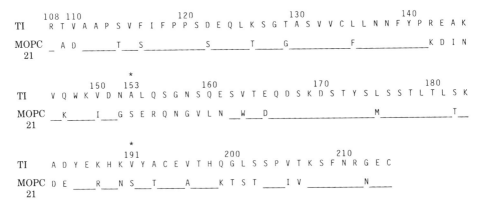

FIGURE 1. Comparison of the amino acid sequence of the C_κ regions of human and mouse myeloma proteins, designated TI and MOPC 21, respectively. The one-letter code is given in Appendix I. Note that no artificial gaps are required to improve the homology. The asterisks denote the two positions in the human sequence at which allotypic substitutions (the K_m markers) occur. The degree of homology between the human and mouse protein is 61%. References to the sequences are in Appendix IV.

FIGURE 2. Partial amino acid sequences of the heavy chains of human IgD, ▶ IgG1, IgM, IgE, and IgA1. The sequences presented are for the C_H2 and C_H3 domains of the δ, γ, and α chains and for the C_H3 and C_H4 domains of the μ and ε chains. Hinge regions and the last seven residues of μ and α are omitted. Sequences are aligned so as to maximize homologies. Invariant half-cystine (C) and tryptophan (W) residues are placed in register. Gaps (hyphens) are inserted artificially to improve homology. (From Shinoda, T., Takahashi, N., Takayasu, T., Okayama, T. and Shimuzu, A. 1981. *Proc. Natl. Acad. Sci. USA* 78, 785.)

247

```
              10              20              30              40
δ  S H T Q P L G V Y L L T P A V Q D - L W L R D K A T F T C F V V G S D L - K D -
γ  E L L G G P S V F L F P P K P K D T L M I S R T P E V T C V V V D V S H E D P Q
μ  D Q D T A I R V F A I P P S F A S - I F L T K S T K L T C L V T D L T T Y D S -
ε  S N P R G V S A Y L S R P S P F D - L F I R K S P T I T C L V V D L A P S K G T
α  P S C C H P R L S L H R P A L Z B - L L L G S Z A N L T C T L T G L R D - A S G


              50              60              70              80
δ  A H L T W E - V A G K - V P T G G V E E G L L E R H S N G S Q S H S R L T L P
γ  V K F N W Y - V D G V Q V H - - N A K T K P R E Q Q Y B S T Y R V V S V L T V L
μ  V T I S W T R E E G - A V - - - K T H T B I S E S H P B A T F S A V G E A S I C
ε  V N L T W S R A S G K P V - - - N H S T R K E E K Q R N G T L T V T S T L P V G
α  V T F T W P S T S G K - - - - - S A V Z G P P E R D L C G C Y S V S S V L P G C


              90             100             110             120
δ  R S L W N A G T S V T C T L N H P S L P P Q R L M A L R E P A - - - A Q A P V K
γ  H Q N W L D G K E Y K C K V S N K A L P A P - I E K T I S K A K G Q P R E - P Q
μ  E D B W N S G E R F T C T V T H T D L P S P - L K Q T I S R P K G V A L H R P B
ε  T R D W I E G E T Y Q C R V T H P H L P R A - L M R S T T K T S G - P R A A P E
α  A E P W B H G K T F T C T A A Y P E S K T P - L T A T L S K - S G - N T F R P Q


             130             140             150             160
δ  L S L N L L A S S D - P P E A A S W L L C E V S G F S P P N I L L M W L E D Q R
γ  V Y T L P P S R E E - M T K N Q V S L T C L V K G F Y P S D I A V E W E S N D G
μ  V V L L P P A R E Q L N L R E S A T I T C L V T G F S P A D V F V E W Q M Q R G
ε  V Y A F A T P E W P - G S R D K R T L A C L I Q N F M P E D I S V Q W L H N E V
α  V H L L P P P S Z Z L A L B Z L V T L T C L A R G F S P K D V L V R W L - Q G S


             170             180             190             200
δ  E - V - - - N T S G F A P A R P P P Q P G S T T F W A W S V L R V P A P P S P Q
γ  E - - - P E N Y K T T P P V L - - D S D G S - F F - L Y S K L T V D K S R W Q Q
μ  E P L S P E K Y V T S A P M P E P - Q A P G R Y F - A H S I L T V S E E E W N T
ε  Q - L P D A R H S T T Q P R K - - - T K G S G F F - V F S R L E V T R A E W Q E
α  Q E L P R E K Y L T W A S R Q E P S Q G T T T F A - V T S I L R V A A E D W K K


             210             220             230             240
δ  P A T Y T C V V S H E D S R T L - - L N A S R S L E V S Y V T D H G P M
γ  G N V F S C S V M H E A L H N H Y T - Q K S L S L S P G
μ  G Q T Y T C V V A H E A L P N R V T - E R T V D K S T G K P T L Y N V S L V M S
ε  K D E F I C R A V H E A A S P S Q T V Q R A V S V N P G K
α  G D T F S C M V G H Z A L P L A F T - Q K T I D R L A G K P T H V N V S V E M A
```

APPENDIX III: REFERENCES TO AMINO ACID SEQUENCES

CHAPTER 4, FIGURE 6

Shark L chain: Sledge, C., Clem, L. W. and Hood, L. (1974). *J. Immunol. 112,* 941.
Protein OU: Putnam, F. W., Florent, G., Paul, C., Shinoda, T. and Shimizu, A. (1973). *Science 182,* 287.

CHAPTER 5, FIGURE 1

Protein

ROY: Hilschmann, N. and Craig, L. C. (1965). *Proc. Natl. Acad. Sci. USA 53,* 1403.

Hilschmann, N., Barnikol, H. U., Hess, M., Langer, B., Ponstingl, H., Steinmetz-Kayne, M., Suter, L. and Watanabe, S. (1969). *Proc. Fifth FEBS Symp. 15,* 57.

AU: Schiechl, H. and Hilschmann, N. (1972). *Z. Physiol. Chem. 353,* 345.
OU: See above.
REI: Palm, W. and Hilschmann, N. (1975). *Z. Physiol. Chem. 356,* 167.
HAU: Watanabe, S. and Hilschmann, N. (1970). *Z. Physiol. Chem. 351,* 1291.
SCW: Eulitz, M. and Hilschmann, N. (1974). *Z. Physiol. Chem. 355,* 842.
RFZ: Smithies, O., Gibson, D., Fanning, E. M., Goodfliesh, R. M., Gilman, J. G. and Ballantyne, D. L. (1971). *Biochemistry 10,* 4912.
GAL: Laure, C. J., Watanabe, S. and Hilschmann, N. (1973). *Z. Physiol. Chem. 354,* 1503.
LAY: Klapper, D. G. and Capra, J. D. (1976). *Ann. Immunol. (Inst. Pasteur) 127C,* 261.
EU: Gottlieb, P. D., Cunningham, B. A., Rutishauser, U. and Edelman, G. M. (1970). *Biochemistry 9,* 3155.
HBJ: Smith, G. P., Hood, L. and Fitch, W. M. (1971). *Ann. Rev. Biochem. 40,* 969.
CAR: Milstein, C. P. and Deverson, E. V. (1974). *Eur. J. Biochem. 49,* 377.
BI: Braun, H., Leibold, W., Barnikol, H. U. and Hilschmann, N. (1972). *Z. Physiol. Chem. 353,* 1284.
KA: Shinoda, T. (1975). *J. Biochem. 77,* 1277.
KUE: Eulitz, M. (1979). *Z. Physiol. Chem. 360,* 725.

249

CHAPTER 5, FIGURE 2

Protein

TEI: Capra, J. D. and Kehoe, J. M. (1974). *Proc. Natl. Acad. Sci. USA 71*, 845.
BRO: Capra, J. D. and Hopper, J. E. (1976). *Immunochemistry 13*, 995.
Hopper, J. E., Noyes, C., Heinrikson, R. and Kessel, J. W. (1976). *J. Immunol. 116*, 743.
TUR: Capra, J. D. and Kehoe, J. M. (1974). *Proc. Natl. Acad. Sci. USA 71*, 845.
POM: Capra, J. D. and Kehoe, J. M. (1974). *Proc. Natl. Acad. Sci. USA 71*, 4032.
TIL: Wang, A. C., Wang, I. T. and Fudenberg, H. H. (1977). *J. Biol. Chem. 252*, 7192.
MU: Shinoda, T. (1973). *Biochem. Biophys. Res. Commun. 52*, 1246.
WAS: Capra, J. D. and Kehoe, J. M. (1974). *Proc. Natl. Acad. Sci. USA 71*, 845.
EU: See above.
BUS: Bennett, J. C. (1968). *Biochemistry 7*, 3340.

CHAPTER 12, FIGURE 2

Mouse β_2M: Gates, F. T., Coligan, J. E. and Kindt, T. J. (1981). *Proc. Natl. Acad. Sci. USA 78*, 554.
Guinea
pig β_2M: Wolfe, P. B. and Cebra, J. J. (1980). *Mol. Immunol. 17*, 1493
Rabbit β_2M: Gates, F. T., Coligan, J. E. and Kindt, T. J. (1979). *Biochemistry 12*, 4811.
Human β_2M: Suggs, S. V., Wallace, R. B., Hirose, R., Kawashima, K. and Itakura, K. (1981). *Proc. Natl. Acad. Sci. USA 78*, 6613.

CHAPTER 12, FIGURE 4

H-2K[b]: Coligan, J. E., Kindt, T. J., Uehara, H., Martinko, J. and Nathenson, S. G. (1981). *Nature 291*, 35.
H-2D[b]: Maloy, W. L., Nathenson, S. G. and Coligan, J. E. (1981). *J. Biol. Chem. 256*, 2863.
H-2K[d]: Kimball, E. S., Nathenson, S. G. and Coligan, J. E. (1981). *Biochemistry 20*, 3301.
HLA-B7: Orr, H. T., Lopez de Castro, J. A., Lancet, D. and Strominger, J. A. (1979). Biochemistry 18, 5711.
HLA-A2 and Lopez de Castro, J. A., Strominger, J. L., Strong, D. M. and
HLA-A28: Orr, H. T. (1982). *Proc. Natl. Acad. Sci. USA 79*, 3813.

CHAPTER 12, FIGURE 7

A_α^k and E_α^k: Benoist, C. D., Mathis, D. J., Kanter, M. R., Williams, V. E. and McDevitt, H. O. (1983). *Proc. Natl. Acad. Sci. USA 80*, 534.

INDEX

This book was set in Linotron 202 Century Schoolbook at DEKR Corporation. The production team consisted of Jodi Simpson, copy editor, Joseph J. Vesely, designer and production coordinator, and Fredrick J. Schoenborn, illustrator. The book was manufactured by The Murray Printing Company.